FROM MONITOR TO MISSILE BOAT

Thunderer
This excellent contemporary German study of the Royal Navy turret ship Thunderer *of the 1870s (victim of an unfortunate boiler explosion illustrated in Chapter 3), shows well the low freeboard of the Devastation* class, *of which* Thunderer *was the second example. The class is the link between unambiguous coast defence ships and the classic ocean-going turret battleship of which* Dreadnought *was the first example in the Royal Navy (GPH Collection)*

FROM MONITOR TO MISSILE BOAT

Coast Defence Ships and Coastal Defence since 1860

George Paloczi-Horvath

Foreword by Antony Preston

Naval Institute Press

Annapolis, Maryland

First published in Great Britain in 1996 by
Conway Maritime Press,
an imprint of Brassey's (UK) Ltd,
33 John Street,
London WC1N 2AT

Published and distributed in the United States
of America and Canada by the Naval Institute Press,
118 Maryland Avenue, Annapolis, Maryland 21402-5035

Library of Congress Catalog Card No. 96-68994

ISBN 1–55750–270–6

Manufactured in Great Britain

Contents

Acknowledgements

I WOULD LIKE TO EXPRESS my particular thanks to Antony Preston for his expert guidance and the loan of a number of books from his impressive naval library. At Conway, I thank Rob Gardiner, Julian Mannering and Stephen Chumbley for both their assistance and a display of patience which went well beyond the call of duty, while John Lee and David McLean kindly saw the project through to its completion.

In London, I acknowledge the assistance of library and research staff at the Imperial War Museum, the National Maritime Museum, the Public Records Office and the London Library. At the Royal Institution of Naval Architects in London, Toby Ramsay was especially helpful. In Paris, M. Jérôme Legrand of the Centre de Documentation at the Musée de la Marine showed me documents on the French coast defence fleet and the Battle of Koh-Chang. In Amsterdam, help on Dutch-designed vessels was provided by Mrs E. Streef, Mr C.P.P. van Romburgh and Mr L. Horneman of the Nederlands Scheepvaartmuseum. In Germany, assistance was provided by the Bundesarchiv-Militärarchiv, Freiburg, where Dr Hansjoseph Maierhöfer and Herr Moricz were very helpful with a range of subjects relating to coastal defence in Germany and Scandinavia after the First World War. The Stadtbibliothek, Mainz, also proved to be a very useful library.

Significant assistance on modern Swedish coastal defence was given by Col. Göte Dygeus, Swedish Coast Artillery, while in Norway Frank Abelsen provided some remarkable photographs and background on Norwegian coastal battle-ships. In Britain, Ted Hooton gave helpful pointers on general sources and especially on fixed coastal defences, Eric Grove introduced me to one hitherto unfamiliar aspect of the subject, while the original inspiration for the work came from Trevor Lenton.

Photographs and illustrations come from Conway Maritime Press, my own collection, the above-mentioned museums and sources, and a host of contemporary weapon system manufacturers and shipbuilders, whose publicly available material is acknowledged as such. To the latter I extend my gratitude for both illustrations and also for their numerous technical briefings on different aspects of the subject over the years. Assembling my own collection was made an easier task thanks to the kind assistance of Anthony Cross and colleagues at the Warwick Leadlay Gallery in Greenwich.

Finally, the enterprise was made a great deal easier to complete thanks to the loving help and encouragement given by my family Agi and Richard Argent, and the invaluable practical assistance provided by Hashi Syedain and Gavin Stoddart. I am also grateful for the kind help provided by Dr Sayed Fazle Amin, Barbara Krebs, Deanne Bergin, Stephen Gardiner and Suzanna van Moyland. I apologise to any helper whom I may have neglected to mention. Any fault with the text is mine alone.

GEORGE PALOCZI-HORVATH
London, April 1996

Foreword

by Antony Preston

COAST DEFENCE MUST SURELY be the most misunderstood subject in military history. Myths abound, the most famous being the guns facing the wrong way at Singapore, a fiction which, despite having been exposed repeatedly, is widely believed by that well-known military specialist, the 'man in the street'.

Coast defence also conforms to that time-honoured rule which ensures that military engagements lead to incorrect analysis. As the author shows, the leading navies of the second half of the nineteenth century were inordinately influenced by two very atypical actions, the Battle of Hampton Roads in the American Civil War and the Battle of Lissa, fought only four years later in the Adriatic. At Hampton Roads, the turret ironclad USS *Monitor* fought the converted broadside ironclad CSS *Virginia* to an inconclusive draw, leading to a spate of orders for 'monitors' around the world. At Lissa, the Austrian fleet vanquished the Italians in a thoroughly decisive manner, with the result that the navies of the world spent the next 30 years trying to perfect the ram as a tactical concept in its own right.

In fact, the obsession with coast defence is almost as old as naval warfare itself. When the Sibyl told the Athenians that their city-state would be saved by its 'wooden walls', that could be said to mark the beginning of an argument between the disciples of fixed land defences and those who favoured the security offered by command of the sea. Hence, in the reign of Henry VIII large sums were expended on small coastal castles such as Southsea.

In modern times the argument became acrimonious and costly, particularly in the aftermath of the Crimean War. Because French ironclad floating batteries had helped to subdue the Russian fortress at Kinburn in the Black Sea and British light forces had waged successful hit-and-run warfare against Russian defences in the Baltic, it was widely held that all future naval conflict would be conducted in coastal waters. A visible reminder of that sterile debate is still visible in the fortifications around Portsmouth and the massive Spithead forts, all stigmatised together as 'Palmerston's Follies'. Two decades later, the threat from steam torpedo boats led to numerous harbours being enclosed by breakwaters on both sides of the English Channel.

The reaction to the low-key naval operations in the Crimean War is now universally described as a strategic aberration. That incorrect conclusion is echoed by current thinking in the wake of the Gulf War in 1991, but the buzzword is now 'littoral' rather than 'coastal'. Forecasting is a risky pastime, and particularly so in the field of warfare, which has an unpleasant habit of confounding soothsayers and pundits.

Coast defence ships have always been of interest to students of naval technical history. Because they were ultra-specialised they embodied unusual features, and because they were heavily armed ships on small dimensions they required a high level of design skill. They were the true 'pocket battleships' before that term was misused by the British press to describe the German 'Panzerschiffe' of the 1930s, in reality armoured cruisers which had only a modest speed but sufficient armament to deter any cruiser or smaller warship. In their proper environment coast defence ships were by no means powerless to influence events. Used correctly in conjunction with fixed defences ashore they could provide a measure of flexibility which might be decisive.

The coast defence ship was a creation of the steam age. It is no coincidence that the Royal Navy's first steam-powered ships-of-the-line, the two-deckers *Ajax* and *Blenheim*, were designated 'blockships' or floating batteries when their conversion was completed in 1846. They and their successors were designed to frustrate the feared French invasion of the British Isles. With hindsight we can now see that the logistic problems of landing 30,000 soldiers in a single night were much greater than any military theorist of the day could comprehend. Indeed, they were beyond the Wehrmacht and the Kriegsmarine, and would tax the amphibious warfare capability of, say, the modern French Navy.

Steam gave manoeuvrability but it was iron that made the coast defence ship practicable. When iron gave way to steel, designers could keep the weight of armour down and increase the power of guns without allowing displacement to grow too much. Shallow water was always the limiting factor, yet providing coast defence ships with protection against more powerful warships.

As the author shows, coast defence is a complex business, varying according to needs and circumstances. A 'blue water' navy such as the US Navy can use selected coast defence measures, but these will not include coast defence ships because the main fleet is the striking force which will (it is hoped) beat off any enemy seaborne threat. In such a case, fixed coast defences on land are useful to protect specific assets against a land threat. But they cannot be a substitute for a fleet, as the British found at Singapore in 1942. When Admiral Jellicoe advised the home government on the sea defences of the Empire in 1919, he advocated the creation of the Singapore fortress, but only to provide a secure base for a Far Eastern fleet. Had the Royal Navy and the Royal Air Force been able to dominate the sea and the skies over northern Malaya it is hard to see how the Japanese land invasion of Malaya could have succeeded.

This is much more than a fond memoir of an extinct type of warship. The author traces the connection between older forms of coast defence and modern methods, showing how the principles of coast defence are enshrined in today's missile-armed fast attack craft, land-mobile missiles and even submarines. Coastal submarines have been called 'mobile minefields' and by a similar analogy fast attack craft can be described as 'mobile coast defence batteries'. The anti-ship missile, with no recoil, is much easier to mount on a road vehicle than any gun. Both fast attack craft and coastal submarines conform to a pattern established by the coast defence ship: ill-suited to distant 'blue water' operations but very potent in defence.

George Paloczi-Horvath is to be congratulated for documenting the history of coast defence ships and putting them in a historical context. The traditional coast defence ship has gone the way of its bigger sisters, but coast defence is still in business.

Conversion Table

Conversion table for gun calibres mentioned in this book.

Calibres below 3 inch (in) or 76.2 millimetres (mm) are generally only ever recorded in metric measurements and will be familiar to readers in their metric form. For the record they are: 7.62mm, 7.92mm, 8mm, 12.7mm (0.5in), 13.2mm, 20mm, 25mm, 37mm, 40mm, 47mm, 50mm, 50.8mm (2in), 57mm, 75mm. Some explanations of other conversions are necessary. Many source books only record calibres in either imperial or metric and surprisingly frequently contain errors. Thus the German 280mm gun which equipped *Deutschland* is habitually referred to in American or British publications as an '11inch' gun, when the precise conversion should be 11.02in. Similarly, the '8.3in' gun of many Swedish coast defence ships actually refers to a 210mm weapon, for which the precise conversion should be 8.26in. Some of these instances are made apparent below, where a calibre is stated to be 'often rendered as' something else. However, for clarity and because many readers may only be familiar with a weapon as, for example, an '8.3in' gun, it and similar cases are described in the text as such. The confusion is made worse in cases where a calibre existed in both very similar imperial and metric measurements, hence the conversions of calibres below of similar dimensions.

Imperial	Metric
3in	76.2mm
3.1in	78.7mm
3.14in	80mm
3.46in	88mm
3.93in	100mm
4in	101.6 (ORA 102mm)
4.13in	105mm
4.72in (ORA 4.7in)	120mm
5in	127mm
5.4in	137.1mm
5.5in	139.7mm (ORA 140mm)
5.51in	140mm
5.7in	147.3mm (ORA 147mm)
5.9in	150mm (5.9in AC: 149.86mm)
6in	152.4mm
6.4in	162.5mm
6.74in	165mm
6.7in	170mm
7in	177.8mm (ORA 178mm)
7.63in	194mm
7.8in	198.2mm (ORA 200mm)
7.87in	200mm
8in	203.2mm
8.2in	208.2mm
8.26in (ORA 8.3in)	210mm (8.3in AC: 210.82mm)
9in	228.6mm
9.2in	233.6mm
9.4in	238.7mm
9.45in	240mm
9.5in	241.3mm
10in	254mm
10.2in	259.08mm (ORA 260mm)
10.8in	274.32mm (ORA 275mm)
10.82in	275mm
11in	279.4mm
11.02in	280mm
11.09in	283mm
12in	304.8mm (ORA 305mm)
13in	330.2mm
13.38in	340mm
13.4in	340.3mm
13.5in	342.9mm
13.65in	346.7mm
13.779in (ORA 13.8in)	350mm
14in	355.6mm
15in	381mm
16in	406.4
16.53in	420mm
17in	431.8mm
17.2in	436mm
17.71in	450mm

Torpedoes

Imperial	Metric
14in	355.6mm (ORA 355mm)
18in	456mm
19.68in	500mm
21in	533mm
21.65in	550mm

ORA = Often Rendered As. AC = Actual Conversion. For reference to this table, and to the conversion of imperial armour thickness measurements, 1in = 25.4mm.

From Monitor *to Missile Boat . . .*

Coastal defence is the discipline which links these two illustrations. Above is a print of John Ericsson's revolutionary US Navy ironclad Monitor *of 1862, from which countless coastal defence ships and, later, turreted battleships were derived. Below is a line drawing of a very heavily-armed fast attack missile boat design, a derivative of Vosper Thornycroft's* Vita *concept, four of which were ordered in 1992 by the Qatar Emiri Navy.*

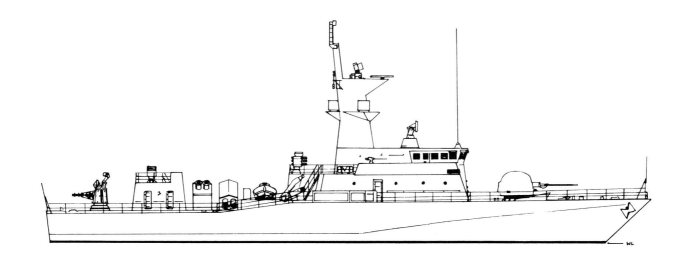

CHAPTER 1

Coast Defence in History

THIS BOOK IS THE story of a discipline and how it has been practised since 1860. The narrative concentrates on classic gun-armed coast defence ships of the type which had their roots in Ericsson's *Monitor*. They were generally small, unpretentious, comparatively cheap and, considering that they were mostly deployed by nations which avoided trouble rather than looked for it, were put to the test comparatively rarely. The last such vessels were built just before the Second World War. A very few survived for a short while thereafter and their passing was barely noticed.

Coast defence was far from being a role exclusive to classic coast defence ships. This was also the discipline which bred the torpedo and the mine. The torpedo boat and the minelayer can also be regarded as coast defence vessels of a sort, but the former had a very limited operational radius and was armed with a short-range weapon, while the latter's uses were not exclusively associated with defensive strategy. In any case, many navies simply routinely added mine rails to their surface combatants to maximise the number of hulls available for the task.

It was not until well after the Second World War that a new breed of vessel emerged which, by virtue of its range, propulsion technology and weapons, could rightfully assume the mantle of the coast defence ship of old. Equipped with the means of detecting, classifying and attacking targets at long range, the modern missile-armed fast attack craft performs a similar role to the diminutive battleship of earlier generations. Moreover its punch is as deadly as that of a battleship shell.

Just as the torpedo boat destroyer of the nineteenth century grew in size in order to transit the open ocean to protect the fleet, the fast attack craft has grown from a small missile boat tied as often as not to a particular nearby base into a more capacious corvette in order to house the sophisticated command, control and communications equipment required of a modern warship. It is also far better protected than its forebears of a generation ago and, as is argued in Chapter 11, looks set to regain the advantage against attacking blue water fleets, thanks to technologies which include 'stealth' – the means to mask or reduce a vessel's radar signature.

The obvious proviso, which has applied throughout most of the twentieth century, is that while quite small coast defence forces can enormously complicate the depredations of an aggressor, air superiority or at least the ability to

seriously contest control of the air is vital. The quality of some of the coast defence ships built by the Scandinavian countries in the twentieth century was not matched by an appreciation of the need to control the air. It also helped if the coastal fortresses which complimented the coast defence fleets were manned and had enough ammunition, as was not the case in many Norwegian forts in 1940.

Nevertheless, there is no question that their existence did materially alter potential aggressors' policy and strategies. Norway's acquisition of a fleet of British-built coast defence ships played a significant role in persuading Sweden to accept the termination of the union of the two kingdoms in 1905, while Sweden's own later *Sverige* class coast defence ships earned the healthy respect of more powerful Baltic neighbours.

Coast defence ships were also adopted by some major naval powers, such as France and Russia. In Russia the adoption of the most curious coast defence ships ever built, the circular ironclads *Novogorod* and *Popov*, related at least indirectly to the limitations of the Treaty of Paris. The concept of a pure coast defence strategy dominated US naval thinking for most of the late nineteenth century. Coast defence even became a *cause célèbre* in Britain, prompting the building of the *Cyclops* class, and again became an issue both when the German High Seas Fleet raided English east coast ports during the First World War and was also even a worry after 1945. Thus coast defence was not merely the understandable obsession of the weaker naval powers.

There can be no better description of the essentials of coast defence and its antithesis than that provided by a crisp footnote in Mahan's *The Influence of Sea Power Upon History* which bears quoting at length.

The word 'defence' in war involves two ideas, which for the sake of precision in thought should be kept separated in the mind. There is defence pure and simple, which strengthens itself and awaits attack. This may be called passive defence. On the other hand, there is a view of defence which asserts that safety for one's self, the real object of defensive preparation, is best secured by attacking the enemy. In the matter of sea-coast defence, the former method is best exemplified by stationary fortifications, submarine mines, and generally all immobile works destined simply to

Selection of coast defence
ships
This collection of warship
views from an item on
ironclads in a French
illustrated dictionary from
1897–98 shows several
French and two US coast
defence ships of the period,
which is not surprising
given their prominence in
both fleets at the time. Seen
are, clockwise from the
lower centre: Fulminant,
the USN monitor
Miantonomoh, Admiral
Tréhouart, the 'seagoing
coast line battleship' USS
Iowa, Jemmapes and
Terrible. The floating
battery Arrogante can also
be glimpsed top left.
Several armour
arrangements typical of the
period 1860–98 can be
seen top right, as can
typical armament and
armour layouts in the side
and plan views top left
and bottom right (GPH
Collection)

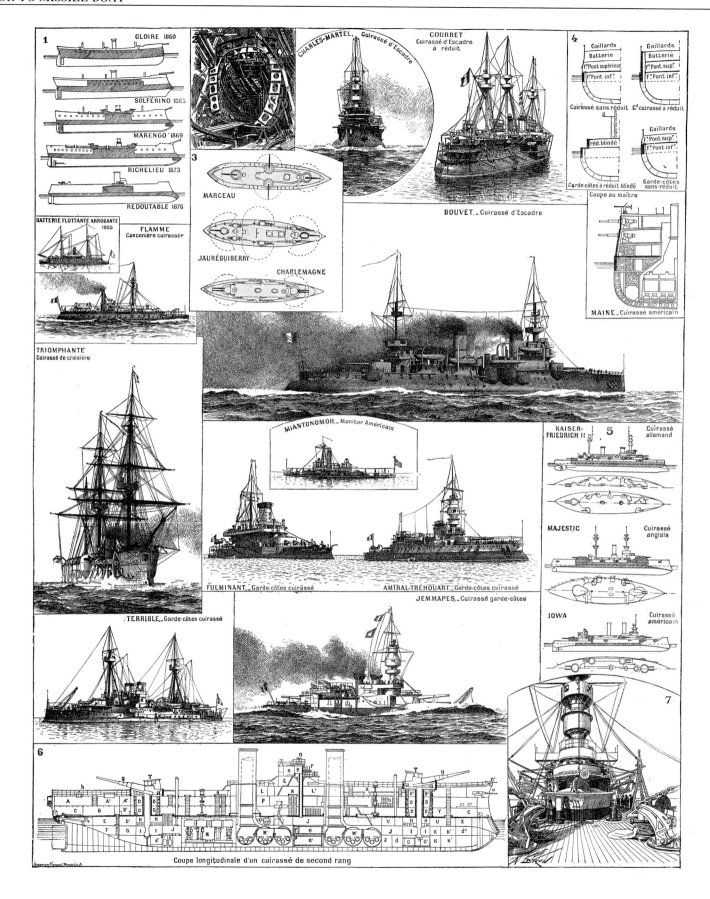

stop an enemy if he tries to enter. The second method comprises all those means and weapons which do not wait for attack, but go to meet the enemy's fleet, whether it be but for a few miles, or whether to his own shores. Such a defence may seem to be really offensive war, but it is not; it becomes offensive only when its object of attack is changed from the enemy's fleet to the enemy's country.[1]

Mahan's astute understanding of this critically important distinction enabled him to differentiate correctly between the defensive purpose of English stationing of fleets off French ports – to protect her coast and colonies against the French – and the fundamentally offensive character of the United States' blockade of the Confederacy, which was intended to isolate the rebels rather than guard against their relatively few frigates and privateers.

Confusion over what was and what was not defensive led 'to much unnecessary wrangling as to the proper sphere of army and navy in coast defence', Mahan said. His solution was that 'passive', that is, fixed defences should belong to the army, and 'everything that moves in the water to the navy, which has the prerogative of offensive defence. If seamen are used to garrison forts, they become part of the land forces. . .'.

One might speculate as to what Mahan would have thought of the elaborate network of fixed and mobile coastal defences in Scandinavia which were to be developed into such a fine art during the twentieth century, especially since in some countries they became virtually a separate arm of service, as indeed they did in Sweden with the creation of the Coastal Artillery.

According to Mahan's thesis, purely passive defence smacked of weakness. One can only speculate on whether he knew of Sir Walter Raleigh's views on the subject some three centuries before, but he surely would have agreed with his Elizabethan forebear, when he wrote: 'It is impossible for any maritime country, not having the coasts admirably fortified, to defend itself against a powerful enemy that is master of the sea'. What was required, in Raleigh's view, was a fleet – by implication much more than a coastal fleet – which could 'debar an enemy from landing'.[2]

As Mahan observed, the nature of nations' maritime strategies was critically influenced not only by geography, resources and economic strength, but also by national character. Thus when Halifax wrote of England's paramount maritime needs in his *Rough Draught of a New Model at Sea*, published in 1694, he generated an almost mystical belief in sea power as the protection against the knavish tricks of foreigners which was to survive in Anglo-Saxon maritime strategy in the twentieth century, to say nothing of British politics.

But the resonance of his language can be turned to support either idea: the need to reinforce seagoing power with an effective coastal defence. 'To the question, What shall we do to be saved in this world? there is no other answer but this, Look to your moat', Halifax wrote. 'The first article of an Englishman's political creed must be, that he believeth in the sea. . .'.[3]

As for Mahan, his interpretation would always have been that only a fully-fledged seagoing fleet could meet a serious maritime power's needs. He had only to point to the parlous state of his own country's navy, writing as he did in 1889 when the United States' fleet was finally about to emerge from the long period of decay after the Civil War, when only the subterfuge of the 'great repairs' kept any kind of fleet afloat. This force was not even fit for the true coast defence mission, as this would have involved the despatch to sea of low-freeboard monitors with dubious seakeeping qualities to contest any blockade. The US Navy knew this, Mahan knew it, and an increasingly vocal political and industrial lobby knew it too and the latter had the solution if only a majority in Congress would listen.

America still had no colonies, no significant mercantile fleet to speak of, and no seagoing navy yet – all of which were the usual ingredients of sea power according to Mahan's view. But in the year when Mahan wrote his *magnum opus*, a US Navy special policy board asked for the construction of no less than 192 warships over 15 years, including ten first class and twenty-five coast defence battleships. An anti-militarist Congress soon put paid to these plans, only conceding in 1890 the construction of what an Act of Congress of that year termed three 'seagoing coastline battleships' – the *Indiana*s. Their significance in American naval history cannot be minimised, as they constituted the beginnings of the 'New Navy'. And they were also examples of economy in battleship construction which might indeed be effective in a purely coastal defence.

But the one advantage which, according to Mahan's definition of the essentials of sea power, America undoubtedly had at this time was a dynamic economy with apparently endless scope for internal growth. This was to provide the basis of American naval supremacy in the century to come. With this, and the growth of the fleet from the 1890s onwards America largely turned its back on coastal defence.

The United States' emergence from the shell of an isolationist industrial power into something like a conventional expansionist European power provided perhaps the classic example of a nation 'outgrowing' coastal defence. But there were – and still are – many nations for which coastal defence in at least its broader and more sensible definition can never be regarded as a luxury.

It may be tempting to speculate on what might have happened to the Danish fleet had Denmark joined in the scramble for colonies. After all, poorer countries like Portugal did just that and even Denmark had had her own little far-flung possession in the Danish Virgin Islands, which were only given up to the United States in 1917.

In the event, the clear lesson of history for a country like Denmark was that ocean-going pretensions were largely pointless other than to protect her extensive Atlantic fisheries. Despite Denmark's weakness on land, evidenced by her defeat at Prussian and Austrian hands in Schleswig-Holstein in 1864, her naval strength was still more than a match for Prussia's and Austria's.

One lesson had already been learned though. In an earlier conflict over Schleswig-Holstein in 1849, two vessels, the Danish line-of-battleship *Christian VIII* and the accompanying frigate *Gefion*, had been destroyed by coastal batteries. Surely only a strong coastal defence could ward off a blockading fleet – or an invader. And surely any blockading fleet or any flotilla intended for operation in restricted coastal waters would now have to be composed of appropriately protected vessels.

So, like her neighbour Sweden, Denmark was now to use the design concepts of John Ericsson such as his *Monitor*, which were at this time being put to such innovative use in America's Civil War, in the creation of her own ironclad fleet. The result of this realisation of the power of coastal artillery were vessels like the well-armoured, and armed, ram-bowed *Peder Skram* and a plethora of similar vessels in many other countries.

Conversely, for Prussia and even Austria the lessons of 1864 were that an ocean-going fleet of some sort was essential for a great power, so the fairly inconsequential scraps of that conflict were certainly to have a far-reaching influence on subsequent events.

It can therefore be understood why the central doctrinal conflict between the proponents of coastal, or passive defence and the supporters of an ocean-going strategy has always seemed practically impossible to resolve. Practically impossible in the sense that there have been very few countries with the wherewithal to foot the bill for both forms of defence. France during the period of the 'jeune école' is one example, the Soviet Union after the Second World War is another. But most seagoing powers had little time for the perceived distraction of coastal defence.

Coast defence sceptics could, for example, hark back to the derisive views of the kind expressed by Sir Edward Pellew who, in a parliamentary debate in 1804 on Pitt's naval inquiry, observed:

As to the gun-boats which have been so strongly recommended, this mosquito fleet, they are the most contemptible force that can be employed; gun-brigs, indeed, are of some use, but between a gun-brig and a gun-boat there is almost as much difference as between a man-of-war and a frigate.[4]

This view of the perceived uselessness of the small coastal combatant was only to be altered by the discovery of the great equaliser, the torpedo, and the torpedo boat 'scare' of the late nineteenth century, which suggested that there was indeed an apparent equivalence between smaller and larger defenders, between 'gun-brig' and 'gun-boat'.

But however inadequate some coast defence ships may have seemed to some at the time or in retrospect, there is no doubt that the type played a critical role in the development of the big gun battleship. When, on 9 March 1862, Ericsson's purpose-built ironclad *Monitor* engaged the Confederate ironclad conversion *Virginia* at Hampton Roads, a new age was ushered in. They may have exchanged fire laboriously and the engagement may have been inconclusive, but these coast defence vessels – for that is all they were fit for and even a modest passage was asking much of them – signalled the coming end of the dominance of the sail-rigged ship of the line.

If that end was not so rapid, it was only because steam was not yet so reliable a form of propulsion for open ocean passages that it could be relied on alone, while it was to be some time before turret ships became the norm, although they were to be introduced sooner on coast defence vessels than on ocean-going ships. Following the early ironclads' hull-mounted gun arrangements, as on France's *Gloire* and the British ironclad frigate *Warrior*, a long period of experimentation with casemates and barbettes followed before the logic and simplicity of the turret was to establish its dominance in naval design.

In Britain, one dedicated coast defence ship, *Royal Sovereign*, became the Royal Navy's first turret ship to enter service. Her conversion had been started only two months after Hampton Roads and she was to be somewhat more seaworthy than *Monitor*. Designed before *Royal Sovereign*, but not completed until eighteen months after, *Prince Albert* was the Royal Navy's first iron turret ship, a purpose-built coast defence vessel robust enough to survive almost until the end of the century.

These coast defence ships earned their place in history not only because of their innovative features, but because they so directly influenced the design of the revolutionary *Devastation* class turret ships, which blazed a trail for the ocean-going turret battleships. These vessels were of course marked apart from coast defence ships not only because they carried a wider variety of armament and, usually, better armour protection, but also because they had greater freeboards.

This characteristic separated the true ocean-going turret ships from many of the diminutive coastal ironclads like Denmark's *Rolf Krake* or Prussia's *Arminius*, both British-built vessels with Coles turrets. Similarly armed was *Huascar*, a legendary coast defence ship which started its life in Peruvian hands, was captured by Chile during the War of the Pacific and which survives today, in remarkable condition, as a museum ship.

However small some of these coastal ironclads may have been, they nevertheless earned fame because of the balance

REMAINS OF THE FLOATING BATTERY "ETNA," AT MESSRS. SCOTT RUSSELL'S, MILLWALL.

of their strengths. In the case of the Hellenic Navy's central battery ship *Basileos Georgios*, completed in 1868, her designer claimed that, for her size, she boasted superior offensive and defensive properties than any warship of comparable size or purpose at the time.

The advent of new forms of propulsion in the following decade, such as vertical engines which took up less space than horizontal machinery, meant that greater compactness was possible in coast defense vessels, which, with the final passing of sail, could now cram a worthwhile battery into restricted space. For the smaller powers, as long as a large

coal capacity was not required, it became at least theoretically possible to argue that a well-armed coast defence ship could be the equal of an ocean-going battleship. The type also suited countries which did not possess the industrial infrastructure of a major power, as measured by production of iron and later steel.

Power was measured not only by whether, as Mahan believed, a country had colonial pretensions and trade routes to protect, but also by straightforward economic measures which usually pointed to a nation's ability to transform itself from being a predominantly agricultural society into an

Etna

Etna *was a wooden-hulled Royal Navy floating battery, shown here damaged after the accident during her launch at Millwall in 1854. A replacement* Etna *(also known as* Aetna*), was launched at Chatham Dockyard in April 1856 and served for 10 years before being relegated to harbour duties (GPH Collection)*

Jacob van Heemskerck
*This model of the Royal
Netherlands Navy
'pantserschip' Jacob van
Heemskerck as she
appeared in 1908 shows
all the main features of
coast defence ship design in
the type's heyday:
compactness, simplicity
and, unusually for the
period, an enclosed bridge.
The ship never served in
the defence of the
Netherlands, but only in
the Dutch East Indies,
hence her being painted
white and her array of top
semaphores (Nederlands
Scheepvaartmuseum,
Amsterdam)*

industrial one. Theories and even coefficients for the 'ranks of backwardness' have showed how, in Europe in the nineteenth century, there were measurable, quantifiable reasons why certain countries were always going to be ahead of others. They also show how countries which kept a better balance of economic strengths and did not rely too much on imports could be strong, while strength in commerce clearly played its own part in encouraging the development of ocean-going navies.[5]

While the pure coast defence powers accepted their status, this did not of course mean they need accept inferiority – ship for ship – compared with the major fleets. Argentina showed this with her acquisition of *Almirante Brown*, while by the 1890s France even came to regard the coast defence ship as an essential element of her fleet: witness the *Jemmapes* class.

But from Reed's *Dreadnought* to her namesake of 1906, a trend had grown towards larger and more powerful capital ships and, on the whole, it can be said that notwithstanding the coast defence shipbuilding 'boom' of the quarter century preceding Fisher's *Dreadnought*, it was inevitable that the all big gun battleship was going to prompt the disappearance of the coast defence ship from most fleets.

It was hence something of a neat turn of fortune that some of the busiest warships of the First World War had been assigned to coast defence tasks. Many pre-dreadnought battleships, relegated to humble secondary duties because of the strategic pre-eminence of their multiple turret replacements, found themselves in secondary theatres of war where they were put to very good use.

The few classes of new coast defence ships built after *Dreadnought* nonetheless showed that they could still boast considerable advances, not least in demonstrating how compactness or, as in the case of the Finnish *Väinämöinen* class, new propulsion forms – in this case diesel-electric – could show up the major powers' larger capital ships.

Furthermore, as is argued in Chapter 8, coast defence ship designs had an influence on Germany's first capital ship to be built after the Treaty of Versailles, the landmark 'armoured ship' *Deutschland*. Yet even the best coast defence ship was only as good as its armament and during the Second World War the type suffered various humiliations, while also taking part in several brave engagements and serving in a variety of secondary roles.

The Second World War showed, even more than the First, that the country with a good integrated coast defence doctrine stood a very good chance of seriously impeding an invader. All countries had always had fortresses and guns at their ports, but few thought seriously about how to integrate the separate parts into a cohesive whole.

The inability of the Germans to protect their 'Fortress Europe' and even the fanatical Japanese to prevail in bloodbaths like Iwo Jima gave the idea of static coast defence a bad name. It would only be after 1945, with the invention of a new form of weaponry in the surface-to-surface guided missile, that integrated coast defences again became a truly worthwhile objective. Even so, it is remarkable how much coastal artillery still survives. Some have even been replaced of late with new guns.

That technology should have recently become available to make feasible a greater balance between the smaller and the larger naval power probably could have been forseen, but as new weapons, hull concepts and technologies are less and less the preserve of the few, it is today arguable whether we shall always live in a world of a handful of major naval powers and a host of minor ones. The altering of this balance can only benefit the coast defence navy.

1 A T Mahan, *The Influence of Sea Power Upon History 1660–1773* (first published in 1890 – Sampson Low, London, Sixth Edition), p87 ff.

2 H W Hodges & E A Hughes (ed.), 14. Ralegh on Strategy, Select Naval Documents (Cambridge University Press, 1936), pp18–19.

3 Ibid., 82. The Importance of Sea Power, p109.

4 Ibid., 135. Defence Against Invasion, p210.

5 See Clive Trebilock, *The Industrialisation of the Continental Powers 1780–1914* (Longman, London, 1981), Chapter 7, 'Statistics and Structures', pp429–53, for a concise and informative exposition of such theories.

CHAPTER 2

Ericsson, the Monitors and the American Civil War

THE EXACT MOMENT WHEN the sailing ship of the line ceased to dominate naval affairs could be said to have been on 9 March 1862 when the USS *Monitor* and the CSS *Virginia* lumbered within sight of one another at Hampton Roads and laboriously exchanged fire for several hours without a conclusive result. But the engagement between these totally unfamiliar-looking craft, which were bereft of any sailing rig, shook the global naval establishment to its foundations. All at once, the world's sailing fleets had been apparently rendered obsolete. Of course, this was not to be for the rest of the 1860s and most of the 1870s, as it took a long time for the very low freeboard Ericsson-type monitors to evolve into genuine seagoing turret ships which could manage without a sailing rig. But the promise was there.

For the Swede John Ericsson's creation had introduced a great number of technological changes, made others highly necessary, and threatened to overturn the generally accepted ideas of what was involved in the maintenance of a close blockade against an enemy. The monitors' role in the Union's defeat of the Confederacy was equally influenced by the latter's basic essential industrial weakness, which made it very hard for the 'gallant South' to equal the North in technology or resources.

Ironically, the role of the monitors in the Union's victory had a negative influence on the further development of the United States as a sea power, as their legend was in effect a psychological deadweight, apparently justifying Congressional reluctance to spend money on larger, more seaworthy replacements. And so it was that the completely erroneous view that monitors could even challenge a more sophisticated enemy on the high seas was allowed to take root in some quarters. The result of this of course was that Congress refused to fund any replacements for the Civil War monitors and the deception of the 'great repairs' was used to secretly build replacements in the shape of *Puritan* and the *Amphitrite* class.

Even in 1898, when America went to war against Spain and sent fleets to Cuba, Puerto Rico and the Philippines, it was believed that monitors had a useful role to play on the high seas. Those that were sent to join Dewey's squadron in the Philippines had the roughest and most difficult of passages across the Pacific, thereby putting an end to the nonsense of the 'New Navy' monitors being regarded as an element of the ocean-going battle fleet. They and their successors spent most of their lives laid up or in secondary roles, just as their Civil War forebears had after that conflict.

Ericsson's Monitor

Yet during that war, the importance of the monitors' role could not be underestimated. The outbreak of the Civil War in April 1861 found the Union unprepared because of the Confederate Navy's rapid conversion of the former sail-rigged frigate *Merrimack* into the ironclad vessel *Virginia*. An immediate response was required to this sudden and frightening technological challenge and so it was that John Ericsson was contracted to provide, in just one hundred days, some sort of vessel which could reasonably be expected to take on *Virginia* and survive.

The requirement was demanding, although the contract price, $275,000, was relatively modest for such an important new warship. Because there was so little time available, whatever vessel was produced would have to be small, yet she would need to be armoured to a level sufficient to withstand some of the most powerful contemporary guns, as fitted to *Virginia*. However, because her small dimensions effectively made it impossible for a large battery of weapons to be fitted, some means would have to be provided to maximise the effectiveness of a small battery. Ericsson had first put forward the idea of a cupola or turret mounting in 1854, and hence in 1861 the method chosen of resolving the design puzzle was a simple central turret mounting a pair of 11in (279.4mm) Dahlgren muzzle-loading smoothbores. The turret was mounted on a central spindle on what was for all practical purposes an armoured raft with a displacement of just 987 tons, and dimensions of 172ft x 41ft 6in x 10ft 6in (52.42m x 12.64m x 3.2m).

Ericsson had opposed the US Bureau of Construction and Repair, which had favoured a low-freeboard ironclad with a pair of Coles turrets (as designed by Britain's Captain Cowper Coles, see Chapter 3), each mounting a single 11in gun. But Ericsson's approach had the benefit of simplicity, allowing for very rapid construction. However Ericsson's final design was somewhat more practical than his early sketch concepts for a vessel with 6in (152mm) side armour and 2in (50.8mm) deck protection which would have made it impossible to operate the vessel given its other weights.

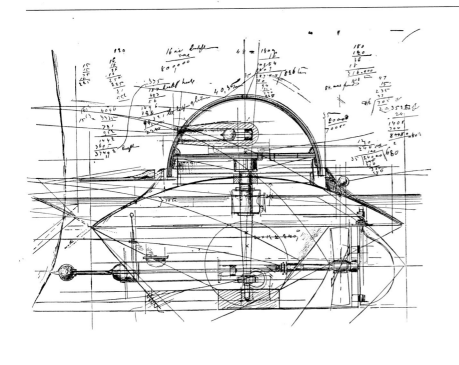

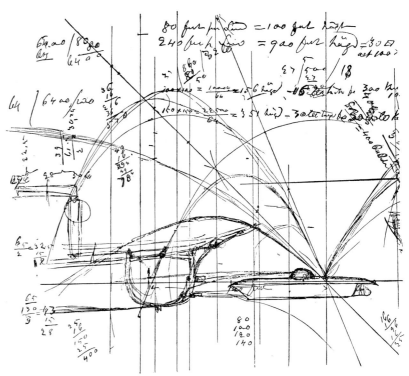

Monitor *concept drawings These facsimiles of drawings by Ericsson show a transverse section, with a semi-hemispherical turret (left), and the original concept drawing (right) shows an appreciation of the fire trajectories which could be brought to bear against, and by such a vessel (From* The Life of John Ericsson, *1892)*

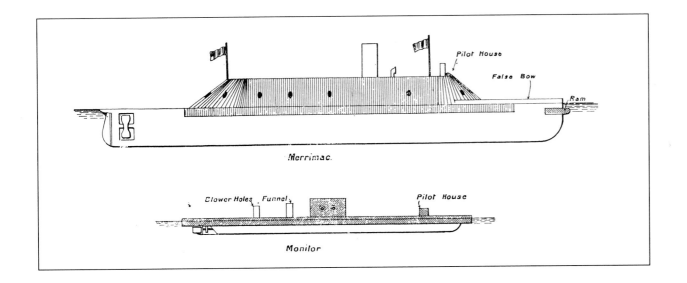

Monitor *& 'Merrimac' The armoured 'raft'* Monitor *was in every respect a lash-up, a rush job to meet the sudden threat posed by Confederate ironclads. The lower side view shows the very small freeboard of the vessel as she was built in 1862, complete with a pair of turret-mounted 11in Dahlgren guns. Above, to scale, is the Confederate ironclad* Virginia *(ex-'Merrimac'), every bit a conversion and substantially more imposing (From 'The Life of John Ericsson', 1892)*

The *Monitor*, the name chosen 'that she might be a warning to others', was laid down at Continental Iron Works on 25 October 1861 (on the same day the contract was signed), was launched less than three months later on 30 January 1862, and was commissioned on 25 February of that year: which, though 23 days longer than the contracted period and some days longer if the short preparation of materials for the vessel is taken into account, was nevertheless very impressive. It is worth recalling that among the sceptical voices greeting *Monitor*'s arrival in the Union fleet was that of David Farragut, later to become the Union's senior naval commander, who came to understand the strengths of the monitor concept at first hand.

The Union Navy knew that, because the approaches to the Confederacy's key harbours and much of its waters were shallow, a vessel like the *Monitor* would need to have a shallow draught for coastal operations. This it had at 10ft 6in (3.2m) mean draught, with a freeboard of just 2ft (0.6m), decreasing to just 1ft 2in (0.35m) when fully laden. This had the advantage of presenting the smallest possible side armour to the enemy, this armour being from 4.5in (114mm) to 3–2in (76–50mm) thick below the waterline. This side protection was fitted to an overhang of the *Monitor*'s raft structure which had the dual advantage of enhancing the vessel's stability and adding to its protection against ramming.

The lower hull over which the composite armour and wood raft were hung was slab-sided with dimensions of 126ft x 34 ft max (38.4m x 12.64m), with a flat bottom 18ft (5.48m) wide. The raft overhang extended 14ft (4.28m) beyond the *Monitor*'s sides forward, 32ft (9.79m) aft and 3ft 9in (1.14m) amidships; the aft overhang contributed to a lowering of *Monitor*'s speed below its contracted speed. The side, deck and turret armour consisted of iron plates 1in (25.4mm) thick, or thinner, riveted or bolted together in laminated plates, the turret armour being 9–8in (228.6–203.2mm) thick on an internal diameter of 20ft (6.12m). America's inability to roll armour thicker than 1in contrasted with Britain's practice of rolling armour at the time in solid 4in (102mm) plates. A curious pagoda-like canopy with railings sat atop the turret, where crewmen could observe the vessel's passage in somewhat more comfort than from the pilot house.

Monitor's propulsion comprised two Martin boilers and a single shaft, vibrating lever engine of Ericsson's own design, developing 320ihp for a speed of 6kts, which was 2kts below the contracted speed. Two square funnels 6ft high, fore and aft of the turret, together with a very small pilot house made from 9in (228.6mm) thick iron, with a 3in (76mm) glacis later installed around it, made for a very clean superstructure around the 9ft (2.75m) high turret. The clean lines belied a poor ventilation system though, with very high temperatures in the engine room and below the main deck, while the hawse pipe was too close to the waterline for comfort.[1] The complement of 49 was modest indeed, but made sense given that there was no other armament.

Virginia and Hampton Roads

What of *Monitor*'s opposition at Hampton Roads, the CSS *Virginia*, whose sailors contemptuously described *Monitor*, upon sighting her, as a 'cheesebox on a raft'? Whereas *Monitor* was purpose-designed from scratch, *Virginia* was, for the time, a fairly ingenious, if quickly improvised floating battery, clearly constructed with the experience of the French and British floating batteries of the Crimean War in mind. The objective was to concoct a vessel which could break the blockade of the Confederacy which the Union swiftly tried to establish after the outbreak of war.

Displacing 4,500 tons,[2] *Virginia* was based on the sunken wooden hull of the Union wooden steam frigate USS *Merrimack*, which had been seized at Norfolk naval dockyard in April 1861. After a survey of the hull, the sailing rig was removed in June, and sloping armour cladding was installed which had itself been constructed from railway line rails, bolted together in groups of three, an early sign of the industrial weakness which was to be the Confederacy's downfall. Dimensions were 275ft x 38ft 6in x 22ft (83.81m x 11.73m x 6.7m).

The Confederate ironclad was armed with 68pdr muzzle-loaders which were able to fire a broadside every 15 minutes and was also fitted with a short iron ram. The full battery comprised a pair of 7in (177.8mm) Brooke rifled muzzle-loaders, a pair of 6.4in (162.5mm), six 9in (228.6mm) smoothbores and two 12pdr smoothbore howitzers. The 7in were installed forward and aft, firing through three ports in the casemate, while the other guns were fired through eight other ports, four each side. The two cylinder horizontal return connecting rod steam engine and four Martin boilers drove a single shaft to provide a maximum speed variously put at 7kts,[3] 7.5kts[4] and even 9kts.[5] *Virginia*'s armour comprised a casemate of 4in-thick rails consisting of two 2in rails bolted together, with side armour less than 1in thick, the casemate's lower end being just 6in below the waterline. The vessel's high complement, at 320 men, reflected its fairly extensive armament.

Virginia's momentous, if inconclusive encounter with *Monitor* came a day after she had made short work of the Union wooden frigates *Congress* and *Cumberland* at Hampton Roads. The next day, after firing on the 'cheesebox', *Virginia*'s crew were surprised to see that their shells had no noticeable effect on *Monitor*, but then again, nor did *Monitor*'s on *Virginia*. It has been said that had *Monitor* fired 30lb charges rather than the 15lb charges to which she had been limited (because her guns had not yet been proof-fired), or had *Virginia* fired solid shot, then perhaps this first ironclad battle, which lasted three and a half hours, would have had a more conclusive result. In the event, there was none, despite even *Virginia*'s attempt to ram the little *Monitor*.

After a refit in which she was given extra plating providing side armour ranging from 3–1in, *Virginia* tried to engage *Monitor* one more time on 11 April, and with solid shot this time, but the Union vessel sensibly refused to be drawn into battle. *Virginia* was then unceremoniously burned on 11 May with the abandonment of Norfolk in the state after which the ship had been named. *Monitor*'s end was equally sad, as she foundered under tow on 31 December in Force 7 winds with, it is believed, a separation of the core inner hull from the armoured raft which had rested upon her.

The Union Girds its Loins

In August 1861, Congress authorised the construction of ironclads at a cost of $1.5 million to match the *Merrimack*, *inter alia*. The Union Navy, though able to draw on a strong industrial base, was weak at the war's outset, with just ninety ships of all types, of which only forty-one were actually in commission. These paltry assets were what was immediately available to begin the blockade of the southern rebels, who had opened the conflict at sea with the bombardment of Fort Sumter in Charleston harbour in April 1861. Within three weeks of the inconclusive battle at Hampton Roads, the Union had contracted for another ten Ericsson-type monitors of the *Passaic* class, these being among no fewer than sixty-four monitors and turreted ironclads the Union ordered during the Civil War. Another twenty ironclads of other types were also built, but the bulk of the new fleet which comprised monitors formed a coastal and riverine offensive force which was nonetheless to have a profound influence on the development of coastal defence vessels in the decades to come.

The *Passaic*s, launched in 1862–64 and commissioned in 1862–65, had almost double the displacement of *Monitor*, at 1,875 tons. With the same powerplant and speed as *Monitor*, the *Passaic*s carried 50 tons more coal at 150 tons, and a more powerful armament of one 15in (381mm) smoothbore and one 11in smoothbore in the case of seven vessels, including the name ship, two 15in in the case of *Camanche*, and one 15in and one 8in Parrott rifled muzzle-loader on *Lehigh* and *Patapsco*. The 15in suffered from the disadvantage, however, of not projecting from the 21ft-diameter (6.42m) turret, and had to be aimed via the 11in or 8in ports.

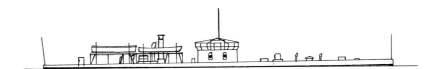

Side armour was better than *Monitor* at 5–3in (127–76mm), with 11in (279.4mm) on the turret and 1in (25.4mm) on the decks. The crew numbers remained modest, at 75, but with better ventilation, more extensive ship's boats arrangements, and a turret-mounted pilot house (which did not turn with the turret), the *Passaic*s were a good deal more practical than *Monitor*. Dimensions were 200ft x 46ft x 10ft 6in (60.96m x 14.01m x 3.2m).

Nine improved versions of the *Passaic*s, the 2,100 ton *Canonicus* class, were built between 1862 and 1865, benefiting from the experience gained during the war. They were longer (223–225ft; 67.97–68.58m), but thinner (43ft–43ft 4in; 13.1–13.2m), and with a deeper draught (12ft 5in–13ft mean; 3.78–3.96m). Armament was standardised at a pair of 15in, but once again the ambitious designed speed of 13kts was beyond the capabilities of the powerplant, identical to the *Passaic*s, except for some which used Stimers in place of Martin boilers. Actual speed was 8kts on trials and in service and the *Catawba*, later sold to Peru, could only make 6kts with her new owner. Side armour protection was as on the *Passaic*s, though turret armour at 10in (254mm) was 1in thinner and deck armour half an inch thicker at 1.5in (38mm). *Catawba* and *Oneota* were sold to Peru in 1868; the others, with the exception of the unfortunate *Tecumseh*, were sold between 1891 and 1907, four of them not having been commissioned in time to take part in the war.

The *Passaic*s were complemented by the first multi-hull monitor, the 4,395 ton *Roanoke*, a former wooden frigate which, after its conversion between May 1862 and April 1863 and its commissioning in June of that year, went to sea with three turrets with a mixed armament of, from fore to aft, one 15in smoothbore and one 8in rifled muzzle-loader, one 15in and one 11in smoothbore, and one 11in and one 8in. Towards the end of the war, in January 1865, three 12pdr smoothbore howitzers were also provided. The 265ft (80.77m) ship was broken aft after its launching and the turrets (with 11in armour) were too heavy for the hull, with its 4.5–3.5in side and 1.5in deck armour. This curious vessel was a local coast defence ship at Hampton Roads and saw no action during the war, being sold in 1883.

Camanche
Camanche *was a later* Passaic, *commissioned in 1865 after being sent to California in pieces following her construction in Jersey City. The pieces were retrieved after being lost on the* Aquila *which sank in San Francisco in 1863. She is seen here as she was in 1898 (CMP)*

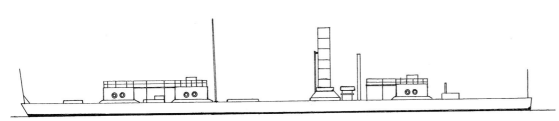

Roanoke
Roanoke *had the distinction of being the turret warship with more than two turrets. A former wooden frigate, she was the heaviest monitor so far, at 4,395 tons, but was not well liked and saw no action (CMP)*

The first purpose-designed multi-turret Union monitor was the twin-turret, 2,551-ton *Onondaga*, launched by Continental Iron Works in July 1863 and commissioned in March 1864. This vessel was somewhat more practical than *Roanoke*, with each turret containing one 15in smoothbore and one 8in Parrott rifled muzzle-loader. Side armour was thicker at a maximum of 5.5in (140mm), though deck armour was thinner at 1in; as on *Roanoke* and the *Passaic*s, turret armour was 11in. The four Martin boilers and 610ihp twin shaft horizontal return connecting rod gave a speed of 7kts, no different from *Monitor*, though the crew, at 150, was twice the size. Dimensions were 228ft 7in x 51ft 2in x 12ft 10in (69.67m x 15.6m x 3.91m).

The next monitor design efforts were aimed at improving the type's seakeeping, so as to permit operations in the open sea. Two classes were built, the four 3,400 ton *Miantonomoh* class, designed by the Bureau for Construction and Repair, and Ericsson's own curiously-named *Dictator*, which displaced 4,438 tons. All were laid down in 1862, the latter in August, but the former class was a better bet and were proven to have good seakeeping characteristics.

Wooden-hulled vessels, the *Miantonomoh*s were armed with four 15in in two turrets with thinner 10in armour than previous monitors; side armour was 5.5in, deck protection 1.5in and pilot houses were provided on top of each turret. Actual speed was 9–10kts, designed speed not being known, provided by four Martin boilers and, in *Agamenticus* and *Miantonomoh*, Ericsson vibrating lever engines, with Isherwood[6] horizontal return connecting rod engines in *Monadnock* and *Tonawanda*, both engine types apparently generating 1,400ihp. Coal bunkerage of 300 tons was good, though not as good as *Roanoke*'s 550 tons, but the class proved its long range capabilities when *Monadnock* went to San Francisco via Cape Horn in 1865–66 and when *Miantonomoh* went for a cruise of 17,767 miles to Europe in 1866–67.

Dictator differed from the *Miantonomoh*s not only in being 1,038 tons heavier, yet only being fitted with a single turret with a pair of 15in smoothbores, but also in disposing of a significantly heavier armour package, comprising 15in (381mm) on the turret, 6–1in (152–25mm) on the sides and 2in (50mm) for the deck. But where *Dictator* failed was in speed: her designed speed of 11kts was not reached, her

actual service speed being 9kts. Six Martin boilers were provided but Ericsson stuck with his own vibrating lever engine, developing 3,500ihp. As completed in November 1864, *Dictator* is believed to have been fitted with a hurricane deck around the funnel amidships. Her mechanical failings curtailed an action during the conflict and she was laid up after the war, being sold in 1883. Dimensions were 312ft x 50ft x 20ft 6in mean (95.1m x 15.24m x 6.25m).

One other monitor based on the *Dictator* design was *Puritan*, laid down in July 1862. Though launched in 1864, this 4,912 ton vessel (as planned) was never completed, and was surreptitiously broken up in 1874–75 to allow for the clandestine construction of a new replacement under the so-called 'great repairs' ordered by Secretary of the Navy George Robeson (see Chapter 5).

Four other wooden-hulled monitors never completed during the war would have been the largest, the *Kalamazoo*s, intended to displace 5,660 tons. With deeper draughts and more generous 3ft 9in (1.146m) freeboards than the *Miantonomoh*s on which they were based (their freeboards being 2ft 7in or 0.78m), the *Kalamazoo* class were laid down in 1863 and 1864 but were eventually broken up on the stocks in 1874 (*Shackamaxon*) and 1884 for the other three vessels. Conceived with the intention of being able to use their four 15in in a seaway, they have been stated to be 'the only monitors that could have fought contemporary European warships on equal terms outside protected coastal areas'.[7]

Two other significant types of monitor were built for the US Navy during the Civil War, the *Milwaukee* and *Casco* classes, of which four of the former were built while of the twenty *Casco*s, just eight were completed in time to be commissioned during the Civil War, none seeing any action.

The 1,300 ton *Milwaukee*s were launched at Union Iron Works at Carondelet on the Mississippi (not to be confused with the later San Francisco yard of the same name) in May 1862, being commissioned between May and August 1864. They were designed by J B Eads for riverine service, but spent most of their Civil War service with the West Gulf Blockading Squadron. Admiral Farragut had *Chickasaw* and *Winnebago* under his command at the Battle of Mobile Bay and said 'no vessels in his fleet performed more efficient service'.[8] The other two vessels in this turtle-decked class were *Kickapoo* and *Milwaukee*.

Powered by seven horizontal tubular boilers, the *Milwaukee*s' four shaft horizontal non-condensing engines were intended to provide a speed as designed of 9kts; horse-

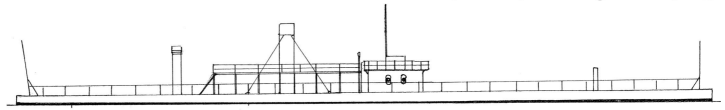

power is not known. Side armour composed of three 1in plates extended 4in beneath the waterline on three vessels, while *Winnebago* had heavy 3in-thick iron plates. The turrets had 8in (203mm) armour protection and the deck half an inch (12.7mm). The class garnered considerable praise from Farragut and others, not least because of the installation of an Eads turret forward for two of the four 11in Dahlgren smoothbores on all four vessels in the class; the other turret was an Ericsson design.

The *Scientific American* of 28 November 1863 described the guns in the Eads turret as being 'placed on a huge platform, loaded in the hold, and raised in the turret by steam power. They are also run out by steam; the recoil is received on steam cylinders, and the whole apparatus, guns and all, is operated by one man.' Elevation of the guns in the Eads turret was 20 degrees, twice that of the Ericsson turret. Dimensions of these vessels was 229ft x 56ft x 6ft mean (69.8m x 17.07m x 1.83m). All but *Milwaukee*, which met her end at Mobile Bay in 1865, were sold in 1874.

The *Casco* class of shallow draught monitors did not share the success of the *Milwaukee*s. With a designed displacement of 1,175 tons (but which reached 1,618 tons in the case of *Squando*), their dimensions were 225ft x 45ft x 6ft 4.5in (68.58m x 13.72m x 1.94m) and their designed freeboard, as completed, was supposed to be 15in, but was nearer 3in, as shown by the example of *Chimo*. The failure to correctly calculate displacement doomed many of the class to either non-completion or non-delivery to the navy. The twin ironies of this situation were that, as designed, the class was lightly armoured to meet the demand for shallow draught (armour thickness being as on the *Milwaukee*s), and a ballast tank was installed to enable the *Casco*s to go into action partially submerged, keeping their silhouettes low. The reason behind this was the riverine threat posed by the Confederate ram *Albermarle*, among other vessels, which could not be countered with deeper draught monitors.

Armed with two 11in smoothbores, another of the *Casco*s' considerable failings was their inability to meet the designed service speed of 9kts, which in fact did not exceed 5kts, machinery comprising two Stimers boilers and twin shaft Stimers direct acting inclined engines. Dogged by delays, the programme was noteworthy for a complete change in its direction with the decision to complete five ships (*Casco, Chimo, Modoc, Napa* and *Naubuc*) as spar torpedo vessels without turrets, a single 11in on an open pivot mounting, and with a thinner deck. *Casco* cleared mines in the James River, but 5kts was not exactly a hopeful starting point for a spar torpedo attack. Fifteen monitors in the class had their hulls deepened at least to allow them to carry the required weights and of these, *Tunxis* was recommissioned with one 11in and one 8in Parrott rifled muzzle-loader. All of the class received new names mostly derived from Greek mythology in June 1869, recovering their former names less than two months later, though some kept their new names or were renamed yet again. All of this troubled class, complete or not, were sold or broken up in 1874–75.

Besides the monitors and the intended riverine craft of the *Milwaukee* and *Casco* classes, the Union Navy also commissioned five other river monitors the function of which is of tangential relevance to this account. For the record they were the two vessels of the *Neosho* class, the single vessel *Ozark*, and the two ships of the *Marietta* class. All were armed with two 11in Dahlgren smoothbores and were 180ft or 170ft (*Marietta* class) long, with old tonnage displacements of 523 tons, 578 tons and 429 tons for *Neosho*, *Ozark* and *Marietta* respectively.

The Union of course commissioned numerous other seagoing, coastal and riverine armoured vessels, with casemated or conventional side armour for the time. These ranged from the seagoing ironclad *New Ironsides* to the thirteen casemated riverine craft known as the 'Pook turtles' after their designer Samuel M Pook.

Battles Joined

The Union's advantage in industrial power, as evidenced by the large number of monitors and other ironclads built during the conflict, could never be equalled by the Confederacy, which tried, but mostly failed, to obtain ironclads from Britain and France. However a handful of armoured vessels were acquired, notably the 1,400 ton armoured ram *Stonewall*, built by Arman at Bordeaux. The replacement casemate ironclad *Virginia*, laid down at Richmond in 1863 after the destruction of its original namesake, and commissioned in 1864, had a short enough career, being scuttled on the evacuation of Richmond. Meanwhile the casemate ship *Tennessee*, which like the first and second *Virginia*s, was armed with 7in Brooke rifled muzzle-loaders, was eventually obliged to surrender at the Battle of Mobile Bay on 5 August 1864.

As for the Union's ironclads, after Hampton Roads the *Passaic*s took on the major part of the burden of the Union ironclads' assault on Charleston. As a result of their experience, some of them were given additional armour and they also carried a pair of light guns, usually 12pdr smoothbore howitzers on field carriages.

Meanwhile the twin-turret monitor *Onondaga*, the Union's first purpose-designed multi-turret monitor, saw active service at the James River, being sold in 1867 to the French Navy, which retained the vessel's name, but re-armed it with four 240mm (9.4in) M1864 or M1866 breechloaders, themselves replaced by M1870s; the vessel was only stricken in 1904. Of the *Miantonomoh*s, only *Monadnock* saw action in the Civil War, while *Dictator*'s effort to participate in the attack on Fort Fisher was called off because of excessive wear on her short shaft bearings.

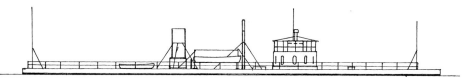

Saugus
Saugus *was one of the*
Canonicus *class monitors,*
built as improved
Passaics, *with iron and*
wood upper hulls and iron
lower hulls. Armament
was a pair of 15in
smoothbores (CMP)

Of the *Canonicus* class, *Tecumseh* was unfortunate enough to strike a mine in Mobile Bay on 5 August 1864, sinking in under half a minute. The vessel's commander, Captain T A M Craven, a Mexican War veteran, displayed particular heroism which is worth recalling. The *Tecumseh*'s sinking was so rapid that it was clear to Craven that there would only be time to get either his pilot or himself out of the turret via a narrow opening in the turret tower before the vessel's swift sinking. Craven made way for his pilot and died accordingly.

The next year, on 28 March, *Milwaukee*, one of the best of the Union's monitors, also struck a mine on the port side abaft the after turret. But unlike *Tecumseh*, *Milwaukee* took three minutes or so to sink at the stern, but the forward compartments did not fill for almost an hour, 'indicating better subdivision than usual in monitors at that time'.[9]

Overall, the Civil War's outcome was plainly predestined, in that the Confederacy's industrial weakness made its defeat ultimately inevitable, especially given the Union's strategy of invading the South using the Mississippi and its tributaries. The Union's blockade of the South was successful because, in addition to the US Navy's core of warships, the four blockading squadrons were also able to draw on large number of armed merchant ships. The Union's successful attack on the Mississippi forts in April 1862, culminating in the fall of New Orleans, were mere

precursors to their dazzling success at the Battle of Mobile Bay in August 1864. The battle is of course memorable not only for its military results, but also for Farragut's famous command after *Tecumseh* hit a 'torpedo' (mine): 'Damn the torpedoes, full steam ahead'. Four Union ships surrounded and repeatedly rammed the *Tennessee*, forcing her to surrender. It is tempting to speculate whether this occasion, and the examples of other Civil War vessels which had successfully rammed their opponents, may have inspired Austria's Admiral Tegetthoff at that key moment during the Battle of Lissa two years later.

1 *Conway's All the World's Fighting Ships 1860–1905*, (CMP, London, 1979), p119. See Afterword for reference to William C Davis, *Duel between the First Ironclads* (Stackpolt Books, Mechanicsburg, Pennsylvania, 1994).

2 Antony Preston, *Battleships 1856–1905*, (Phoebus Publishing, London, 1977), p12. Description of *Virginia* in Conway's Fighting Ships 1860–1905, ibid, p134, does not mention displacement.

3 William N Still, in Robert Gardiner (Ed), *Steam, Steel & Shellfire, The Steam Warship 1815–1905*, (CMP, London, 1992), p74. See pp61–74 for a detailed account of steam warships in the American Civil War.

4 *Conway's Fighting Ships 1860–1905*, op.cit., p134.

5 Preston, *Battleships 1856–1919*, op.cit., p12.

6 Lt. Richard H Webber (Ed.), *Monitors of the U.S. Navy 1861–1937*, Naval History Division, Navy Department (Washington, 1969), p20 records Isherwood engines, not recorded in other sources. This short monograph is a useful guide to the subject.

7 Ibid., p28.

8 Ibid,. p35.

9 *Conway's Fighting Ships 1860–1905*, op.cit., p123.

CHAPTER 3

Royal Navy coast defence turret ships 1860–80

THREE PARTICULAR WARSHIP CLASSES in the Royal Navy critically influenced the creation of both the seagoing turret battleship and the further development of the classic coast defence ship. In 1862, less than two months after the inconclusive but momentous encounter across the Atlantic between *Monitor* and *Virginia*, the conversion of *Royal Sovereign* into a turret ship, the RN's first, was started. Far more seaworthy than *Monitor*, this vessel showed that turret ships could indeed wrest control of the inshore seas from purely sail-rigged crafts.

But even before *Royal Sovereign* was conceived, the design of the RN's first purpose-built iron turret ship, *Prince Albert*, had been completed, although the ship itself did not enter service until eighteen months after *Royal Sovereign*. Both vessels were essentially simple coast defence vessels, but *Prince Albert* was a more robust vessel and remained in service until practically the beginning of the twentieth century.

There is a clear design link between *Prince Albert* and the two *Cerberus* class coast defence monitors of 1870. The latter were the first British-designed turret ships without sail, and as such they further directly influenced the revolutionary *Devastation* class turret ships, the first unambiguously seagoing turret ships. These were the true progenitors of the battleships of the late nineteenth century, leading directly to the even more impressive *Dreadnought*. Thus can a clear lineage be established between *Royal Sovereign* and *Prince Albert* and both the classic seagoing battleships and their

coastal relatives. If *Monitor* is rightly regarded as having been a trend-setter in warship design, it is still perhaps more relevant for the historian to examine how simple turret ships like *Royal Sovereign* and *Prince Albert* had such a lasting influence on the development of somewhat more seaworthy battleships, regardless of whether they were dedicated solely to coastal defence tasks.

In America, after all, the massive effort put into creating large fleets of viable inshore turret ships, monitors which were not really fit for long sea passages, was not further developed to the next logical step, a true seagoing turret ship. In this sense, therefore, the RN's experience with the turret ship is of somewhat greater and more lasting relevance, although Britain was not alone at this time in experimenting with turret ships more seaworthy than their original American inspirations. Although the objective was to create a seagoing turret battleship, among other seagoing ironclads, Britain still showed considerable interest in the coast defence concept, as shown variously by the construction of the breastwork monitor *Glatton*, the ironclad ram *Hotspur* and the four *Cyclops* class coast defence monitors. Other coast defence oddities were the *Scorpion* class turret barques originally intended for the Confederate Navy, and the pair of *Belleisle* class armoured rams first destined for the Ottoman fleet.

Captain Cowper Coles' work on practical designs for turntable mountings for heavy guns was hampered by his own ship-design pretensions, but nonetheless a first turret

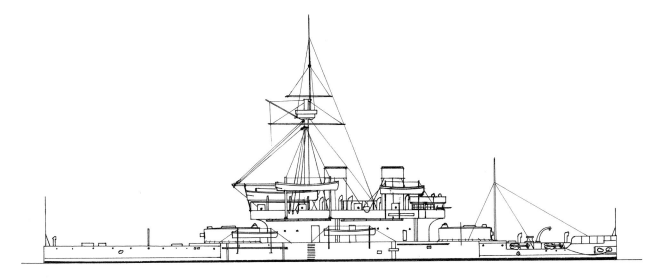

Dreadnought
The direct result of all the experimentation with coast defence turret ships in the Royal Navy was Dreadnought, *the first revolutionary vessel of the late nineteenth and early twentieth centuries to bear the name. Effectively a derivative of* Devastation, Dreadnought *was yet wetter in a seaway than her predecessor (CMP)*

Glatton
The single turret breastwork monitor Glatton *was intended for both coastal defence and offence and is seen here in an* Illustrated London News *drawing of December 1871 (GPH Collection)*

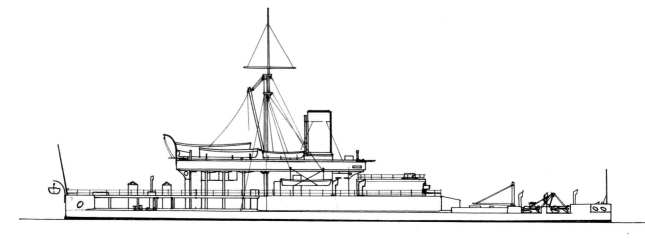

Glatton
Line drawing of Glatton. *Faster than her designed speed,* Glatton *spent her career at Portsmouth (CMP)*

experiment was performed with the installation of a single-gun turret on the armoured battery *Trusty* in 1861. Successful firing and defence trials at Shoeburyness, in which the turret was proved capable of firing a dozen rounds in just over six minutes, twice as fast as a similar broadside gun, and in which it was shown that the turret could freely move after twenty-nine hits from 68pdrs and 110pdrs, settled the argument that a turret ship should be built.[1] The first was *Prince Albert*, swiftly followed by the order for the *Royal Sovereign* conversion.

Improvements in armour protection in Europe, specifically the introduction of wrought iron armour of growing thickness, provided significant advances over the application of armour protection in the United States, the birthplace of the *Monitor*. America's laminated armour was cruder than wrought iron plate, while the Confederacy's armour fashioned from rolled railway irons was an inadequate expedient born of desperation.

In gunnery, the muzzle-loaded smoothbore still ruled in the very early 1860s before *Royal Sovereign* and *Prince Albert* were conceived. The problems of Armstrong's rifled breech-loader, which had entered widespread British service by 1862, but which subsequently suffered numerous accidents, showed that the way forward was a road strewn with development obstacles. Against the breech-loader's superior theoretical penetration, range and accuracy were set the practical difficulties of manufacturing reliable rifling in large calibre weapons. The gunnery trials of 1863–65 led to the adoption of the Woolwich muzzle-loading rifled gun, a reliable weapon which was nonetheless retained in service for far too long – until 1879. Towards the end of the period, even the guns on the *Dreadnought* turret ship which had itself been inspired by *Devastation* were being outclassed by the experimental Fraser system gun which, in its 16in (408mm) version, could penetrate no less than 21in (533mm) of iron at 1,000 yards (914m).

The simple horizontal steam engine and return connecting rod engine of *Prince Albert* and *Royal Sovereign* provided a far more reliable and compact form of propulsion than that on the early paddle steamers. The combination of these advances in armour, armament and propulsion, together with the further innovation of the (often hand-driven) armour-protected turret, were the components of the application of new technology to warships which would allow the revolution initiated by *Monitor* to inspire true seagoing turret ships.

Although not directly relevant, this survey of British coast defence vessels after 1860 would not be complete without brief reference to the 'flatiron' gunboats built for the RN during this period. Between 1867 and 1881, no fewer than thirty-nine of these curious little craft were launched for the RN, because of the invasion scares of the 1860s and 1870s, and their only conceivable role was coastal defence, yet they were too slow and unwieldy for even this task. The first two prototypes, *Staunch* and *Plucky*, displaced 200 tons and 212 tons respectively and each carried one 9in (228.6mm) rifled muzzle-loader. The twenty succeeding *Ant* class and the four *Gadfly* class boats, launched in 1870–74 and 1879 respectively, all displaced 254 tons and carried a single 10in (254mm) rifled muzzle-loader, which was also the armament of the two 265 ton *Bouncer* class boats launched in 1881. Finally the eleven 386 ton *Medina* class boats launched in 1876–77 were more modestly armed with three 64pdr rifled muzzle-loaders.

Royal Sovereign

Originally laid down in Portsmouth dockyard in 1849 as a steam powered, wooden line-of-battle-ship which was not launched until 1857, *Royal Sovereign*, as a 121-gun vessel, was thoroughly obsolescent by the early 1860s. At Coles' suggestion, it was decided to convert *Royal Sovereign*, among other vessels, into turret ships for coastal defence. This was not, however, the first warship to carry Coles turrets, this distinction being enjoyed by the little Danish coast defence ship *Rolf Krake*, of which more in the next chapter.

The Admiralty was concerned that the proposed conversions might not have been appropriate given the stresses which heavy iron turrets could place on wooden hulls. Because of this worry it was decided to hold the conversion

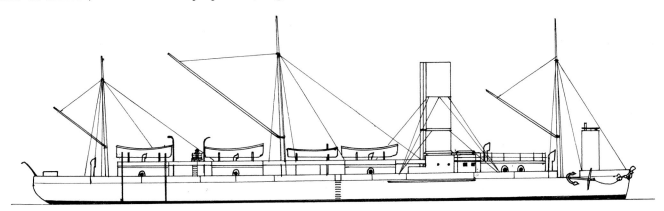

Royal Sovereign
The first Royal Navy turret ship to enter service, Royal Sovereign *is shown as she was in 1864 after conversion from a three-decker sailing ship of the line. It has been said that her draught was too great for her coast defence role* (CMP)

Devastation
Inspired by the Cerberus *class, Reed's* Devastation *provides the direct link between the monitor-type coast defence vessel and the classic battleship of the late nineteenth century (GPH Collection)*

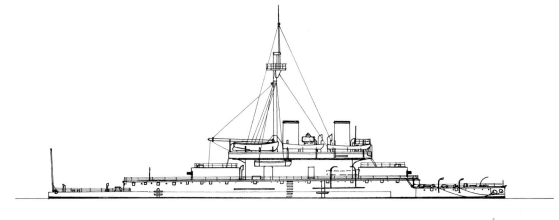

programme to just one vessel – *Royal Sovereign*, the work being completed in August 1864.

The initial design concept behind *Royal Sovereign* was for no fewer than 10 muzzle-loading 68pdrs or 110pdrs mounted in five turrets weighing 80 tons, mounted *en echelon*. This arrangement gave way to four turrets mounting five somewhat heavier 10.5in (267mm), 150pdr smoothbore muzzle-loaders. One pair of guns was mounted in the forward turret, weighing 163 tons, with three single turrets, each weighing 151 tons, aft of the single steam funnel. In a later refit in 1867 these guns were replaced by 9in rifled muzzle-loaders, this being the result of the major trials conducted between 1863 and 1865 to choose a future rifled gun. The chosen design used the Woolwich groove, a modification of a French concept, with steel tubes reinforced by coiled wrought iron hoops and tubes.

Royal Sovereign was a curiosity in several respects. Displacing 5,080 tons standard load, she was a somewhat ungainly three-masted conversion, with a length to beam ratio of 4:1, the smallest in a British armoured vessel: dimensions were 240ft 6in x 62ft x 23ft 3in (73.3m x 18.9m x 7.09m); draught has also been recorded as 25ft (7.62m).[2] Freeboard, at 7ft (2.13m) amidships with 3ft 6in (1.06m) hinged bulwarks to allow the turrets to fire, made *Royal Sovereign* a more seagoing vessel than *Monitor*.

The whole hull was armoured, with an iron belt 5.5in (140mm) thick, slimming down to 4.5in (114mm) at the ends fore and aft, behind which lay an oak hull 36in (918mm) thick. Side armour was 36in (914mm), turret armour ranged from 10in–5.5in (254–140mm), over 14in of teak, with 5.5in for the conning tower. *Royal Sovereign*'s Maudslay two cylinder return connecting rod engines originally gave a speed of 12.25kts, but after reconstruction this fell to 11kts.

Originally a three-decker, as a single decker with the turrets installed on the lower gundeck (reclassified as the upper deck), *Royal Sovereign*'s initial schooner rigging comprised a foresail, mainsail with jib amidships and a further sail aft. This gave way to a simpler fore and aft steadying canvas rig which seems to have been rarely used. A distinctive and noteworthy feature was the large crowned lion installed in the bow.

In trials in 1866 the central battery ironclad *Bellerophon* fired three 9in rounds with 43lb charges at *Royal Sovereign*'s after turret, none of them interrupting its operation.[3] *Royal Sovereign* saw no action and was sold for breaking up in 1885. Nevertheless it had a significant impact on succeeding RN warships.

Prince Albert

In approving only the conversion of *Royal Sovereign* into a turret ship, the Admiralty was erring on the side of caution. Although Hampton Roads had shown that ironclads could survive a battle, the Admiralty's circumspection about these vessels was seemingly to be borne out by the unimpressive performance of US monitors at the Battle of Charleston in 1863. Besides *Royal Sovereign*'s trials, the Admiralty also wished to await trials with *Prince Albert*, the RN's first purpose-designed turret ship, before accepting that Coles' turrets were the way forward for the arrangement of the main armament of seagoing ironclads.

Designed by Isaac Watts and ordered in February 1862, *Prince Albert* was laid down at Samuda Brothers in London in April 1862, being launched in May 1864 and finally completed after delays in February 1866. She was the result of an extended design process which saw Coles put forward several ideas for turret ships to the Admiralty. One concept envisaged a 5,660 ton ship and another outlined a plan for two smaller vessels. The first idea was too expensive, while the second did not deliver the requisite armour protection, so in January 1862 plans were drawn up for a significantly more ambitious warship with displacement of 4,020 tons

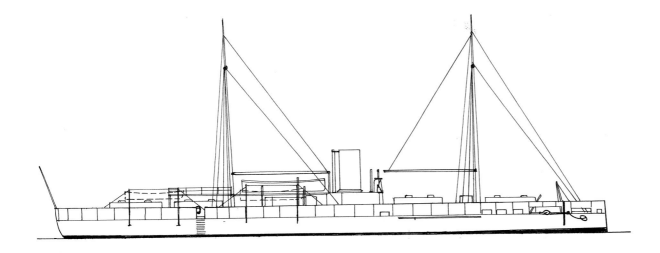

Prince Albert
The first Royal Navy iron turret ship, Prince Albert *was designed before* Royal Sovereign *but her construction was delayed, her design being altered from six to four turrets. She is shown here as completed in 1866 (CMP)*

and a heavy battery of a dozen 10.5in, 300pdr rifled breech-loaders in six 80 ton turrets.

However Coles' ambitions were not to be realised, as Captain Cooper Key of the RN gunnery establishment HMS *Excellent* had conducted an assessment of the proposed use of the 10.5in and concluded that the heaviest gun which could be used aboard the vessel would be a 9.2in 100pdr weighing 6.5 tons, almost half the 12 ton weight of the massive 10.5in. Following this it was decided in February 1865 to reduce the number of turrets to four, each with just one of the newly approved 9in 250pdr rifled muzzle-loaders, all mounted on the same deck, this approach becoming the norm on broadside ironclads. Hinged bulwarks 5ft high protected the massive 111 ton turrets in a seaway; these bulwarks could be dropped for action and, unlike *Royal Sovereign*, *Prince Albert* was capable of end-on fire. The turrets were hand-operated, requiring 18 men to complete a revolution, but the men were out of the turret officer's sight, making control a problem.

Prince Albert's final displacement, variously recorded as 3,687 or 3,880 tons standard,[4] and dimensions of 240ft x 48ft x 20ft 6in (73.15m x 14.63m x 6.25m) max, made for a substantially more compact and less beamy vessel (5:1) than *Royal Sovereign*. The twin-masted schooner sail arrangement for long voyages, with a midships funnel, also made for a neater appearance. Speed – courtesy of a Humphreys & Tennant two cylinder horizontal direct acting steam engine, and four rectangular boilers driving a single shaft – was 11.26kts. This was more than the rebuilt *Royal Sovereign* (11kts), with less installed power (2,128ihp vs 2,460ihp). *Prince Albert* needed a third fewer crew members at 201, than the 300 of *Royal Sovereign*. *Prince Albert* was reboilered in 1878.

Armour protection reflected the original intention to mount six turrets, with the whole of the 7ft sides being armoured for stability. The 4.5in (114mm) belt, decreasing to 3.375in (86mm) at the ends, had an 18in wood backing, with a 10.5in battery. As on *Royal Sovereign*, turret armour ranged from 5.5in to 10in for the turret faces, with 14in (357mm) wood backing, while deck armour at just over 1–0.75in was enough for splinter protection, although the bases of the turret were unprotected beneath the upper deck.

Prince Albert's coal provision of 229 tons allowed seven days' steaming at economical cruise speed; range at a near-maximum speed of 10–11kts was 930 miles in three and a half days. *Royal Sovereign* had the edge in this respect, with bunkers for 350 tons of coal. *Prince Albert* was given a major refit in 1866–67 soon after entering service, with the addition of a flying bridge over the two forward turrets, on which six machine guns were later installed. The name of the deceased Prince Consort ensured that, at Queen Victoria's behest, *Prince Albert* remained in service until 1899 when she was sold for breaking up.

The Cerberus class

Cerberus and *Magdala*, of which the former was laid down at Palmers in Jarrow in September 1867 and the latter at Thames Iron Works in Blackwall in October 1868, being launched in December 1868 and March 1870 respectively, were low-freeboard coast defence ships for service at Melbourne and Bombay respectively and carried no sailing rig, for the first time in a British ironclad vessel. They were completed in September and November 1870 respectively.

Displacing 3,344 tons standard, *Cerberus*' Maudslay twin shaft machinery delivered 1,369ihp and a more modest speed of 9.75kts than either *Royal Sovereign* or *Prince Albert*, though *Magdala*'s twin shaft Ravenhill machinery provided 1,435ihp for a speed of 10.6kts. These Reed-designed vessels were significantly more compact than their forebears, with four 10in muzzle-loaders mounted in two twin turrets on a raised breastwork upper deck. Face turret armour of 10in and 9in on the turret walls, plus belt armour of 8in to 6in (203–152mm) and breastwork armour of 9in to 8in, was sufficient to cope with these vessels' probable armoured cruiser adversaries; the dimensions of the class were 225ft x 45ft x 15ft 4in (68.58m x 13.72m x 4.67m).

A single pole mast was mounted forward of the forward turret on the shelter deck, and an extended flying bridge was originally installed after completion, though this was cut back to the superstructure's length on *Magdala*. *Cerberus* was fitted with a three-mast sailing rig for her transit to Melbourne. She passed the later years of her service as a depot ship at Williamstown. *Magdala*'s main armament gave way to 8in breech-loaders in 1882, and machine guns were also installed on the shelter deck. *Magdala* was finally sold for breaking up in 1904, but *Cerberus* ended her days in Melbourne as the depot ship *Platypus II* until she was sunk in 1926. She is still resting on the bottom there, the turret supports having been eroded by tidal action, and in 1994 concern was expressed that without the finances to preserve her, *Cerberus* will 'inevitably vanish'.[5]

Abyssinia, Glatton and Hotspur

A third turret ship, not normally counted in the *Cerberus* class, but nonetheless very similar despite its lower 2,901 ton standard displacement, was *Abyssinia* which, like *Cerberus*, also performed coast defence duties at Bombay. Laid down at Dudgeon in Poplar in July 1868, *Abyssinia* was launched in February 1870, was completed in October of that year and was significantly more economic with manpower than *Cerberus*, with a crew of 100 against its predecessor's 155. With a similar breastwork arrangement to the *Cerberus* class and a pair of turrets each mounting two 10in rifled muzzle-loaders, *Abyssinia* had a lower freeboard than *Cerberus*, a single pole mast, and fewer ship's boats.

The midships belt armour, at 7in (177.8mm), was 1in thinner than *Cerberus* and similarly the breastwork armour was 1in thinner at its maximum of 8in, while the turrets' wall armour was also 1in thinner at 8in. The twin shaft Dudgeon engine delivered 1,200ihp for a speed of 9.59kts. Dimensions were 225ft x 42ft x 14ft 7in (68.58m x 12.8m x 4.45m). Like *Magdala*, *Abyssinia* was rearmed with four 8in breech-loaders in 1892 and was sold for breaking up in 1903.

At around the same time as the construction of the *Cerberus* class, the decision was taken to approve *Glatton*, a large 245ft (74.68m), 4,912 tons (standard) monitor with a 54ft (16.46m) breadth, 19–19.5ft (5.79m+) draught and 2–3ft freeboard. Laid down at Chatham Dockyard in August 1868, *Glatton* was launched in March 1871 and was completed in February 1872 with an armament of two 10in rifled muzzle-loaders. A very reasonable speed for her armour of 12.11kts was provided by a twin shaft Lairds steam engine developing 2,870ihp. This performance significantly exceeded the design speed of 9.75kts. This was surprising given the heavy armour of a 12–10in (306–255mm) belt, 6.5ft (1.98m) deep, which had 15–21in (382.5–533mm) wood backing, along with 12in breastwork armour and turret armour of 14–12in (357–306mm) for the face and sides respectively. The conning tower was protected by 9–6in, while deck armour ranged from 3in to 1.5in.

Designed unwillingly by Edward Reed, the single-masted *Glatton*, though based at Portsmouth as a coast defence vessel, had a deep draught for deep water operations.

However, her low freeboard made her wet forward in practically any kind of sea. Her stern was built up to the same deck level as the breastwork, being connected to the main superstructure by a rather messy hurricane deck. Refitted in the 1880s with three 6pdr quick-firers, four machine guns and 14in torpedo launchers, *Glatton* went into reserve in 1889 and was sold for breaking up in 1903.

A little smaller than *Glatton* was another curious one-off, the 4,331 ton standard load ironclad ram *Hotspur*, laid down by Napier in Govan in October 1868 to counter the 'threat' posed by similar French vessels. She was launched in March 1870 and completed in November 1871. Although she was not built as a turret ship, given her fixed 10in-armoured gun-house for her single 12in rifled muzzle-loader, *Hotspur* was a coast defence ironclad which was eventually to be reconstructed as a turret ship in the 1880s. Secondary armament comprised a pair of 64pdrs behind bulwarks aft. Armour protection was good, with an 11in (279.4mm) belt amidships, thinning at the ends to 8in, which was also the armour of the breastworks. Deck armour was 1.5–2.75in (38.2–70.1mm) ranging from the breastwork deck to the main deck.

Hotspur's main 'weapon' was her 10ft (3.06m) ram, reinforced by the extension of her side armour. The ram became a feature of most capital ships between the 1860s and 1890s because of the exaggerated conclusions reached by naval strategists after the Battle of Lissa on 20 July 1866 between Austria and Italy. A digression is necessary.

Wyvern
Wyvern was a masted turret ship built originally for the Confederate States of America but not delivered because of British neutrality in the American Civil War (GPH Collection)

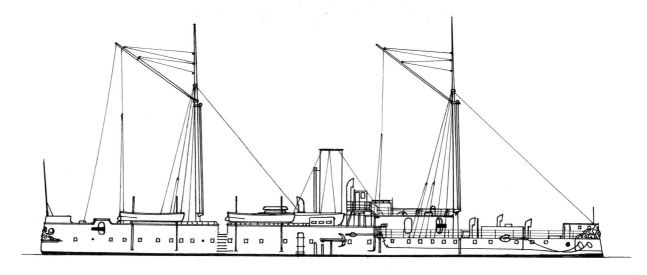

In this engagement, critically influenced by the relative timidity of the Italian commander, Count Carlo Pellion di Persano, one Italian vessel, the frigate *Re d'Italia*, was sunk by ramming by Rear Admiral Tegetthoff's ironclad flagship *Erzherzog Ferdinand Max* when the Italian ship was unable to steer because of an unlucky hit on her rudder. Significantly, other Austrian attempts to ram Italian ships, and vice versa, failed, but after Lissa the ram became a feature of late nineteenth-century warship design which was regarded as essential, and which has been much derided since the period.

Was the ram such a completely indefensible addition as many historians have since maintained, with the benefit of hindsight, of course? Given that there was no example of a major fleet action to draw on other than Lissa, and given also the known shortcomings of the range of both rifled and smoothbore weapons of the period and the length of time it took to both reload them and, in the case of some vessels, manually train the turrets which contained them, the feeling that the ram was the one weapon which could certainly have a decisive effect on an engagement if used properly was entirely forgivable, if misplaced. After all, one abiding lesson of Lissa was how ineffective the guns of the period were.

However, the obsession with the ram was not so understandable by the 1890s. By this time, far better longer range gunnery was available and penetrating any target's armour at over 1,000 yards (914m) was not such an achievement as it was considered to be in the late 1860s when this was the range at which, typically, a 9in 250lb shell was expected to penetrate 10in of iron.

The reconstruction of *Hotspur* in Lairds in 1881–83 involved the replacement of the gun house with a compound armour turret of 2.75in (70.1mm) steel on 5.75in (146.6mm) iron and a complete citadel with 8in protection, which replaced the breastwork. The new guns were a pair of 12in rifled muzzle-loaders and a pair of 6in (152mm) breech-loaders which replaced the 64pdrs. Other new armament comprised torpedoes and even a torpedo boat. *Hotspur* was also reboilered with steam steering gear, but the ship was useless for its original coast defence role, and was a poor sea boat.

A considerably larger seagoing version of *Hotspur* was *Rupert*, a 5,440 ton (standard) ironclad turret ram built at Chatham Dockyard between 1870 and 1874, while a pair of armoured rams built by Samuda between 1874 and 1882 were the 4,870 ton ex-Turkish *Belleisle* and *Orion*, which were eventually reclassified as second-class battleships and then as coast defence ships. Their armament of four 12in rifled muzzle-loaders was central battery-mounted, however, and despite sundry refits did not prove genuinely useful even in the modest coast defence role, *Belleisle* being used as a target from 1900 to 1903 and *Orion* (renamed *Orontes* in 1902), being relegated to harbour duties between 1902 and 1913.

The Cyclops class

Cerberus also inspired the construction of four very similar vessels of the 3,480 ton (standard) *Cyclops* class, with two twin 10in rifled muzzle-loaders and exactly the same armour protection as the ship on which they were based, apart from deck armour which at 1.5in (38.1mm) was a quarter to half an inch thicker than on *Cerberus*. Dimensions were also identical, apart from draught which at 16ft 3in (4.97m) was deeper than *Cerberus*' 15ft 4in (4.6m). Five fewer crew members, at 150, were required.

The one area in which the *Cyclops* class showed variations on the model set by *Cerberus* was in propulsion, and in the very different results which it delivered on each of the four ships. Thus *Cyclops* and *Hydra* both had John Elder twin cylinder compound engines which delivered 1,660ihp and 11kts in the case of *Cyclops*, but 1,472ihp and 11.2kts in

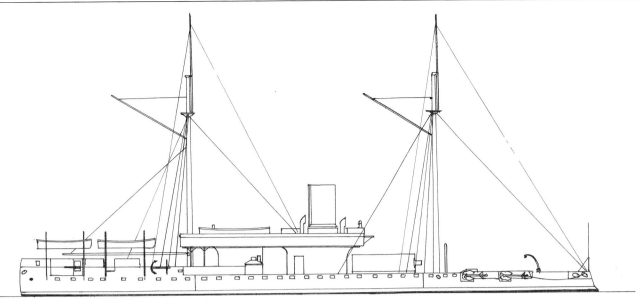

Rupert
Another ironclad ram was
Rupert, *seen here as*
completed in 1874, which
was a larger vessel than
Hotspur *and went some*
way towards correcting its
deficiencies (CMP)

Hydra and Cyclops
The Cyclops *class*
breastwork monitors – the
line drawing is of Hydra
as completed in 1876 and
the illustration is of
Cyclops *– were repeats of*
the Cerberus *class and,*
like Devastation, *were*
later improved with the
extension of the breastwork
to improve seakeeping
(CMP)

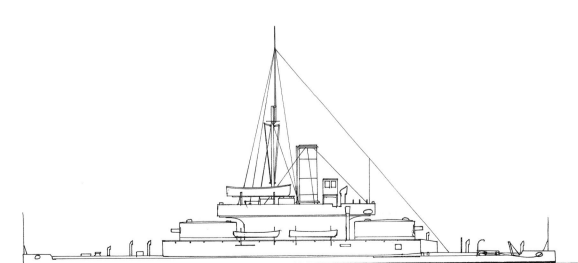

Hydra's case. *Hecate* and *Gorgon* had Ravenhill twin shaft, twin cylinder horizontal direct acting engines, which yet managed to deliver 1,670ihp and 11.14kts in the case of *Gorgon*, and 1,755ihp but a slower 10.9kts in *Hecate*'s case.

There is no ready explanation for the differences in performance between ships equipped with the same engines, but it should be noted that each of the four was built in a different shipyard, all four being laid down in September 1870, launched between July and December 1871, but completed at significantly different dates. *Cyclops*, built by Thames Iron Works, was only finished in May 1877, in which month *Hecate* was also completed by Dudgeon, of Poplar. *Gorgon*, built by Palmers of Jarrow, was actually the first to be completed in March 1874, while *Hydra*, built by Napiers, at Govan, was ready by May 1876.

Were these differences in performance attributable to shipbuilders' or engine builders' skills alone, or was this simply a case of some stokers being more experienced than others? Given that trials were notorious at this time for presenting misleading performance information, perhaps not too much should be read into these differences, though clearly shipyards' quality-control varied.

Confiscated Confederate prizes

Two coast defence turret ships of the period, *Scorpion* and *Wyvern*, were more similar to *Prince Albert* in conception, although like the *Cerberus* class they had twin turrets and unlike both had modest ram bows and were intended to be ocean-going vessels. Laid down in April 1862 by Laird Brothers at Birkenhead, and with Egypt as their official client, these ships' real destination was to have been the Confederate States Navy, their intended names being *North Carolina* and *Mississippi*. The Confederate agent James Bulloch had contracted for these vessels in July 1861 and their delivery was due in early 1863, but the British Government discovered the ruse and on completion they were confiscated by Britain and then bought for the RN in 1864. *Scorpion* was launched in July 1863 and *Wyvern* in August of that year, both being completed in October 1865.

Displacing 2,751 tons standard, *Scorpion* and *Wyvern* carried four 9in muzzle-loaders in a pair of octagonal turrets with 10–5in (254–127mm) armour, other armour protection comprising 4.5in (114mm) to 2in (50.8mm) on the sides, with 3in (76mm) and 2in (51mm) protection for the bow and stern respectively. The hull was armoured to over 3ft (1m) below the waterline. Lairds provided two cylinder horizontal direct acting engines of their own construction, which provided 1,450ihp to give a maximum speed of 10–10.5kts.

A high forecastle and poopdeck, combined with the use of 5ft hinged bulwarks, theoretically enabled this class with its 6ft freeboard below the bulwarks, to transit long distances. A 336 ton coal provision provided a range of 1,052nm at 10kts, but because of the combination of flat bottoms (meeting a Confederate requirement to navigate the Mississippi), and a small rudder, in reality the class proved difficult to handle in a seaway. *Wyvern* differed from *Scorpion* in having two tripod masts to reduce the amount of rigging on this triple-masted barque. Its dimensions were 224ft 6in x 42ft 4in x 16ft 3in (68.43m x 12.95m x 4.95m). In 1866–68 a flying bridge from forecastle to poop was fitted and the rig was reduced to fore and aft sails. *Scorpion* was a guardship at Bermuda from 1869 to 1899, a role also performed by *Wyvern* first in home waters and then in Hong Kong. *Scorpion* was sunk as a target in 1901, raised and sold for breaking up in 1903, foundering en route to Boston. *Wyvern* performed harbour service from 1898 until being sold for breaking up in 1922.

Captain's demise

The capsize of the fully rigged turret ship *Captain* in the Bay of Biscay in September 1870, caused by the lethal combination of turrets sited close to the waterline and the weight and height of a full sailing rig, both ended Coles' life and marked a tragic end to his earlier proposals for an unambiguously ocean-going turret ship. These had first comprised a twin turret, triple tripod-masted 1862 concept, but without topsails, followed by an 1863 variant with a full canvas spread. The Admiralty would not agree to Coles' basic concept though and instead approved the construction of *Monarch*, designed by Coles' rival Reed, which enjoyed the distinction of being the first large seagoing turret ship. Unlike *Monarch*'s three decks, the Lairds-designed *Captain* had two, but *Captain* was completed with a forecastle and poop against Coles' advice.

The capsize of *Captain* prompted the establishment, in January 1871, of the Admiralty Board's Committee on Designs for Ships of War which compared various designs in the light of *Captain*'s fate. The vessels under investigation included both *Glatton* and *Cyclops* and the committee recommended that breastwork turret ships like *Cyclops* must have unarmoured, plated-deck extensions fitted to the breastworks to improve their stability, while coast defence ships such as *Glatton* needed stronger bottoms to ensure that they could survive a grounding.

But what was not at issue was that the principle of the turret ship had been firmly established over the previous years, from *Trusty*, through *Royal Sovereign*, *Prince Albert*, and *Cerberus* to the landmark, Reed-designed turret ships *Devastation* and *Thunderer*, built at Portsmouth and Pembroke Dockyards from 1869 to 1877. Although these 9,330 ton ships were rightly regarded as key components of the future battle fleet, it was nonetheless acknowledged at the time that these were essentially much larger versions of the *Cerberus* class coast defence monitors which were still under

Thunderer
This rendering from the
Illustrated London
News *of 22 July 1876*
shows the steam boiler
explosion on Thunderer,
the second of the
Devastation *class turret*
ships (GPH Collection)

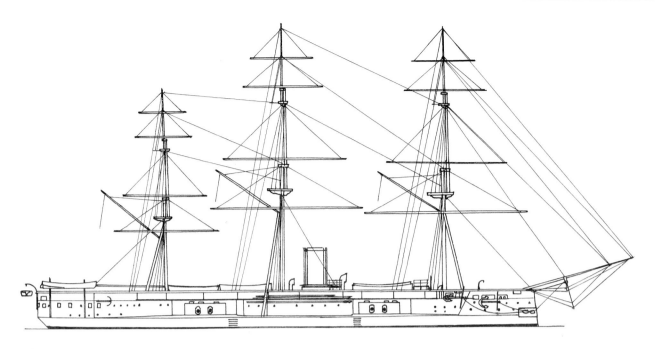

Captain
The loss of the masted turret ship Captain *had a major impact on British naval thinking, and though designed for ocean-going service, is relevant to this account for the way in which it highlighted the importance of good stability, a feature normally shared by most coast defence ships, including those at this time armed with Coles turrets. Coles died in the* Captain *accident in December 1870 (CMP)*

construction when *Devastation* and *Thunderer* were laid down. Indeed, such was the influence of the coast defence design, that *Devastation*'s freeboard as initially conceived was comparable to *Cerberus*.

But the Admiralty did not like this and insisted that the freeboard be raised amidships, much against Reed's wishes. *Thunderer*'s construction was delayed to await the outcome of *Devastation*'s trials, such was the popular unease at the design of this, the first seagoing turret ship without any provision for sail.

1 *Steam, Steel and Shellfire*, op.cit., p79.

2 Details of *Royal Sovereign*, *Prince Albert*, the *Cerberus*, *Scorpion* and *Cyclops* classes, and *Abyssinia* and others, are variously taken from *Conway's Fighting Ships 1860–1905*, op.cit., and Tony Gibbons, *The Complete Encyclopaedia of Battleships and Battlecruisers* (London, 1983).

3 *Steam, Steel and Shellfire*, op.cit., p79.

4 The former displacement is given in *Conway's Fighting Ships 1860–1905*, op.cit., p19, the latter by Gibbons, op.cit., p38.

5 Letter from Colin Jones, *Warship International*, No.3 1994, p311.

CHAPTER 4

The Ironclad Message Spreads

THE IMAGINED SPECTACLE OF the inconclusive engagement between *Monitor* and *Virginia* concentrated minds throughout the world. Although neither of the ironclads at Hampton Roads was lost, the battle certainly proved that the right kind of armour could at least provide a modicum of protection. What was not yet proven was whether such vessels could safely be committed to the open sea, or whether a turret ship was necessarily the best approach for future ironclads. Central battery ships and other turretless ironclads remained valid alternative solutions for many navies and it took the best part of twenty years for the turret ship to establish itself firmly as the way forward for both coast defence vessels and battleships.

At the same time, the new ironclad naval race provided welcome work to the shipyards of Britain, France and other countries. As it became apparent after Hampton Roads, and also after the example provided by the British with *Prince Albert* and *Royal Sovereign*, that it was now certain that the existing sailing battle fleets of the world's navies faced the danger of sudden wholesale obsolescence, all navies rushed to catch up. Besides providing a boost to the industries of the established naval powers, the advent of the new technology also enabled some countries, notably Denmark, to establish convincing coastal ironclad fleets using hulls of domestic design and construction.

In this sense, the ability of some modest shipyard facilities in Europe to respond to the new technological challenge ensured that the new ironclad coast defence fleets could provide additional security, in that unlike the navies of, for example, Latin America, they could viably underpin their countries' security, or neutrality, in the face of the other powers. In the case of France and Russia, which took coast defence very seriously, these vessels were centre-stage in these countries' perceptions of what was needed for their defence.

Of course it helped that some other users of this type of vessel, all in northern Europe, did not have colonies and therefore did not enter into any significant disputes with any of the major powers. The result was stability and a period when the foundations of the modern shipbuilding countries of, among other regions, Scandinavia, were built.

Plainly, for those countries in southern Europe or Latin America with more slender financial resources and without the requisite shipbuilding infrastructure, the dependence on the major powers which supplied the new ironclad fleets brought its own political dangers, and made it hard to build viable fleets. The result was that some navies had to soldier on for a great many years with only a handful of ironclads bought in the 1860s and 1870s, and as a result never caught up with actual or probable adversaries.

The coastal defence mission of the navies which accepted this as their primary purpose was fairly easily served by low-freeboard ironclads like Denmark's *Rolf Krake*, the first ship with Coles turrets, or Prussia's *Arminius*, her first ironclad, earning good reputations for their workmanlike simplicity and utility.

These turreted ironclads were of course not the only types to be exported, as modest central battery ships like Brazil's *Barroso* and Greece's *Basileos Georgios* gave minor naval powers the possibility of joining the ironclad boom. The latter was even claimed to possess, for her size, superior offensive and defensive properties than any other comparable warship of the time. The new technologies were also to be exploited in the strangest fashion by Russia, denied the freedom to build seagoing ships after the Crimean War, which constructed the extraordinary circular *Novgorod* and *Popov*, estuarine defence vessels intended for the protection of the Dneiper which unfortunately in practice proved to be more than a handful to steer against any kind of strong current.

While the Netherlands, Sweden and Denmark developed their domestic ship-building capabilities for coast defence, the latter with the experience of the war of 1864 very much in mind, other nations began to challenge the technological predominance of Britain and France. Most could not compete with these countries' industrial infrastructures, while one, the new German Empire after 1871, began its rise to become a major naval power with the construction of coast defence vessels.

With only the American Civil War and the Battle of Lissa to draw on, naval strategists had to make assumptions about future naval warfare which could not be based on accurate guesses about the pace or even direction at which technology would advance. Thus within only about five years of the construction of *Gloire* and *Warrior*, guns were being produced which could penetrate over 9in (228.6mm) of iron, yet in the same period armour thickness generally increased only from 4–5in (102–127mm) to 6in (152mm). Something had to give and that something was the idea of a broadside armament and a complete armour belt to protect it. This

Huascar
The small ironclad
Huascar *saw noble service*
with the Peruvian Navy,
followed by extensive
service with the Chilean
Navy. She was effectively a
coast defence ship, but
played a key role in the
War of the Pacific. She still
survives, as seen here in
this photograph taken in
1995 (Hanny and Leo van
Ginderen Collection)

gave way to the idea of shorter, and thicker, armour protection to cover the vitals of a warship, be it a central battery or turret ship or a ship using the barbette concept favoured by the French.

As the following description of the various coast defence vessels of the period to 1880 shows, the designer's task was now a case of squaring a circle which became familiar to the warship designers of the second half of the nineteenth and certainly the first half of the twentieth centuries. How could you match operational requirements to fiscal wherewithal, provide desired armour protection and desired gunnery, hoped-for speed and a practical range and endurance? For the coast defence navies, at least the last equation was not as vital a factor as it was for the major powers. Apart from the War of the Pacific in 1879 in which *Huascar* was to play such a major role, and a few colonial skirmishes, the design theories of the period were put to little test.

Denmark: Rolf Krake and her successors to 1880

This little Danish vessel has the distinction of being the first ship to use Captain Coles' turret. Laid down on 1 December 1862 and launched by Napier in 1863, this triple mast, schooner-rigged 1,320 ton coast defence ship cost £74,000 and was ordered at a time of rising tension with Prussia over Schleswig-Holstein. Initially armed with four 68pdr smooth-bores mounted in two turrets behind bulwarks which could be lowered for action (as on *Prince Albert*), *Rolf Krake* could make 9.5kts on her single shaft 750ihp engine. Coal provision at 135 tons was sufficient for this vessel's coastal mission. Side and turret armour of 114mm (4.5in) with 228.6mm (9in) backing, with 76mm (3in) at the ends, would not have protected *Rolf Krake* later in the 1860s from large calibre, 9–10in guns at close range. The side armour extended 0.91m (3ft) below the waterline. The deck had 38mm (1.5in) plate armour and an armoured conning tower aft had 228.6mm (9in) protection.

In the war of 1864 against Prussia and Austria, *Rolf Krake* was driven off by Prussian batteries in June, thereby being prevented from blocking the crossing of the channel between Schleswig and Alsen. After the war, the 68pdrs were replaced by two Armstrong 203mm (8in) rifled muzzle-loaders in 1867 (forward turret) and 1878 (after turret), while two 86mm (3.4in) 24cal and four 1pdr revolvers were added in 1885. Dimensions were 56m x 11.63m x 3.2m (183ft 9in x 38ft 2in x 10ft 6in) and the three masts were reduced to two pole masts in 1878, the ship becoming a gunnery training vessel in 1893 and finally sold in 1907.

Rolf Krake's relatively weak armour was slightly improved upon on *Lindormen*, the next Danish coast defence vessel laid down in 1867 and launched in 1868, a single turret vessel with 127mm (5in) side armour with 254mm (10in) backing and 139mm (5.5in) for the single turret, in which a pair of Armstrong 228.6mm (9in) rifled muzzle-loaders were mounted. Two light quick-firers were also fitted. This 2,048 ton low-freeboard ship was built at Copenhagen Dockyard,

Rolf Krake
The first vessel to be fitted
with Coles turrets, the little
Rolf Krake *took part in*
the blockade of Prussia
during the war of 1864,
but could not resist
Prussian shore batteries at
the Schleswig-Alsen
channel. She is shown as
built (CMP)

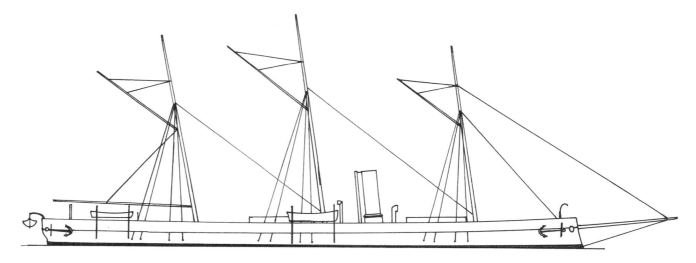

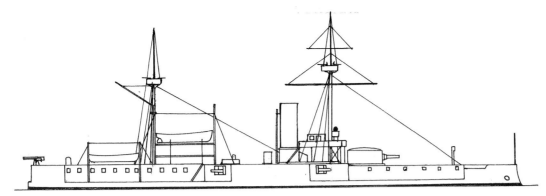

Helgoland
Easily the largest Danish coast defence ship of the period, Helgoland *(shown as built) had a complete belt, a turret for her single 12in and four 10.2in in central battery-mounted barbettes (CMP)*

as were succeeding Danish coast defence vessels. The twin shaft 1,560ihp engine was twice as powerful as *Rolf Krake*'s, giving a speed of 12kts, and coal provision at 125 tons was more modest but reflected improvements in engine efficiency as all Danish coast defence vessels had similar endurance requirements. Like *Rolf Krake*, *Lindormen* later received different armament, comprising 150mm (5.9in) in place of the 9in, fitted in 1885, plus four 3.4in 24cal and four 1pdr revolvers fitted in 1879. One source, Gibbons,[1] reports that two 3in muzzle-loaders were added in 1875. Dimensions of *Lindormen*, which was disposed of circa 1907, were 66.42m x 11.99m x 4.44m (217ft 11in x 39ft 4in x 14ft 7in).

Slightly larger than *Lindormen* was the low-freeboard *Gorm*, launched in 1870 at a cost of £104,000 and which displaced 2,313 tons. Main armament comprised a pair of Armstrong 10in rifled muzzle-loaders in a single turret with 203mm (8in) armour and 444mm (17.5in) backing, side armour being 177.8mm (7in) with a maximum of 10in backing. A better engine gave 1,600ihp and a speed of 12.5kts, the coal provision being a maximum of 113 tons. *Gorm* received the same armament additions as *Lindormen*, the 3.4in being replaced later by 6pdrs, and also eventually 150mm guns in place of her. Dimensions were 71.11m x 12.19m x 4.37m (233ft 4in x 40ft x 14ft 4in max) and 160 crew were carried. *Gorm* was scrapped in 1912.

The next Danish coast defence ship, *Odin*, launched in 1872, was a major break with the established precedent in that she was a low-freeboard central battery ship, with four Armstrong 10in rifled muzzle-loaders and a significantly larger displacement at 3,170 tons. She was also distinguished by the oddity of a retractable spur ram. Both side and central battery armour was set at 203mm, and the 2,300ihp engine gave a speed of 12kts, with a higher coal provision at 177 tons. The 10in guns were converted by Krupps to 16cal breech-loaders and *Odin* received the same armament additions as *Gorm* and *Lindormen*, with the addition of a pair of 1pdr quick-firers. The increased armament was reflected in the larger crew of 206.

The final coast defence ship built in Denmark before 1880 and the largest to be built by the Danes in the nineteenth century was *Helgoland*, a 5,332 ton vessel laid down

in 1876 and launched in 1878. It combined a central battery for a quartet of 259mm 22cal (10.2in) Krupp guns with a forward barbette for a single 305mm 22cal (12in) Krupp gun. Other armament comprised five 120mm (4.7in), ten 1pdr revolvers, and a mixed torpedo battery of two 381mm (15in) and three 356mm (14in). An iron belt of 254–203mm and 254mm armour for the battery and barbette, plus a high 3.35m (11ft) freeboard gave her protection and an appearance comparable to true battleships of the period. The twin shaft 4,000ihp engine gave a better speed than the rest of the coast defence fleet at 13.75kts: 224 tons of coal were carried. The light armament was altered to consist of a pair of 6pdrs, four 1pdr revolvers and three 1pdr quick-firers. Dimensions were 79.12m × 18.5m × 5.89m (259ft 7in x 59ft 2in x 19ft 4in). With a crew of 331, *Helgoland* remained in service for thirty years.

France

France, together with Russia, was alone among the major naval powers before 1880 in putting a lot of effort and investment into the construction of a substantial force of coast defence ships. The motley coast defence fleet constructed in these years reflected the desire to maintain a guard for the homeland against possible British depredations, besides an expanding battle fleet to protect a growing empire. As it turned out, besides colonial skirmishes, the only major French naval action of the period was during the Franco-Prussian War of 1870–71 in which the coast defence ships played no significant part.

The French coast defence fleet of the period can be divided into three groups: the *Palestro*, *Arrogante* and *Embuscade* class floating batteries; the armoured rams *Taureau* and *Cerbere*; and the *Tonnere* and *Tempête* class breastwork monitors. In addition, there was the former US broadside ironclad *Dunderberg*, sold to France and commissioned briefly as *Rochambeau*, and the ex-USN monitor *Onondaga*, which retained its name in French service and was rearmed and kept in service until 1904.

The Arman-built floating batteries of the *Palestro* class (*Palestro*, *Paixhans*, *Peiho* and *Saigon*) were 1,508–1,539 ton

Novgorod
This study of Novgorod *from the* Illustrated London News *in January 1876 shows the design principle well: how to put a substantial armament of two 11in and two 3.4in on a small hull which could handle estuarine defence and, as it turned out, much more problematical operations at sea (GPH Collection)*

wooden-hull vessels with 110mm (4.7–4.3in) wrought iron armour protecting a battery of a dozen 162.5mm (6.4in) M1860 guns. They were able to make 7kts from their twin shaft high pressure, 150nhp engine. Faster than the larger Crimean War floating batteries, this twin funnelled class saw little actual service despite being completed in 1862–63 and only stricken in 1871 (1869 for *Peiho*). The three Gouin-built *Arrogante* class floating batteries, displacing 1,490 tons in *Arrogante*'s case and 1,412 tons for *Implacable* and *Opioniâtre*, differed markedly from the *Palestros* in being iron-hulled central casemate vessels, with twenty-four gun-ports for the initial battery of nine 162mm (6.4in) M1864s, of which all but two guns were later replaced by four 193mm (7.6in). Lengths ranged from 46.41m (152ft 3in) to 47.5m (155ft 10in). A twin shaft high pressure engine developing 470ihp could deliver a speed of 6.7–7kts. With a 120mm (4.7in) belt and 110mm (4.3in) battery armour, they were laid down in 1861 for completion in 1864–65, being stricken in 1881–85. The 44m (144ft) *Arrogante* was used for trials of a 240mm gun in 1867. The 1,426–1,555 ton *Embuscade* class floating batteries laid down by Arman in 1862 (*Embuscade, Imprenable, Protectrice, Refuge*) had the same battery armour as the *Arrogantes*, but a thicker 140mm (5.5in) belt. Four 7.6in M1864 or 1866 guns could be fired through a choice of sixteen gun ports. The *Embuscades*' 440ihp twin shaft high pressure engine could propel the class at 7.5kts. Completed in 1866–67, this 39.5m (129ft 7in) class were

stricken between 1882 and 1889, though *Imprenable* was still used for torpedo firing at Cherbourg until 1939.

The 2,433 ton, Toulon-built armoured ram *Taureau*, laid down in 1863, was designed by Dupuy de Lôme, who had a major impact on French warship design of the period. It displayed marked tumblehome, and was not an effective vessel despite its barbette-mounted 240mm M1884/86 gun. Belt armour of 150mm was adequate for the period, but not the barbette's 120mm protection. A long spur ram was fitted, as on other rams of the period. The twin shaft 1,790ihp engine delivered a speed of 12.5kts; dimensions were 60m x 14.78m x 5.4m (196ft 10in wl x 48ft 6in x 17ft 9in). Completed in 1866, *Taureau* was stricken in 1890.

Larger than *Taureau*, and with pronounced tumblehome, were the four 3,532 ton *Cerbère* class armoured rams completed between 1872 and 1874. They were, in order of completion, *Belier* (built at Cherbourg), *Bouledogue* (Lorient), *Cerbère* (Brest) and *Tigre* (Rochefort). Similar engines delivered the same speed as *Taureau*, but where the *Cerbère*s differed markedly was in being armed with two 9.4in in a Dupuy de Lôme-designed turret. The two funnels were installed abreast one another. Armament was altered with the replacement of the main armament with 240mm M1870s and the addition of four 1pdr revolvers. The class' dimensions were 65.56m x 16.4m x 5.66m (215ft 1in x 53ft 10in x 18ft 7in). They were stricken between 1887 and 1892.

Taking their inspiration from the British *Cerberus* class breastwork monitors, but much more heavily armoured, were the *Tonnere* and *Tempête* classes. They were, respectively, *Tonnere* and *Fulminant* built at Lorient and Cherbourg, and *Tempête* and *Vengeur* built at Brest. All four of these were laid down in 1873–75 and completed in 1879–82. *Tonnere* displaced 5,765 tons (or 5,871 tons for *Fulminant*), while *Tempête*'s displacement was 4,793 tons and *Vengeur*'s 4,635 tons. With 330–254mm belts (13–10in), a 330mm breastwork and 356–305m (14–12in) turret armour, protection was a far more important feature of these vessels than the comparable *Cerberus* class, especially considering the French ships' main armament of two 275mm (10.8in) guns, *Vengeur*'s being an even heavier pair of 341mm (13.4in) pieces, when compared with the four 10in on the lighter, less well armoured *Cerberus* class. These 73.6m (241ft 6in) ships could make 13.7kts in the case of the *Tonnere*s and 11.7kts for the *Tempête*s, but doing so would have been exciting given their very low freeboards. All four ships were stricken in 1905–08.

Cerberus
The sister of the class name ship Bloedhond, Cerberus *was a 1,559 ton monitor originally fitted with a pair of 9in, but later rearmed with one 11in and smaller guns* (CMP)

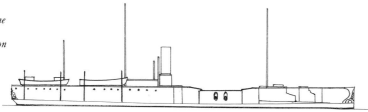

Fulminant
Fulminant *was* Tonnere*'s sister ship, serving from 1882 to 1908. This pen and ink study by 'J.H.' dates from around 1880* (GPH Collection)

Russia

The Imperial Russian Navy's freedom to build any kind of fleet in the Black Sea was limited after the Crimean War by the provisions of the Treaty of Paris. This led directly to the construction of the extraordinary circular ironclads *Novgorod* and *Popov*, while the Russians were quick to take note of events in America and rapidly built the ten *Bronenosetz* class coast defence monitors, as well as seven coast defence turret ships.

The first of these turret ships, *Smerch*, was a 1,460 ton, three-masted clone of *Rolf Krake*, completed by Mitchell in St Petersburg in 1865, and which was armed with four 60pdrs, and later a pair of 228mm (9in) and four 1pdr revolvers. The 57.35m (188ft 2in) *Smerch* had a partial double bottom and armour ranged from side armour of 114mm (4.5in) to turret armour of 152–114mm (6–4.5in), with a 1in deck. *Smerch* was stricken around 1900.

In 1863, the same year *Smerch* was laid down, ten 61.26m (201ft) *Bronenosetz* class monitors were laid down in an ambitious programme. Officially displacing 1,565 tons, though nearer 2,000 tons, these single turret monitors comprised two built by Cockerill at Seraing, and assembled in Russia, where another eight were constructed at four yards in the Baltic. Armament of a pair of 228mm smoothbores gave way to 228mm 20cals or 22cals in the case of *Latnik* and *Lava*. Side armour of 228–76mm (9–3in), turret armour of 254mm (10in), with 203mm (8in) protection for the pilot house was as good as, if not better than, the USN's *Passaic* class, the hull form of which was similar to that of these Russian vessels. Completed in 1865–66, all were stricken around 1900.

The two *Charodeika* class, 2,100 ton twin turret ships built between 1866 and 1868 at Mitchell, St Petersburg (the other vessel being *Russalka*), were low freeboard vessels of modest pretensions, armed with four 228mm 20cals and four 86mm, of which two of the former gave way to 22cal weapons, with the addition of pairs of 3pdrs and 1pdr revolvers. Armour (side: 114mm, turrets: 152mm) and speed (8.5kts provided by a twin shaft, rectangular boiler 875ihp powerplant) were not good enough to contend with some of the threats this 62.94m (206ft 6in) class might reasonably have been expected to face.

The same criticism can be directed at the *Admiral Lazarev* class coast defence turret ships built by Carr & McPherson at St Petersburg between 1866 and 1870. Displacing 3,820 tons in the case of *Lazarev* and 3,768 tons in

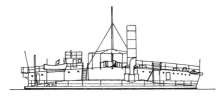

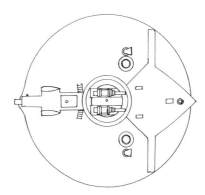

Uragan
Uragan was one of a class of 10 Bronenosetz *coast defence monitors of the Russian Navy built to an American pattern. Uragan was completed by the New Admiralty yard in 1865–66 and remained in service until around 1900 (CMP)*

Novgorod
These line drawings of the extraordinary circular ironclad Novgorod, *the first of the type in the Imperial Russian Navy, show how only the slightest of concessions to tradition allowed a small rearward protuberance for the rudder (CMP)*

the case of *Admiral Greig*, these ships had relatively weak side and turret armour of 114mm. They replaced their initial battery of three twin 228mm with three 279mm (11in) 20/22cal. Speed was 10.5/11kts, provided by four rectangular boilers and a single shaft horizontal direct acting engine developing 2,020ihp. The Baltic Works built another pair of coast defence turret ships, the *Admiral Chichagov* class, which were very similar to the *Lazarev*s but with one fewer turret.

Certainly the strangest warships ever built were the circular *Novgorod* and *Popov*, laid down at Nikolaiev in 1872 and 1874 respectively and completed in 1874 and 1877. These circular ironclads were intended to defend the place where they were built and the Dneiper estuary. The reason for the vessels' shape was the belief[2] that no other hull form could accommodate such considerable displacements (2,419 tons for *Novgorod* and 3,550 tons for *Popov*) on so limited a

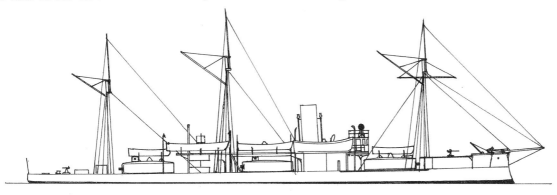

Admiral Lazarev
A near lookalike of Prince Albert, Admiral Lazarev *(also known as* Lazareff) *was a triple-turret ship displacing 3,820 tons, slightly more than her sibling* Admiral Greig *(CMP)*

draught (4.13m, 13ft 6in). With a flat-bottomed hull, *Novgorod*'s diameter was 30.78m (101ft) and the deck was cambered from a 533mm (1ft 9in) freeboard to 5ft in the centre for the circular barbette containing two 279mm 20cal breech-loaders. Side armour was 228–178mm (9–7in), the barbette's being 228mm. Though the generally recorded speed of *Novgorod* is 6–7kts from her six shaft horizontal compound engine, with eight cyclindrical boilers generating 3,000ihp, she managed 8kts on trials, but was still impossible to control in a river when riding with the current, though she was better in open calm water or when stemming the current.[3] Other armament comprised two 3.4in, two 2.5pdrs and spar torpedoes! One can imagine what the use of the latter would have involved in action in a lively current.

The lessons of *Novgorod* were not learned quickly enough to prevent the decision to complete *Popov* (originally named *Kiev*), which had the same powerplant arrangement, but this time developing 4,500ihp to give 8kts. Armour was thicker, at 406–355mm (16–14in) for the sides and 355mm (16in) for the barbette, in which a pair of 305mm 20cal guns were mounted in a hydraulic disappearing mounting. In both *Novgorod* and *Popov* an effort was made to improve reliability and performance by removing the two outer propellers, cutting ihp to 2,000 for 5.5kts (*Novgorod*) and 3,066ihp for 6kts (*Popov*). Both curiosities were scrapped around 1900. It is indeed a pity that one was not preserved.

Italy

Built by La Seyne as coast defence ships in 1866, just in time to fight at Lissa, were *Palestro* and *Varese*, barque-rigged ironclads which were armed with four 200mm (7.8in) and one 165mm (6.47in). *Palestro* (2,165 tons standard) was sunk by a magazine explosion with the loss of just five dead and 39 wounded. *Varese* (1,968 tons standard) was rearmed in 1870 with four 203mm (8in), one 165mm (6.5in) and two 80mm landing guns. She became a hospital ship from 1886 to 1891 and thereafter a depot ship.

Other Italian coast defence vessels of the period were the two 1,821 ton (standard) wood-hulled, armoured floating batteries *Guerriera* and *Voragine* launched in 1866 and stricken in 1875, and the four 631 ton *Alfredo Cappellini* class armoured gunboats which were built for a planned attack on Venice, but were made redundant after the war with Austria when that city was transferred to Italy. They were stricken in 1870–75.

Skorpionen
The first Norwegian coast defence monitor was Skorpionen, *an Ericsson-inspired vessel launched in 1866, and armed with two 10.5in rifled muzzle-loaders, later replaced by two lighter 4.7in and smaller guns (CMP)*

Prussia

The twin turret ship *Arminius* has a place in history as Prussia's, and then Germany's, first ironclad. Laid down speculatively by Samuda in London in 1863, launched in 1864 and bought by Prussia using public subscription money in 1865, *Arminius* was an 1,887 ton twin Coles turret vessel which did not arrive in time to fight the Danes, nor was she considered capable of facing the French in 1870–71. By this time her schooner rig had been taken down and she began to resemble the classic monitor-type coast defence vessels of other countries.

Powered by horizontal single expansion two cylinder engines driving a single shaft for 1,440ihp, *Arminius* could make 11kts, which was reasonably fast compared to monitor contemporaries. Belt and turret armour of 114mm (4.5in), with 76mm (3in) ends and 228mm (9in) teak backing was weaker than necessary for the later 1860s when she entered service. Armour extended 8.38m (2ft 9in) below the waterline.

Armed with four 208mm (8.2in) after it was decided not to fit the originally-planned quartet of bronze 72pdrs, *Arminius* received four 37mm revolvers and a 350mm torpedo tube in 1881. By this time she was being used as an engineers' instruction vessel and remained in service until 1901, being broken up the next year. *Arminius*' dimensions were 63.21m x 61.6m x 4.55m (207ft 4.5in x 35ft 9in x 14ft 11in).

Also being used for coastal defence in this period, if smaller than most coast defence ships, were the eleven 1,139 ton *Wespe* class, shallow draught gunboats launched between 1876 and 1881. Similar to the British *Rendel* boats, they mounted a single 305mm (12in) and remained in service until 1909–11.

Sweden and Norway

Not surprisingly, the influence of the Swede John Ericsson, which had such a momentous impact in America and throughout the world, was also felt in Sweden where three Ericsson-type monitors were launched in 1865–67: the *John Ericsson*, *Thordon* and *Tirfing*. At 1,476 tons and with a 380ihp engine giving 7kts, these were compact vessels with a pair of 240mm (9.4in) 17cal on their 60.9m (199ft) hulls. *John Ericsson* differed in that she was armed with two 381mm (15in) smoothbores instead, but all were rearmed with two 152mm (6in) or 120mm (4.7in), plus two to eight 6pdrs or 3pdrs. Hull armour at 4.75in was typical for the type, as was the 260mm (10.25in) turret armour. Another twin 240mm-armed monitor, the 1,574 ton *Loke*, was launched in 1871. All were built at Norkoping.

Although Norway was under the Swedish crown until 1905, it conducted an independent naval procurement programme, one which was indeed to play a significant role in the attainment of Norway's full independence. Thus separately from Sweden, Norway acquired the three 1,425–1,490 ton *Skorpionen* class, Ericsson-type monitors, of which two were launched in Norway at Horten and one, *Mjolner*, at Norkoping in Sweden, in 1866–69. Armed with two 266mm (10.5in) rifled muzzle-loaders, and later rearmed with two 120mm, two 9pdrs and two 1pdrs, the hull had 127mm armour and the turret 305mm. A similar vessel, the 1,975 ton *Thor* was launched in Horten in 1872 and was rearmed in the same way as the *Skorpionen* class. Armour was better though, at 178mm for the hull and 355mm for the turret. The former class could make 6kts and the latter 8kts, courtesy of 450ihp and 600ihp powerplants respectively.

The Netherlands

The Dutch took advantage of the new technology to update their small fleet quickly after 1860, building, *inter alia*, four turret rams and no fewer than thirteen monitors in six classes by 1880. The relative calmness of inshore, estuarine and riverine waters in the Netherlands lent themselves to the monitor.

Two of the turret rams launched in 1868–70 were the 2,284 ton, Napier-built *Buffel* and the 2,402 ton Amsterdam-built *Guinea* of the *Buffel* class, armed with two 228mm rifled muzzle-loaders and four 120mm 16cal, later just one 279mm 22cal, four 1pdrs and two 1pdr revolvers. The twin masted, 59.69m (195ft 10in) vessels had a 152mm belt with 203mm for the turret and its base, and could make 11.2/11.5kts with 2,000ihp. The other two rams were the *Schorpioen* class, of which the nameship was launched in 1868 at La Seyne and *Stier*, its sibling, was curiously enough built by Laird. Similar to the *Buffel*s, *Schorpioen* displaced 2,140 tons and *Stier* 2,078 tons and they each carried a pair of 228mm, which gave way to new armament identical to

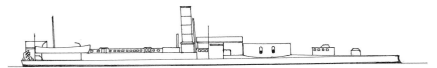

the *Buffel*s although an extra 1pdr was fitted. The turret armour, at 279–203mm, was somewhat heavier than the *Buffel*s, as was the speed, 12.5–13kts courtesy of 2,225–2,260ihp engines.

The first eleven monitors of the *Heiligerlee*, *Bloedhond* and *Adder* classes were all launched in 1868–71, displaced 1,520–1,656 tons, and were all armed with two 228mm, being rearmed with single 279mm guns and smaller weapons as on the turret rams. The significantly larger monitors *Draak* and *Matador* (2,198 and 1,968 tons respectively) were launched in 1877 and 1878 and each carried a pair of 278mm 22cals, to which two 1pdrs and two 1pdr revolvers were later added.

Draak
A later Dutch coast defence monitor, dating from 1877, was Draak, *equipped with two 11in and a ram bow (CMP)*

Greece

Laying claim to better offensive and defensive powers for its displacement than any other warship in the world at the time was the *Basileos Georgios*, a small 1,774 ton, 200ft (60.96m) central battery ship launched by Thames Iron Works in December 1867. Armed with a pair of 228mm (9in) rifled muzzle-loaders and a pair of 20pdrs, and with a complete belt of 178–152mm (7–6in), with 152mm (6in) protection for the battery, the claim by her designer George Mackrow is hard to fault, given that armour took up 330 tons of her displacement. Two engines developing 2,100ihp, driving two propellers, provided a speed of 12.2–13kts. The belt extended 1.06m (3ft 6in) below the waterline and 6ft 6in above it. The 228mm (9in) guns were later replaced by 203mm (8in) breech-loaders.

Basileos Georgios
Built by Thames Iron Works, Basileos Georgios' *designer George Mackrow believed that for her size she was more capable than any other ironclad. This design drawing of the 'King George' accompanied a paper by Mackrow on the vessel's centre of gravity in the Transactions of the Institute of Naval Architects in 1868 (The Transactions of the Royal Institution of Naval Architects)*

GREEK IRON-CLAD "KING GEORGE."
PROFILE.

Turkey

Turkey acquired a considerable number of vessels whose proper description continues to confuse, few being positively identified as coast defence vessels even when this was their obvious purpose. But during the period to 1880, two vessels, *Lutfi Djelil* and *Hifzi Rahman*, stand out. They were originally bought by Egypt, nominally part of the Ottoman Empire, but were actually delivered to Turkey. Launched at Bordeaux in 1868 and completed in 1869, these three masted turret ships had ram bows, displaced 2,540 tons and were armed with pairs of 203mm (8in) and 178mm (7in), all Armstrong muzzle-loaders, the former being in the forward turret. Armour protection was not over-impressive though (140mm belt, 117mm ends, 76mm side and 140mm turret), and this probably accounted for *Lutfi Djelil*'s loss during the Russo-Turkish War. Her sister was rearmed after the war with two 150mm (5.9in) Krupp breech-loaders in the rear turret and a 120mm (4.7in) Krupp breech-loader right forward, plus two 37mm.

Portugal

Portugal acquired a single coast defence vessel for the defence of Lisbon during this period, *Vasco da Gama*, which remained in service as Portugal's most important warship until well into the next century. Built by Thames Iron Works and launched in December 1875, *Vasco da Gama* was a barque-rigged central battery ship armed with a pair of 258mm (10.2in) 20cal breech-loaders, a single 150mm (5.9in) 25cal and four 9pdrs. Her twin shaft Humphreys & Tennant compound engines developed 3,625ihp for a speed of 13.25kts according to Gibbons or 3,000ihp for 10.3kts (*Conway's Fighting Ships 1860–1905*). This discrepancy has not been resolved.[1] *Vasco da Gama* was extensively refitted at Orlando, Leghorn, after the turn of the century.

Latin America

Brazil built a coast defence fleet after 1860, with the ironclads *Brasil* and *Barrozo*, *Tamandare* and other vessels. *Brasil* and *Barrozo* were built in 1864, the former a 1,518 ton central battery ship built by La Seyne, and both saw considerable riverine action during the War of the Triple Alliance in which Argentina, Brazil and Uruguay were ranged against Paraguay, which was utterly crushed in the conflict. *Brasil* was armed with four 7in Whitworth muzzle-loaders and four 68pdrs. She was protected by 114–76mm (4.5–3in) iron armour over her belt and battery. *Barrozo* had two 178mm (7in), two 68pdrs and three 32pdrs. She narrowly escaped sinking on a mine during the Allied fleet's repulse at Humaíta in July 1868. *Brasil* became a floating battery in 1887 and *Barrozo* was stricken in the mid 1880s. *Tamandare* was a 980 ton central battery ship built in 1865, armed with two 147mm (5.8) Whitworth muzzle-loaders.

In 1865–66, six other classes of coast defence ships were built for the Brazilian Navy: *Lima Barros*, *Rio de Janeiro*, *Bahia*, *Silvado*, the two Rennie-built *Mariz e Barros* class and the pair of Rennie-built *Cabral* class ships. Displacements ranged from 1,008 tons (*Bahia*) to 1,353 tons for *Herval*, *Mariz e Barros'* sister. All were armed with 178mm (7in) or 147mm (5.8in) guns and were discarded in the 1885–95 period.

Two other classes should be mentioned, the single *Sete de Setembro* and the pair of French-built *Javary* class ships, all of 1874. The former displaced 2,172 tons and was a central battery ship armed with four 228mm (9in) and one 2pdr, with 114mm (4.5in) armour. The latter displaced 3,543 tons and had four 254mm (10in), four 25.4mm (1in) or two 2pdrs in the case of *Javary's* sister *Solimoes*.

By the second half of the nineteenth century, Argentina's economy was growing fast and so was a sense of rivalry with neighbouring Brazil which was to culminate in a small scale naval race after the turn of the century. Argentina acquired the Laird-built *La Plata* class coast defence ships during this period. Launched in 1874, these 1,500 ton low-freeboard monitors carried two 7.8in in a single turret, plus two 102mm (4in), two 9pdrs and a pair of 3pdrs. The narrow superstructure allowed end-on fire and armour protection of these 56.69m (186ft) ships ranged from a 152mm (6in) belt to 203mm (8in) breastwork and 228–203mm (9–8in) turret.

(Right) La Plata Argentina's answer to Brazil's central battery ships were the two 1,500 ton Laird-built coast defence ships La Plata *(seen here in 1896)* and Los Andes, *with 7.8in Armstrong breech-loaders, more powerful than the Brazilian vessels' 7in (CMP)*

(Left) Vasco da Gama Portugal's sole ironclad of any note of the period, Vasco da Gama *was intended for the defence of Lisbon. She was very extensively refitted at Orlando in 1901–03 and is shown as reconstructed. (CMP)*

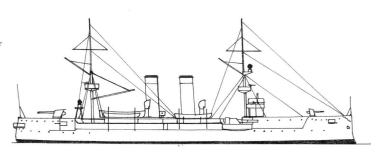

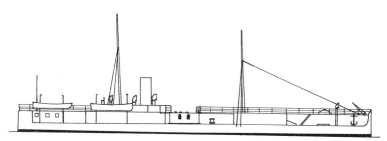

1 Details of vessels in this chapter are mostly taken from Gibbons, op.cit., and *Conway's All the World's Fighting Ships 1860–1905*, op.cit.

2 H T Lenton, *Warships from 1860 to the Present Day* (Hamlyn, 1970), p.142. See also *Neptunia* (the magazine of the friends of the Musée de la Marine, Paris), No.188, 1992, Jacques Chantriot, 'Les Cuirasses du Terrible Amiral Popov', pp36–43. Chantriot describes these vessels in detail and refers to criticism of the concept by the British naval engineer Barnaby, who stated (pp40–42) that for the £330,000 equivalent which *Novgorod* cost, Britain could have built 20 gunboats each armed with an 11in gun and capable of a speed of 9kts. Sir Edward Reed visited Russia in the autumn of 1875 and saw these vessels and was a little less caustic, pointing out in an address to the United Services Institution on 4 February 1876 that these craft were in fact not entirely circular because of an 'aft' protuberance to make it easier to manage these vessels. A later Russian vessel inspired by the *Novogorod* and *Popov* was the turtle-shaped, shallow draught imperial yacht *Livadia*, launched by J.Elder & Co. on the Clyde on 25 June 1880.

3 Lenton, ibid.

CHAPTER 5

The Pre-Dreadnought Age

BY THE 1880S, THE distinction between coast defence battleships and their larger, unambiguously ocean-going siblings was becoming far clearer. In the Royal Navy the latter had developed from the *Devastation*, itself a derivative of the *Cerberus* class coast defence ships, into *Dreadnought*, the seventh ship with that name, which was to break new technical ground in the RN. An account of the pre-*Dreadnought* age as it affected coast defence ships can therefore rightly be described as the further development of the coast defence discipline between the *Dreadnought*s.

Devastation, designed by Reed in 1868, was a direct descendant of the *Cerberus* class, and was designed against the background of widespread public worry over RN designs in the wake of the tragic capsize of *Captain*. At the behest of the Committee on Designs, freeboard was raised amidships and unarmoured structure was added to reach the level of the central breastwork, a feature disliked by Reed. But despite these worries, this 9,330 ton landmark warship, and its sister *Thunderer*, had successful trials and directly inspired the construction of the larger 10,886 ton *Dreadnought* between 1870 and 1879. Building was extended over practically a decade because of the Committee on Designs' decision to recommend better armament, armour protection and stability, following the suspension of construction in 1871. But when in service, *Dreadnought* was recognised as the prototype of the seagoing battleship of the future, with two twin turrets for heavy guns, in this case 12.5in rifled muzzle-loaders.

Against this accelerated pace of technical development, it was no longer possible for many of the smaller navies to compete and most chose not to. But this did not prevent them from acquiring useful coast defence vessels, as they had already shown in the period from the birth of the ironclad to 1880. From Denmark's *Iver Hvitfeldt*, which can perhaps be regarded as the prototype of the classic coast defence battleship as it was developed in Scandinavia, to Russia's *Admiral Ushakov* class, acquired to join her existing coast defence fleet, several smaller navies began developing clear-cut ideas of the place coast defence had in their maritime strategies. They moved beyond low-freeboard monitors which had difficulty negotiating rough open water to vessels with better protection, endurance, range and habitability. Armament calibres remained broadly the same, however.

Among the major powers, France showed considerable interest in coastal defence and several interesting vessels were built in the pre-dreadnought era. Among the most significant was the *Jemmapes* class, while to the east Germany built only one more class of coast defence ship, the *Siegfried*s and their derivatives, as she now concentrated exclusively on building up her ocean-going battle fleet. In the United States, however, as the subterfuge of 'great repairs' to surreptitiously build a few fairly unimpressive new monitors came to an end, the path to maritime mastery began with what were officially defined as 'seagoing coast-line battleships', the *Indiana*s. As the following summary of the state of the coast defence art between 1880 and 1905 shows, the discipline was reaching maturity.

France

As the foremost practitioner of the coast defence art among the great powers, France in 1880 was to develop the coastal battleship to a point where, as with the *Indiana*s, it began to turn into an offensive asset in its own right. This certainly seems to have been the case with the final quartet of French coast defence ships of the *Jemmapes* and *Bouvines* classes.

France had already commissioned eleven modern floating batteries, five armoured rams and four breastwork monitors by around 1880. Now she made a perhaps illogical transition, not to miniature *Devastation*-type turret ships, as other developing coast defence fleets were to do, but to barbette ships instead, as exemplified in capital ship construction from the *Admiral Duperré* of 1883 to the *Marceau* class commissioned in 1891–93.

The two coast defence barbette ships France built at this time were *Tonnant*, which took nine years to build at Rochefort between 1875 and 1884, and *Furieux*, built at Cherbourg between 1883 and 1887. *Tonnant*, displacing 5,010 tons. had a turtle-backed hull forward and was equipped with a pair of 340.3mm (13.4in) 18cal M1875 mounted in two barbettes fore and aft, each with tunnel shields with 368mm (14.5in) armour protection at its maximum. Wrought iron belt armour of 457mm (18in) at the waterline amidships, and 343mm (13.5in) at the ends, had a 50mm (2in) upper edge. Light armament comprised eight 1pdr revolver cannon. Powered by a single shaft horizontal compound engine with four cylinder boilers, producing 2,000ihp, *Tonnant* could make only the modest speed of

11.6kts. Some 175 crew were carried on this single funnelled craft, the dimensions of which were 73.76m x 17.8m x 5.26m (242ft x 58ft 5in x 17ft 3in max). *Tonnant* was stricken in 1903.

The next coastal barbette ship was the 5,925 ton *Furieux* which differed from *Tonnant* chiefly in having the hull extended a deck above the belt protection. Main armament again was two single 340mm (13.4in) M1875s, but 21cal this time. But also provided was a more extensive secondary battery of four 3pdrs, ten 1pdr revolvers and a pair of above-water 355.6mm (14in) torpedo tubes. During a 1902–04 rebuilding, she was rearmed with a pair of 240mm (9.4in) 40cal M1893–96 in centre-pivot turrets with 203mm (8in) armour plus sixteen 3pdr/1pdrs. Similarly, the original propulsion system of a twin shaft vertical compound engine, with eight cylinder boilers developing 4,600ihp for a speed of 13kts, somewhat better than *Tonnant*, was converted to vertical triple expansion, with eight Belleville boilers, for 5,145ihp and 14.3kts. Her single funnel was also changed to twin funnels, a heavier mainmast and she was given of a light pole mast forward. Armour protection comprised an 457–330mm (18–13in) belt, 18in for the original barbettes, decreasing to 12in for the ammunition tubes. After rebuilding, the 8in-protected turrets had 6.5in bases, while the conning tower had light 3in protection. As originally constructed, *Furieux* had a crew of 235; dimensions were 72.54m x 17.83m x 7.09m (238ft x 58ft 6in x 23ft 3in max), the latter changing to 22ft 9in (6.94m) after rebuilding. *Furieux* was stricken in 1913.

Before moving on to build her definitive coast defence ships, the French built two classes of coast defence gunboats in the 1,073–1,124 ton *Fusée* class barbette ships (*Fusée*, *Flamme*, *Grenade* and *Mitraille*) and the 1,690–1,767 ton *Acheron* class turret ships (*Achéron*, *Cocyte*, *Phlegeton*, *Styx*), all built between 1882 and 1890, the *Achéron*s at Cherbourg and the *Fusée*s split between Cherbourg (*Flamme*), Lorient (*Fusée* and *Grenade*) and Rochefort (*Mitraille*). The *Fusée*s had a single 9.4in 28cal M1881, plus a 3.5in and four 1pdr revolvers, while the *Achéron*s had a 10.8in 28cal M1881, two to three 3.9in, a single 5.5in on *Phlegeton* and *Styx*, plus two 3pdrs and four to seven 1pdr revolvers. In armament therefore, these two classes were not standardised, with subvariants. The dimensions and smaller coal provision (71 tons versus 98 tons) of *Phlegeton* and *Styx* also differed from *Achéron* and *Cocyte*. Armour protection was also nonstandard, steel for *Fusée* and *Grenade*, compound for *Flamme* and *Mitraille* – 241–101mm (9.5–4in) belt and 203–119mm (8–4.7in) for the barbettes in both cases, while at least the *Achéron*s had standard compound 8in belt and turret armour.

This bewildering array of differing characteristics among just eight gunboats displayed the weakness for one-offs which has plagued French naval shipbuilding from the latter part of the nineteenth century to this. The *Fusée*s' twin shaft vertical compound engines could make 1,500ihp and

12.5kts while the *Achéron*s' twin shaft horizontal compound engines developed 1,600ihp for 11.6–13kts.

The two 6,476 ton *Jemmapes* class coast defence ships (*Jemmapes* and *Valmy*), built at Societe de la Loire in 1890–94, at least displayed standard characteristics, but again it is curious that the substantially better and more seaworthy *Bouvines* class, with a similar displacement (6,681 tons), were built at around the same time at Lorient (*Amiral Tréhouart*, built during 1890–96) and La Seyne (*Bouvines*, building during 1890–94). They also differed in main armament (two 13.4in 42cal M1887 for the *Jemmapes* class and two 12in 45cal M1887 for the *Bouvines*). Secondary armament of four (*Jemmapes*) to eight (*Bouvines*) 3.9in was standard, but not the barrel length, 45cal quick-firers on the *Jemmapes* and 50cal on the *Bouvines*! Otherwise, all three ships had ten 1pdr revolvers (*Tréhouart*: four 1pdrs and eight 1pdr revolvers), and all four had two 18in above-water torpedo tubes.

The one thing that was standard on all four ships, making the other differences so hard to comprehend, was armour protection and three of the ships had the same boilers. Armour comprised a mixture of nickel steel and steel 18–10in (457–254mm) belts, 18in turrets with 16in for the bases, and 4in for the conning towers. Propulsion comprised twin shaft horizontal triple expansion engines on the *Jemmapes* class, with sixteen Lagrafel d'Allest boilers, developing 9,000ihp for 16.7kts, while the *Bouvines* had two shaft vertical triple expansion engines and sixteen of the aforementioned boilers (except *Tréhouart*, which had sixteen Bellevilles), for 8,500ihp and 16.5–17kts.

In general layout the four ships were similar, though the *Jemmapes* class had pronounced tumblehome and the *Bouvines*' forecastle deck extended aft to the main mast.

Jemmapes
The coast defence turret ship Jemmapes *was markedly larger than previous French vessels of the type at 6,476 tons, armed with two 13.4in (Musée de la Marine, Paris)*

Jemmapes' dimensions were 86.5m x 17.47m x 7.06m (283ft 9in x 57ft 4in x 23ft 2in), while the *Bouvines'* dimensions were very similar indeed, with exactly the same length, a slightly greater breadth of 17.78m (58ft 4in) and depth of 7.14m (23ft 5in).

It is impossible to avoid the observation that France could have remained a significantly greater naval power in the 1880–1905 period had she learned the value of economy and increased hull numbers through standardisation. Alternatively, given that these vessels were admittedly vulnerable to hits above the armour deck, the money could have been put instead into either a couple of larger battleships or simply into better protected coast defence vessels. The *Jemmapes* class was stricken in 1911 while the *Bouvines* survived to 1920–22.[1]

Germany

The *Siegfried* and *Odin* classes were the last coast defence ships to be built by Germany and were constructed between 1888 and 1896 at five different yards. Apart from general agreement among historical sources on these types' armament (three 240mm, eight or ten 88mm [*Odin* class], and four 350mm torpedo tubes on all the *Siegfried*s except *Siegfried* itself which had six, or three 450mm tubes on the *Odin*s), there is considerable disagreement on displacement, armour, ihp, the *Siegfried*s' speed and both classes' dimensions.

Both primary sources consulted[1] record these vessels' standard displacement as 3,691 tons, but a key German source from 1900 records the *Siegfried*s' displacement as the round number of 3,500 tons and the *Odin*s' as a more precise 3,530 tons.[2] The primary sources record armour protection as 241–178mm (9.5–7in) belt (7–9in for *Odin* and *Ägir*), barbette and turret armour of 203mm (8in), with 1.25in deck for the *Siegfried*s and 2.75–2in deck for the *Odin*s. Gibbons records belt width as 2.29m (7.5ft).

But the German source also records slightly different, more extensive and, it is believed, more accurate information on the *Siegfried* and *Odin* classes' armour.[2] Turret armour of the *Siegfried*s is described as 200mm (7.9in) for the barbettes and 30mm (1.2in) for the turret cupolas. Beneath the waterline and the 240–180mm (9.44–7in) belt was a continuation of the belt, ranging from 140mm (5.5in) to 100mm (3.9in) at the ends. Conning tower of 80mm (3.14in), magazine armour of 200mm and deck armour of 30mm (1.2in) completed the *Siegfried*s' protection. The *Odin*s had a 220mm (8.66in) belt amidships, stopping abruptly at the 200mm magazine armour, but not continuing to the ends. Turret, cupola, magazine, deck and conning tower protection were as on the *Siegfried*s and there is no record of stronger deck armour. A further difference is recorded in engine power.

Primary sources record 5,000ihp from twin shaft triple expansion engines giving a speed of 14.5kts, the German source records 4,800ihp and 13kt speed for the *Siegfried*s and 14–15kts for the *Odin*s. The sources also disagree on dimensions: the German source says the *Siegfried*s and *Odin*s came in at 73m x 15m x 5.3m, the primary sources record 78.99m or 79m overall x 14.9m x 5.74m or 5.79m. Even allowing for a certain deliberate vagueness in 1900 over the *Siegfried*s' displacement, since they were still in German service, all these differences are noteworthy.

The armament arrangements of these ships were strange in that two of the 240mm were installed forward, astride one another in separate single turrets. The eight 88mm were installed in single open mountings, four or five (*Odin* class) per side. All later standardised on ten 88mm. At least everybody agrees on these ships' crew numbers: 276. All these ships except *Hagen* were rebuilt from 1898 to 1900 with new boilers and two funnels in place of the original one. They were lengthened to 282ft (85.9m) overall and 275ft 6in (84m) on the waterline and tonnage increased to 4,158 tons, according to one source.[3] The ships' further careers are discussed in Chapter 7.

Austria-Hungary

The Austro-Hungarian Navy adopted the purpose-designed coast defence ship relatively late, with the *Monarch* class. The fleet which had won an unexpected victory at Lissa could not however effect the realities of the strategic situation on land. The combination of Prussia's victory over Austria in the war of 1866, followed by the transformation of the Hapsburg Empire into the Austro-Hungarian monarchy after the 'compromise' of 1867, under which Hungary won its autonomy, with a veto over military expenditure it did not like, meant that the newly titled Kaiserlich und Königlich (Imperial and Royal) Navy would always be the cinderella of the services.

The *Monarch*s were 5,547 ton vessels built at Pola (*Monarch*), and Stabilimento Tecnico Triestino (*Wien* and *Budapest*), between 1893 and 1898. These were true battleships in miniature, with four 240mm 40cal Krupp in two turrets fore and aft, six 150mm 40cal Skoda in separate little barbettes amidships, four 47mm 33cal Hotchkiss quickfirers, an 8mm machine gun, two 70mm 15cal Uchatius landing guns for shore parties, two beam 450mm torpedo tubes and, from 1917 on *Wien* and *Budapest*, a 70mm anti-aircraft gun. Primary sources record Harvey belt armour of 270–220mm (10.6–8.7in), turret armour of 250mm (9.8in), 80mm casemates and 40mm (1.6in) decks. An Austrian source, however, records the belt armour as precisely 262.5mm at its maximum, and deck armour as a thicker 62.5mm.[4] Whichever way, this was not bad, especially the

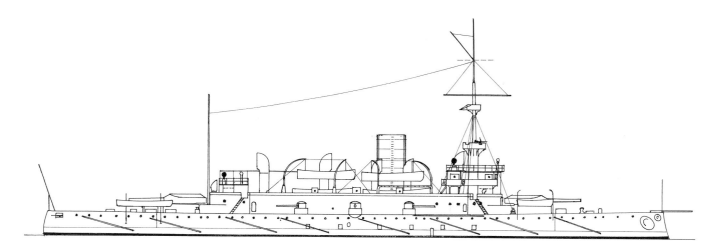

Wien
The first genuine coast defence turret ships of the Austro-Hungarian Navy, the Monarch *class (*Wien *is shown as completed in 1898) were excellent examples of the genre (CMP)*

deck armour when compared with the *Siegfried*s for example. The *Monarch*s had a crew of 426.

These ships could make 17–17.5kts from their twin shaft, triple cylinder vertical triple expansion engines (8,500ihp), which was an improvement on the previous barbette and central battery ships of the fleet, and would only be bettered by succeeding classes, like the 8,232 ton *Hapsburg* class battleships.

So is it fair to criticise the *Monarch*s as inadequate, as some have done? On the face of it, no. These were useful intermediate warships, constructed during the development of true modern battleships, the first of which (*Habsburg*) did not come into service until almost two years after the *Monarch*s. As such, they were not a worthwhile investment and, as Chapter 7 shows, had an interesting war between 1914 and 1918. Their dimensions were 99.22m x 17m x 6.4m (325ft 6in x 55ft 9in x 21ft 9in).

Russia

The unfortunate *Admiral Ushakov* class coast defence battleships, designed to match their Swedish opposite numbers in the Baltic but not the mighty Japanese battle fleet, have their place in history as members of Admiral Rozhestvensky's doomed fleet at the Battle of Tsushima in 1905. *Ushakov* (commanded by Captain Miklukha) was sunk and *Seniavin* and *Apraksin* surrendered, after fully participating in the battle, to become the Japanese *Mishima* and *Okinoshima* (see Chapter 7 for their careers). *Ushakov* went down very bravely on 28 May 1905, refusing to surrender when signalled to do so by the fast Japanese armoured cruisers *Iwate* and *Yakumo*. The Japanese quick-firers caused such damage that *Ushakov* could not reply after she developed a severe list. Miklukha opened the sea cocks for scuttling, but the Japanese cruisers closed in and finished off *Ushakov*, which blew up as the battle came to an end.[5]

Ushakov and *Seniavin* were laid down in 1892 at the New

Admiralty and Baltic Works respectively, *Apraksin* being laid down at the former yard in October 1894. They were completed in 1895, 1896 and 1899 respectively. Designed displacement was 4,126 tons, but *Seniavin* in fact weighed 4,971 tons. Eight cylinder boilers (four on *Ushakov*) and a twin shaft vertical triple expansion provided 5,750ihp for 16kts. Coal provision as designed was 300 to 450 tons, this factor alone playing its part in slowing down the Russian Baltic fleet's ill-fated cruise to the Far East and its doom.

Harvey belt armour of 254–102mm (10–4in) and 203mm (8in) turret and conning tower armour was not too bad for these ships' original purpose, and neither was the armament of four 254mm (10in) 45cal in two turrets (one twin and one single on *Apraksin*), plus four 120mm (4.7in) 45cal, six 3pdrs, ten 1pdrs, six 1pdr revolvers and even four above water 381mm (15in) torpedo tubes. Complement was 404 and dimensions were 87.32m x 15.85m x 5.94m (286ft 6in x 52ft x 19ft 6in max).

Japan and China

The only Japanese coast defence ship of the period which was identified as such was *Hei Yen* (formerly the *Ping Yuen Ho*), which had previously been the Chinese Navy's *Ping Yuen* (which was itself previously known in Chinese service as the *Lung Wei*). The ship was captured at Wei-Hai-Wei on 12 February 1895 during the Sino-Japanese War. Originally laid down as a small armoured cruiser at Foochow in 1883, launched in June 1888 and completed for China's Peiyang (Northern) fleet in April 1889, the ship was armed with a single 260mm (10.2in) Krupp breech-loader in a barbette forward. Two 150mm (5.9in) guns were mounted singly amidships and the four 18in torpedo tubes were divided between fixed bow and stern tubes and two trainable tubes on the broadside. The steel armour comprised a 239mm (9.4in) belt, 50mm (2in) deck, 127mm (5in) barbette with

Hei Yen
The Imperial Japanese Navy's Hei Yen *was formerly the Chinese-built, Chinese Navy coast defence ship* Ping Yuen, *armed originally with British guns before her refitting with Krupp ordnance (CMP)*

38mm (1.5in) shield, and 5in for the conning tower. Propulsion was provided by a twin shaft vertical triple expansion engine with four locomotive boilers, developing 24,000ihp for a speed of 10.5kts. In Chinese service, dimensions were 59.99m x 12.19m x 4.19m (196ft 10in x 40ft x 13ft 9in) and 202 crew were carried.

In Japanese hands, the ship was refitted with British guns in place of the Krupp weapons and was used as a gunnery training ship. The Russo-Japanese War saw *Hei Yen* serve in the coastal bombardment role, in which function she met her end on a mine in Pigeon Bay, Port Arthur, on 18 September 1904. The Japanese lengthened the ship to a 60.95m (200ft) waterline length, but the breadth was narrowed to 4.15m (13ft 6in). The calibre of the secondary armament changed to two 152mm (6in) QF and eight single 3pdr QF. The ship's complement was raised to 250.

United States

That Congress should have been misled by the 'great repair' ruse as a means of replacing Civil War monitors is extraordinary in itself, but that Secretary of the Navy George Robeson felt obliged to resort to such skulduggery was a telling comment on how, when America had one of the fastest growing economies in the world, Congress still could not understand the necessity of such a major power possessing its own seagoing navy.

Five monitors were built under the 'great repairs' programme, the all-new 6,060 ton *Puritan* (in place of the unfinished *Puritan* of the Civil War) and four 3,990 ton *Amphitrite* class vessels: *Amphitrite, Monadnock, Terror* and *Miantonomoh*. The latter programme started out as repairs, but it became evident that the original hulls were unusable, so they and everything else, were replaced.[6] These ships were long in building: *Puritan* took twenty years, being laid down at John Roach in May 1876 and completed by New York Navy Yard in December 1896. Some of the others took even longer to build, being laid down in 1874 at four different yards and being completed between October 1891 (*Miantonomoh*) and April 1896 (*Terror*).

Armament of the iron-hulled *Puritan*, four 12in 35cal in two twin turrets, six 4in 40cal and six 6pdrs was impressive, but the ship was let down of course by her very low freeboard. Armour comprised both Harvey and nickel steel protection: 14–6in (355–152mm) belt, 8in for the turrets, 14in (355mm) for barbettes, 10in (250mm) for the conning tower. Twin shaft horizontal compound engines, with eight single-ended cylindrical boilers, developing 3,700ihp gave a speed on trials of 12.4kts. Dimensions were 296ft 3in overall x 60ft 1.5in x 18ft mean draught (90.3m x 18.33m x 5.49m). Between 200 and 270 crew were carried. *Puritan* saw action in the Caribbean during the Spanish-American War in 1898, was otherwise not often in actual commission and left service in April 1910, being stricken in 1918 and sold in 1922.

The *Amphitrite*s all differed from one another in various major and minor respects, given their widely separated construction (see table). These vessels were iron-hulled with 1.75in (44mm) steel deck over the belt. *Monadnock* did not achieve her intended speed of 14.5kts, her trial speed being a disappointing 11.63kts. The design speed of the others was 12kts. *Monadnock* went to the Philippines for the Spanish-American War, taking almost two months to cross the Pacific. She remained in the Philippines and Chinese waters for the rest of her life until being sold in 1923. The

Puritan
Nominally intended to be a 'great repair' of a Civil War era ship, Puritan *was in fact a new construction, hidden from Congress by an incredible sleight of hand and is shown as completed in 1896 (CMP)*

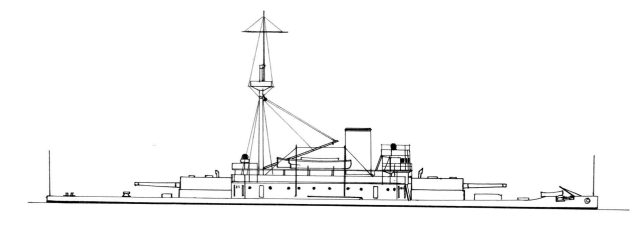

other three ships spent most of their lives out of commission and were finally sold in 1920–23.

A new monitor, as far as both the Navy Department and Congress were concerned (!), was the 4,084 ton *Monterey*, the first officially-sanctioned new monitor since the 1860s, authorised in March 1887, laid down in December 1889, launched in March 1891 and commissioned in February 1893. This twin-turreted vessel had two 12in 35cal forward, two 10in 30cal aft, and six 6pdrs. This was a change from the original conception of one 16in and one 12in. Armour protection comprised 13–5in belt (330–127mm), 13–11.5in (330–292mm) barbettes, 8–7.5in turrets and 10in for the conning tower. Four Babcock & Wilcox twin-shaft vertical triple expansion engines developing 5,250ihp gave a trial speed of 13.6kts. Some 230 tons of coal were carried; *Monterey* accompanied *Monadnock* across the Pacific in 1898 and also remained in the Far East until she became station ship

at Pearl Harbor. Dimensions were 260ft 11in x 59ft 0.5in x 14ft 10in mean (79.52m x 18m x 4.52m). She was sold in 1921.

The final monitor class in the US Navy was the four ship *Arkansas* class. *Arkansas*, *Nevada*, *Florida* and *Wyoming* were built at Newport News, Bath Iron Works, Lewis Nixon and Union Iron Works respectively between 1899 and 1902–03. Displacing 3,225 tons, these ships were authorised in 1898 and were subsequently renamed (see Chapter 7). They shared twin shaft vertical triple expansion engines developing 2,400ihp, but they all had different boilers for their four boiler arrangements, from Thornycroft (*Arkansas*), Niclausse (*Nevada*), Mosher (*Florida*), and Babcock & Wilcox (*Wyoming*). Designed speed was 12.5kts and 350 tons of coal were carried.

With a single turret forward with two 12in 40cals, four 4in 50cal Mk 7s and three 6pdrs, these ships' main armament

Monitors in action in 1898
Two USN monitors are shown in line abreast on the left in this sketch of the bombardment of San Juan by Admiral Sampson's fleet on 12 May 1898 (GPH Collection)

Arkansas
Arkansas *(later* Ozark*) is shown as built and was the lead ship of a quartet of USN monitors which were to perform modest duties during relatively uneventful careers (CMP)*

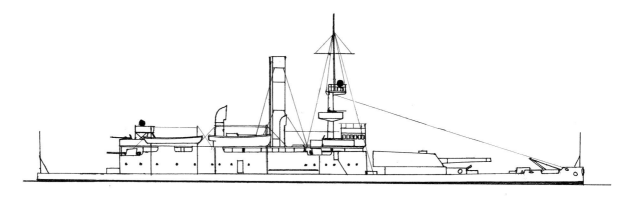

Indiana
Completed in 1895, Indiana and her sisters Massachusetts and Oregon were officially classed as 'coast-line battleships'. These design drawings illustrated an Institute of Naval Architects paper on this and other American designs in 1891 (The Transactions of the Royal Institution of Naval Architects)

was better than many coast defence ships of the period, though the secondary armament was not so. Dimensions were 255ft 1in x 50ft x 12ft 6in (77.75m x 15.24m x 3.81m). They served as tenders during the First World War (Chapter 7).

America's 'New Navy' started with the battleships *Texas* and *Maine*, but her most important battleships were the *Indiana* class, officially described as 'second class seagoing coast-line battleships'. Once again, comment on the ships is often adverse, with the suggestion that too much was being

attempted on too limited a hull but, just as with Austria-Hungary's *Monarch*s, this class should be viewed as a transitional design and as such their construction was a useful exercise. As coast defence ships, they could be viewed as a better than reasonable example of their type, with very powerful armament, and many a more modest coast defence navy might have envied the USN for possessing them.

Displacing 10,288 tons (11,688 full load), they carried two turrets fore and aft with 13in 35cals. Secondary armament was a powerful battery of eight 8in 35cals in four turrets

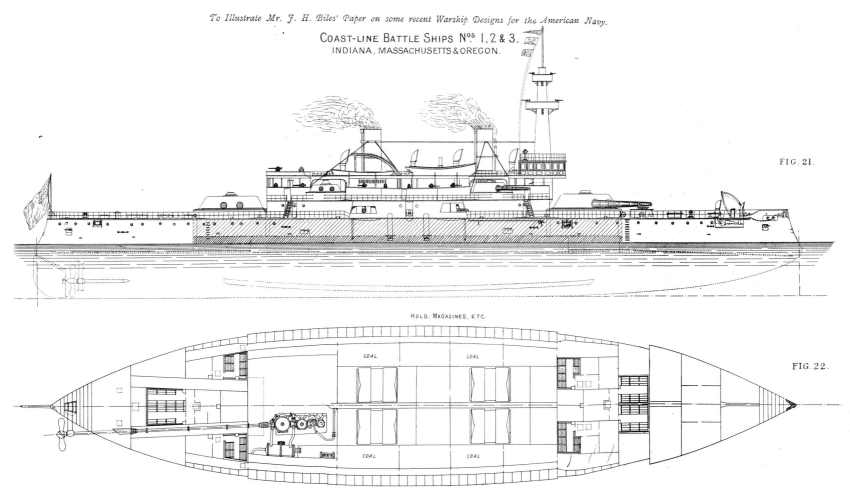

To Illustrate Mr. J. H. Biles' Paper on some recent Warship Designs for the American Navy.

COAST-LINE BATTLE SHIPS Nᵒˢ 1, 2 & 3.
INDIANA, MASSACHUSETTS & OREGON.

FIG. 21.

HOLD, MAGAZINES, ETC.

FIG. 22.

carried high on the superstructure at a gun axis of 25ft (a defensible point of criticism). The four 6in were in amidships sponsoned upper deck casemates. Twenty 6pdrs, six 1pdrs and six above-water 18in torpedo tubes made up the rest of the armament.

Armour comprised both Harvey and nickel steel for the 18–4in (457–101mm) belt, 17in barbettes for the 8in turrets, 15in for the turrets and 8–5in for the secondary guns, with 9in for the conning tower. This was admittedly an inch less than for the conning towers on the new monitors. Speed at 15kts would have been regarded as adequate for the coast defence mission. Six cylinder boilers and twin shaft vertical triple expansion engines developed 9,000ihp. Coal provision ranged from 400 to 1,640 tons. As it turned out, *Indiana* and *Oregon* were sent to participate in the Battle of Santiago in 1898. Dimensions were 350ft 11in (*Oregon* 351ft 2in) x 69ft 3in x 24ft mean (106.95m [107.03m] x 21.1m x 7.32m).

Indiana, *Massachusetts* and *Oregon* were all laid down in 1891 at Cramp and Union Iron Works (*Oregon*), being com-pleted in 1895–96. Their subsequent careers are discussed in Chapter 7. Similar to the *Indiana*s, and better in a number of respects, was the 11,410 ton *Iowa*, built by Cramp in 1893–97, though it was not described as a coast defence battleship.

Sweden

Sweden's iron, steel and armaments industries, specifically Bofors, ensured that her navy was equipped with some of the best medium and light guns in the world, though the country remained dependent on external sources for some larger weapons.

The first real coast defence ships built by the Swedes after their construction of the *John Ericsson* and *Loke* class monitors (see Chapter 4), were the three *Svea* class vessels, which displaced from 3,051 to 3,248 tons. They were *Svea* and *Göta*, launched by Lindholmen in 1886 and 1891, and

Iowa
Though not originally rated as a coast defence vessel, Iowa *was reclassified as 'Coast Battleship No.4' in 1919. As built, she was clearly influenced by the preceding* Indiana *class of coast defence battleships, of which she was a larger sister, yet she had lighter armour and armament and can be regarded as a* de facto *coast defence ship (GPH Collection)*

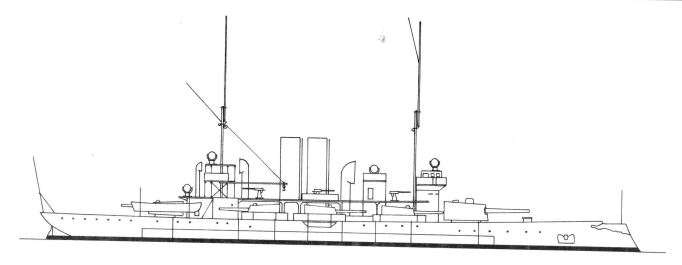

Thule, launched by Bergsund in 1893. A number of characteristics differed among the class (see table), but they were all armed with two single Armstrong 254mm (10in) 32cals and four or six 152mm (6in) 28cals, five or six 6pdrs and one to three 381mm (15in) torpedo tubes.

The *Svea*s were rebuilt in 1901–04 with new armament: one 210mm (8.3in) 44cal in a 190mm (7.5in) Krupp non-cemented turret and seven 152mm (6in) 44cal, all in single turrets, and eleven 6pdrs. *Thule* was alone in the class in possessing a ram.

The next class, the three 3,445 ton *Oden* class (*Oden, Thor* and *Niord*) were built by Bergsund and Lindholmen (*Niord*) and were launched in 1897 (*Oden*) and 1899. Harvey nickel was used for *Thor* and *Niord*'s 241mm (9.5in) belt and 203mm (8in) turrets, while *Oden* used Creusot steel. The engines gave 5,350ihp and 16.5kts and 300 tons of coal were carried. The armament comprised two 254mm 42cal (Canet-supplied for *Oden* and *Thor* and Bofors-supplied for *Niord*), plus six 120mm (4.7in) 45cal and ten 6pdrs and one 456mm (18in) torpedo tube. *Oden* originally had four 6pdrs and eight 3pdrs. Dimensions were 84.4m x 14.78m x 5.28m (278ft 3in wl x 48ft 6in x 17ft 4in max). 254 crew were carried.

With exactly the same displacement as the *Oden* class, the

one-off *Dristigheten* was launched by Lindholmen in 1900. Armament was the more modest, but also more rapid-firing 210mm 44cal in two single turrets, six 152mm 44cal in an upper deck battery, ten 6pdrs and two 456mm (18in) torpedo tubes. The powerplant was a little more efficient than the *Oden*s', delivering 5,400ihp. Harvey nickel 203mm (8in) belt and 203–152mm turret protection made up the armour. Dimensions were 86.87m x 14.78m x 4.88m (285ft wl x 48ft 6in x 16ft max).

The four 3,592 ton *Äran* class ships (*Äran, Wasa, Tapperheten, Manligheten*) were launched by Lindholmen, Bergsund and Kockums for the last two in 1902 and 1904. The armament was as for *Dristigheten*, but the 152mm were in single turrets amidships and armour was different too, with a Krupp cemented and non-cemented 179mm (7in) belt and 190–127mm (7.5–5in) turrets. The powerplant gave a better 6,500ihp for 17kts (*Tapperheten* 5,500ihp for 16.5kts) and 285 crew were carried. Dimensions were 87.48m x 15m x 5m (287ft wl x 49ft 3in x 16ft 5in max).

The last coast defence ship the Swedes built before the landmark *Sverige* class was unique in being three funnelled as opposed to the twin funnelled arrangement of all the other coastal battleships. Launched in 1905, the 4,584 ton *Oscar II* was fast by comparison with the rest of the battle-

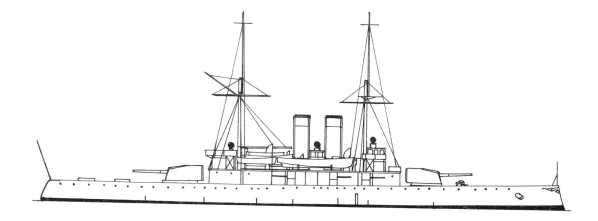

Harald Haarfagre
The first vessel in Norway's coast defence ship build-up in the twilight years of her nominal rule by the Swedish crown was Harald Haarfagre, *a 3,858 ton vessel launched by Armstrongs in January 1897. She is seen here during a visit to Copenhagen (Frank Abelsen)*

ship fleet, at 18kts courtesy of a 9,000ihp powerplant. The armament was as for the *Äran*s, with two more 152mm, and crew numbers were up at 331. The belt armour was reduced, accounting, together with the better powerplant, for the higher speed, with Krupp cemented and non-cemented 152–101mm (6–4in) protection, though turret armour was as on the Arans. Dimensions were 95.6m x 15.4m x 5.49m (313ft 8in wl x 50ft 6in x 18ft max).

Norway

The four *Harald Haarfagre* and *Norge* class coast defence ships were at the centre of Norway's struggle for outright independence from Sweden, whose King was also Norway's head of state, though Norway had its own constitution and managed its own armed forces. It is said that Norway's purchase of these ships from Britain played an important part in convincing the Swedes to accept the inevitable and allow Norway complete independence.

As it turned out, the 3,858 ton *Harald Haarfagre* and *Tordenskjold* were to survive until the end of the Second World War, serving the German as well as Norwegian fleets, albeit in a modest capacity, but the 4,165 ton *Norge* and *Eidsvold* were to meet tragic ends on the same day in 1940, this being described in detail in Chapter 9.

All four ships were built by Armstrongs, the first pair being launched in 1897 and the *Norge* class in 1900. They shared the same main armament of two single 208.2mm (8.2in) 44cal, but had different secondary guns (six shield-mounted 120mm (4.7in) 44cal on the *Harald Haarfagre* class

and six 150mm (5.9in) 46cal on the *Norge*s). Other weapons comprised six 12pdrs, six 1pdrs and two 18in torpedo tubes on the *Haarfagre* class and eight 12pdrs, four 3pdrs and two 18in tubes on the *Norge*s.

With a crew of 245, the *Harald Haarfagre*s' 4,500ihp powerplant gave a speed of 16.9kts; armour protection comprised a 179–102mm (7–4in) Harvey belt and 203–127mm (8–5in) nickel steel on the turrets. Dimensions were 92.66m x 14.78m x 5.38m (304ft x 48ft 6in x 17ft 8in max). The *Norge*s only had a 152mm (6in) Krupp cemented belt amidships, with 229–127mm (9–5in) nickel steel for the turrets. A power plant also developing 4,500ihp did not deliver the same speed given the *Norge*'s increased displacement and provided 16.5kts on a good day. There were 266 crew for the *Norge*s, whose dimensions were 94.57m x 15.39m x 5.38m (310ft 3in x 50ft 6in x 17ft 8in).

Denmark

Iver Hvitfeldt was the first Danish coast defence ship completed after 1880, being launched by Copenhagen Dockyard in 1886. Smaller than *Helgoland*, the last Danish coastal battleship to be built, the 3,392 ton *Iver Hvitfeldt* nonetheless continued the practice started with *Helgoland* of providing a decent freeboard.

Armed with two single 260mm (10.2in) 35cal, four 120mm (4.7in) 30cal, a dozen 1pdr revolvers and a mixed torpedo battery (as on *Helgoland*) of two 381mm (15in) and two 381mm (14in), *Iver Hvitfeldt* was apparently judged to be too heavy, and, in a 1904 reconstruction, the 120mm

Tordenskjold
The second vessel of the
Harald Haarfagre *class,*
the Norwegian coast
defence ship Tordenskjold
is shown as she was in
around 1912, some fifteen
years after her launch by
Armstrongs, and seven
years after Norway's full
independence (CMP)

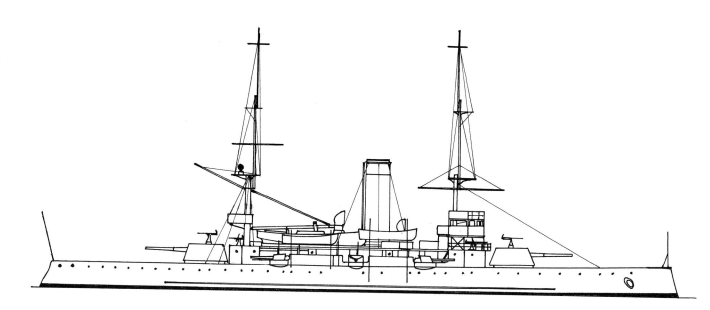

Tordenskjold
Seen here during a visit to
Rotterdam, this view
shows clearly
Tordenskjold's *primary*
8.2in 44cal armament fore
and aft and the three
starboard 4.7in 44cal
behind the small shields
amidships (Frank Abelsen)

were replaced by ten 6pdrs and the 1pdr revolvers were reduced to six, while the 381mm tubes were scrapped. Compound belt armour was provided of a 292–179mm (11.5–7in) belt, with 216mm (8.5in) barbettes, while the 5,100ihp powerplant gave a speed of 15.25kts, far better than *Helgoland*'s 13.75kts. With a crew of 277, dimensions of the single funnelled ship were 74m x 15.11m x 5.59m (242ft 10in x 49ft 7in x 18ft 4in).

The example of *Iver Hvitfeldt*'s acceptable freeboard was not followed though by the succeeding *Skjold* and *Herluf Trolle* class coast defence ships, low freeboard single-funnelled vessels which returned to the monitor club. *Skjold*, launched in 1896, displaced 2,160 tons and was a one-off; *Herluf Trolle* and *Olfert Fischer*, launched in 1899 and 1903, displaced 3,494 tons and 3,592 tons respectively. *Skjold* was armed with a single 238.7mm (9.4in) 40cal, three 120mm 40cal in single turrets aft in a triangular arrangement, four 3pdrs and one 1pdr revolver cannon, and 229–179mm (9–7in) of complete Harvey belt armour and 10in on the turret. The 2,400ihp engine gave 14kts; there were 138 crew and dimensions were 69.24m x 11.6m x 4.16m (227ft 2in x 38ft 1in x 13ft 8in max).

There were numerous differences between *Herluf Trolle* and *Olfert Fischer* (see table), and a third ship of the class, the different *Peder Skram*, was not launched until 1908.

One other ship which could be (but is not) classified as a coastal defence vessel was the very strange 2,462 ton torpedo ram *Tordenskjold*, built at Copenhagen in 1880 and armed with a single 355mm (14in) 25cal and three 355mm torpedo tubes, plus a ram and lighter weapons.

The Netherlands

The Dutch built one more low freeboard monitor after 1880 before getting into their stride with classic coast defence ships. This was the 70m (229ft 8in) *Reinier Claeszen*, a 2,440 ton vessel launched in Amsterdam in 1891 and armed with one 208mm (8.2in) 35cal in a turret with 11in armour, one 170mm (6.7in) 35cal, four 4pdrs and two 14in torpedo tubes. The engine gave 2,315ihp for a speed of 12.5kts and a 121mm (4.75in) compound armour belt was fitted.

The three *Evertsen* class (3,464 ton) and three *Koningin Regentes* class (5,002 ton) which followed (launched 1894 and 1900–1902 respectively) were better armed with three 208mm 35cal for the former and two 9.4in 40cal for the latter, plus respectively two and four 150mm 40cal and numerous smaller 13pdr and 1pdr guns and three 456mm torpedo tubes. They could all make 16–16.5kts, but their armour differed in that the *Evertsens* (*Evertsen, Piet Hein* and *Kortenaer*) had a steel 152–102mm (6–4in) belt with 241mm (9.5in) barbette, while the *Regentes* used Krupp cemented armour for their 6–4in belts.

Two more Dutch coast defence ships were built before

Olfert Fischer
Danish Navy coast defence ships on Baltic manoeuvres
These photographs show the Danish coast defence ship Olfert Fischer (3,592 tons, launched 1903) and assorted coast defence vessels on manoeuvres (CMP)

Table 1: Amphitrite class

	Amphitrite	*Monadnock*	*Terror*	*Miantonomoh*
Builders*	ld: Harlan & Hollingsworth 1874 comp: Norfolk NY 23.4.1895	ld: Continental Iron Works 1875 comp: Mare Is NY 20.2.1896	ld: Cramp 1874 comp: New York NY 20.2.1896	ld: John Roach 1874 comp: New York NY 27.10.1891
Dimensions	262ft 9in x 55ft 4in x 14ft 6in (80.18m x 16.86m x 4.42m)	262ft 3in x 55ft 5in x 14ft 6in (73.93m x 16.89m x 4.42m)	263ft 1in x 55ft 6in x 14ft 8in (80.18m x 16.91m x 4.47m)	263ft 1in x 55ft 4in x 14ft 6in (80.18m x 16.86m x 4.42m)
Propulsion	Twin shaft horizontal compound engines, 4 Babcock & Wilcocks boilers, 1600ihp = 12kts designed speed	Twin shaft horizontal triple expansion engines, 4 single-engined cylindrical boilers, 3000ihp = 14kts designed speed	Twin shaft horizontal compound engines, 6 single-engined cylindrical boilers, 1600ihp = 12kts designed speed	Twin shaft horizontal compound engines, 6 single-engined cylindrical boilers, 1600ihp = 12kts designed speed
Armour**	Belt: 9in (228mm) Barbettes: 11.5in (292mm) Turrets: 7.5in (190mm) Conning tower: 7.5in (190mm)	Belt: 9in (228mm) Barbettes: 11.5in (292mm) Turrets: 7.5in (190mm) Conning tower: 7.5in (190mm)	Belt: 7in (179mm) Turrets: 11.5in (292mm) Conning tower: 7.5in (190mm)	Belt: 7in (179mm) Turrets: 11.5in (292mm) Conning tower: 9in (228mm)
Armament	4 x 10in 30cal; 2 x 4in 40cal; 2 x 6pdr; 2 x 3pdr	4 x 10in 30cal; 2 x 4in 40cal; 2 x 6pdr; 2 x 3pdr	4 x 10in 30cal; 2 x 6pdr; 2 x 3pdr	2 x 10in 35cal, 2 x 10in 30cal; 2 x 6pdr; 2 x 3pdr

*   laid down originally in private yards, completed in naval yards
**   steel and wrought iron

Table 2: Svea class

	Svea	*Göta*	*Thule*
Dimensions	248ft 5in x 48ft 6in x 17ft (75.1m x 14.78m x 18m)	260ft 10in x 47ft 10in x 116ft 9in (79.5m x 14.6m x 5.11m)	260ft 10in x 47ft 10in x 116ft 9in (79.5m x 14.6m x 5.11m)
Propulsion	3640ihp = 14.7kts	4700ihp = 16kts	4700ihp = 16kts
Armament: as built	2 x 10in 35cal, 4 x 6in 28cal, 5–6 x 6pdr, 1–3 x 15in TT	2 x 10in 35cal, 4 x 6in 34cal, 5–6 x 6pdr, 1–3 x 15in TT	2 x 10in 35cal, 4 x 6in 34cal, 5–6 x 6pdr, 1 – 3 x 15in TT
: after 1901–04 reconstruction	1 x 8.3in 44cal, 7 x 6in 44cal, 11 x 6pdr	1 x 8.3in 44cal, 7 x 6in 44cal, 11 x 6pdr	1 x 8.3in 44cal, 7 x 6in 44cal, 11 x 6pdr

Table 3: Herluf Trolle class

	Herluf Trolle	*Olfert Fischer*
Displacement	3494t	3592t
Dimensions	271ft 11in x 49ft 5in x 16ft 2in (82.87m x 15.06m x 4.93m)	271ft 11in x 50ft 6in x 16ft 5in (82.87m x 15.39m x 5m)
Armour	Belt: 8–7in (203–179mm) Creusot Turrets: 7–6in (177–152mm) Creusot	Belt: 7.5–6in (190.5–152mm) Krupp cemented Turrets: 7.5–6.5in (190.5–165mm) Krupp cemented
Armament	2 x 9.4in 40cal, 4 x 5.9in 43cal, 10 x 6pdr, 3 x 1pdr revolvers, 8 x 1pdr QF, 3 x 18in TT	2 x 9.4in 43cal, 4 x 5.9in 43cal, 10 x 6pdr, 6 x 3pdr, 2 x 1pdr, 2 x 1pdr revolvers, 3 x 18in TT

the ill-fated *De Zeven Provincien* (see Chapters 6 and 9). They were *Marten Harpertzoon Tromp*, a 5,210 ton, 100.78m (330ft 8in) long double-turret vessel launched in 1904, with two 240mm 40cal, four 150mm 40cal, and tertiary 13pdrs and 1pdrs and the usual three 18in tubes, and *Jacob van Heemskerck*, a 4,920 ton vessel built at Amsterdam (launched 1906), which was 321ft 6in (98m) long, was armed likewise with a pair of 240mm 40cal and six 150mm 40cal, six 13pdrs, four 1pdrs and just two 18in tubes. Like *Tromp*, she could make 16kts from her 6,400ihp engine. An exceptionally fine model of her can be seen at Amsterdam's Nederlands Historisch Scheepvaart Museum.

Latin America

Brazil's two La Seyne-built *Marshal Deodoro* coast defence battleships (the other being *Marshal Floriano*) were 3,162 ton vessels launched in 1898 and 1899 respectively, 267ft 6in (81.53m) long, single-funnelled and good examples of their type, though with a lowish freeboard.

They were armed with a pair of Armstrong 9.4in (238.7mm) 45cal mounted singly in turrets with 8.6in armour fore and aft, plus four 4.7in (120mm) 50cal, six 6pdrs and two submerged 456mm tubes. The 13.7–5.9in (348–150mm) Harvey belt thinned to 3.9in (99mm) at the ends. Twin shaft vertical triple expansion engines and eight boilers gave 3,400ihp and 15kts. Their further careers are discussed in Chapter 7.

Laird built the two *Independencia* class coast defence ships for Argentina in direct response to the *Deodoro*s. They were named *Libertad* (formerly *Nueve de Julio*) and *Independencia* and were launched in 1890 and 1891. Displacing 2,330 tons, these 230ft (70.1m) vessels were more compact but packed in two 9.4in 35cal, four 4.7in 40cal, four 3pdrs and two 18in tubes. Speed, at 14.2kts from her twin shaft vertical triple expansion engines with four cylindrical boilers, was not as good as the Brazilian ships. Armour comprised an 8in (203mm) steel belt, 8–6in (203–152mm) on the barbettes for the 4.7in guns, with 4in (101mm) for the conning tower.

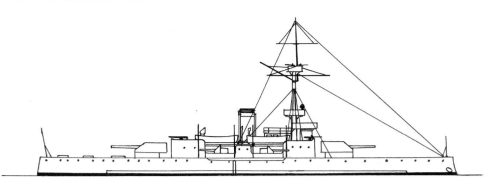

Independencia
Laird built,
Independencia *(shown here as built)* and
Libertad *were conventional coast defence ships with a flush deck and two Krupp 9.4in guns to equal Brazil's* Marshal Deodoros *(CMP)*

Evertsen
The Dutch coast defence ship Evertsen, *seen here in 1902, was launched in 1894 and was armed with three 8.2in 35cal. She had a complete waterline 6–4in belt (Hanny and Leo van Ginderen Collection)*

1 Information on coast defence ships of the 1880–1905 period is taken mostly from Gibbons, op.cit., and *Conway's All the World's Fighting Ships 1860–1905*, op.cit., except where noted.

2 B Weyer, *Taschenbuch der Deutschen Kriegsflotte* (Munich, 1977 reprint of 1900 volume), pp19–20.

3 *Conway's 1860–1905*, op.cit., p246.

4 A E Sokol, *Seemacht Österreich, Die Kaiserliche und Königliche Kriegsmarine 1382–1918* (Vienna, 1972), p213.

5 Eric Grove *Fleet to Fleet Encounters*, (London, 1991), p43 for *Ushakov*'s loss, pp10–46 for a full description of Tsushima, set in context with the technology, training and battle practices of the time.

6 *Monitors of the U.S. Navy*, op.cit., p39 and on, for a description of all the 'New Navy' monitors and the scandal over the 'repairs'.

Intermediate Solutions

THIS CHAPTER DESCRIBES THE approaches of four long-standing coast defence powers to the serious problem of retaining a credible fleet in the face of the major powers after the design of *Dreadnought*. The positions in which Sweden, Denmark and the Netherlands found themselves after 1906 was at once enviable but, certainly in the case of the Netherlands, all too weak.

What was true, however, was that none had major enemies. Sweden had not been to war since Napoleonic times, whereas Denmark had lost what she was going to lose to anyone in 1864. The Netherlands, a declared neutral, had no likely enemies, although she was involved in a long and painful struggle to establish complete control of her very valuable colony in the East Indies. In the case of Spain, she likewise had lost her entire empire in the western hemisphere and in the Pacific in 1898 and her main overseas interests were in North Africa. All these countries were non-combatants during the First World War and all came up with different solutions to the problem of coastal defence, although in the case of Spain, their vessels were only described as such at the time *sotto voce*.

The Swedish ships of the *Sverige* class came into being in controversial political circumstances, never saw action, but were a significant factor in German and Soviet naval planning in the Baltic before and during the Second World War. One Danish vessel, *Niels Juel*, was unfortunately not built to its original design but emerged as a rather unsatisfactory amalgam between a lightly-armed armoured cruiser and a coast defence ship. Her brief moment of tragic glory was not to come until 1943. Another older Danish vessel launched after *Dreadnought* was the third ship of the *Herluf Trolle* class, *Peder Skram*, effectively a low freeboard monitor with a great deal of top-weight. The Dutch ship, *De Zeven Provincien*, saw uneventful service during the First World War, but met a brave end against the Japanese in 1942. Finally, Spain built three dreadnoughts during this period – the *Espana* class – which are as shall be argued of more than passing relevance to this account.

It is worthwhile recalling that all these powers were relatively weak industrially, although the Netherlands was still a significant trading nation. As such their naval vessels understandably reflected national circumstances. Indeed, a 1920 naval study reflected how: 'Navies of the third rank have found it difficult or impossible to attain a fully satisfactory solution,' while criticising *De Zeven Provincien* and

giving *Sverige* qualified praise for her superior armament.[1] It remains noteworthy that only Sweden demonstrated any consistent appreciation of the potential dangers which a small neutral might reasonably expect to face in the early twentieth century and even this understanding was only gained after a full-scale constitutional crisis which brought down a government.

The Sverige class

In Sweden, the army, which was expanding in this period as the threat of a general European war grew, took the lion's share of defence expenditure and Swedish steel production. Yet Sweden's navy, while the cinderella of the two services, had become surprisingly powerful for such a small nation in the latter part of the nineteenth century. From the turn of the new century until the advent of the dreadnought age, five new small coastal defence ships of the *Dristigheten*, *Äran* and *Oscar II* classes were built, all of which were of only limited use up to the First World War, although they and six relics of the 1880s and 1890s were retained, for want of other tonnage.

Defence committee reports in 1904 and 1906 had recommended that any new coastal battleships' armament should be at least comparable to foreign warships and should also be capable of penetrating an armoured cruiser's armour. Given that the heaviest armament on the aforementioned coast defence ships was 254mm (10in) 32 cal and 210mm (8.3in) 44 cal, and that 304mm (12in) guns were now the standard armament of British dreadnoughts, it was not surprising that in 1909 the committee recommended that planned new coast defence ships should be armed with 280mm (11in) guns. The concept supported was the idea of moving on from the basic coast defence ship layout of two single guns fore and aft with negligible secondary armament, to a far larger and heavier combination of a coast defence ship and armoured cruiser, of which Sweden possessed a single example in *Fylgia*, which was launched in 1905. High speed was necessary to break any blockade of neutral Sweden's ports and patrol territorial waters, new responsibilities formally added to the Swedish Navy's mission in 1901.

Like its predecessors, the 1909 Committee made other recommendations: a speed of 21kts, a secondary armament

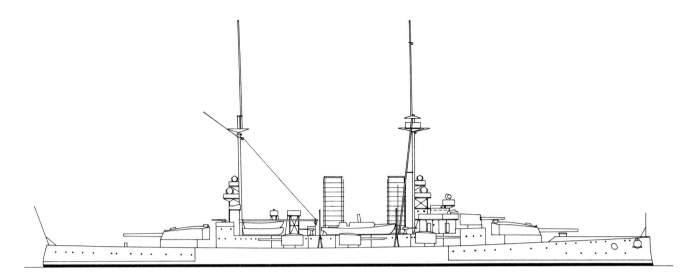

Sverige
Never in modern times has a controversy over the building of a single warship class brought down a government, but that is what Sverige, *the first of Sweden's new coast defence ships, managed to provoke. At 7,125 tons standard, with an armament of four 11.1in and eight 6in, she was equal to the power of older pre-dreadnoughts. The line drawing shows her as she was in 1917 (CMP)*

of four 194mm (7.63in), plus four 37mm guns and two 450mm torpedo tubes. A 200mm armour belt, with the same for the conning tower and main turrets was also recommended, as was 100mm (3.9in) for the citadel and 30–40mm (1–1.5in) for the decks.

The five designs considered by the Committee ranged from 6,440 to 7,500 tons and much higher speeds than their predecessors, from 18kts to 23kts. The final proposal put forward by the committee was the so-called Design F, with a length of 120m (393ft 8in), a beam of 18.6m (61ft) and draught of 6.8m (22ft 4in). Armament was to comprise four 280mm in two twin turrets and eight 150mm (5.9in), for a speed of 22.5kts.

Following its election victory in 1911, the Liberal government of Prime Minister Karl Staaf reversed the earlier conservative government's decision to begin building a new class of much heavier coast defence battleships of the Design F type, later to be known as the *Sverige* class.[2] This was despite the fact that the Swedish Naval Staff now felt that the country faced a real and worsening threat from Russia.

The decision to halt the new coast defence ship programme may have been lightly taken by a government which felt its election victory had earned it the right to govern as it thought fit but Staaf could not have reckoned for the public outcry. From the King downwards, there was widespread criticism of the decision and by 1912 a Swedish pastor, the Reverend Manfred Björkquist, had founded a society to raise public funds to build the first ship of the new class.

Here was a rare example of the public in a democratic society taking the collective initiative to force the government to change course. Thus between January and May 1912 the astonishing sum of over 15 million Kroner ($3,755,000 or £751,000) was raised and the Swedish parliament faced a public ultimatum from the so-called Armoured Ship Society that it must order the ship before the end of 1912 if it wished to use the money.

The necessary parliamentary approval to accept the Society's gift was passed, and the new ship was named *Sverige* (Sweden) because it represented the whole nation (a fair number of whom had contributed to its building). The construction of its successors did not take place before an outright constitutional crisis forced the government's hand in 1914. King Gustav V had ranged himself against the government, calling for an armament programme in speeches, and as a result Staaf's government resigned. After a special election, the new conservative government ordered the construction of two sister ships, to be named *Drottning Victoria* and *Gustav V*.

As it turned out, the dimensions of *Sverige* differed only very slightly from the original Design F concept, at 119.72m x 18.63m x 6.25m (392ft 9in x 61ft 1in x 20ft 6in). At 22.5kts, the 7,688 ton (full load) *Sverige* was slower than *Drottning Victoria* and *Gustav V* at 23.2 kts, these 7,663 ton ships also being slightly longer than *Sverige* at 369ft 8in (120.9m). *Sverige* was powered by a dozen Yarrow coal-fired boilers and Curtis direct drive turbines developing 20,000shp, replaced in *Drottning Victoria* and *Gustav V* by 22,000shp Westinghouse geared turbines.

At 3,280nm, the range of the two later ships was substantially greater than *Sverige*'s 2,720nm at an economical 14kt cruise speed, although both shared the same 910nm range at their respective maximum speeds.

Armament as built was the same for all three vessels, but was substantially altered during later refits. As built, besides the four 283mm (11.1in), they had one twin 152mm (6in) plus six more in single turrets, three on either beam. Six 75mm provided close-range defence against torpedo boats, while the recommended pair of 450mm torpedo tubes were fitted below the waterline as originally recommended.

Part of the reason for the original scepticism over the 1909 Committee's designs was the indisputable fact that Swedish shipyards had never built such a large vessel. In the event, Hugo Hammar's Götaverken yard – which had never built anything larger than 2,000 tons – took up the challenge of building *Sverige* with gusto, but not until after some very tough negotiations over price.

Sverige and her sisters were notable for the seriousness with which their designers took the threats of the day and the original requirement of a combination of a coast defence ship with an armoured cruiser. Thus the vessel's final lines were equal to the coefficients of contemporary armoured cruisers (the inherent disadvantages of this type of vessel not yet being widely understood at this time), while efforts were made to ensure that underwater protection equalled that of contemporary battleships in other countries.

In the event, despite being laid down in December 1912, *Sverige* was not completed until June 1917 because of a shortage of materials caused by non-delivery during the First World War. Her sisters, both laid down in May 1915, were not completed until 1921 in the case of *Drottning Victoria* (she was built at Kockums) and 1922 in the case of *Gustav V* (built at Götaverken). Thus even if Sweden's neutrality had been breached, this little flotilla of modern coastal battleships would have been too late to influence matters, as the last pair were delayed because the Westinghouse turbines were not delivered by the United States, then a combatant.

The *Sverige* class were among the best sea boats of the twentieth century's classic coast defence ships and, following substantial refits, played a key role in preserving Sweden's neutrality during the Second World War, of which more in Chapter 9.

Niels Juel and Peder Skram

Unlike Sweden, Denmark was not very defence-minded after the loss of Schleswig-Holstein to Prussia in 1864. With continental Europe's greatest power, Imperial Germany, as a neighbour, and with no apparent enemy, a simple trust in neutrality formed the basis of Danish foreign policy. Thus from 1897 to 1911 no torpedo boats were built for the navy and after 1899 only one coastal battleship joined the Danish fleet before the outbreak of the First World War, when there were six coast defence ships in service of the *Herluf Trolle*, *Skjold*, *Iver Hvitfeldt*, *Odin* and *Gorm* classes.

The most recent of these ships was the *Herluf Trolle* class vessel *Peder Skram*, launched in 1908, the third in the series and built at the Copenhagen Dockyard nine years after the first. Displacing 3,735 tons (normal), this 16kt coal-fired vessel was armed with two 240mm (9.4in) 43 cal forward and aft and four 150mm (5.9in) 50cal, plus ten 75mm and sundry smaller weapons and four 457mm (18in) torpedo tubes. Belt

Peder Skram
Two views of the Danish Herluf Trolle class *coastal battleship* Peder Skram, *the third of the type, though built nine years after the first. Note the size of the seaplane for scale: the ship was just 84m long, the size of a modern missile corvette (CMP)*

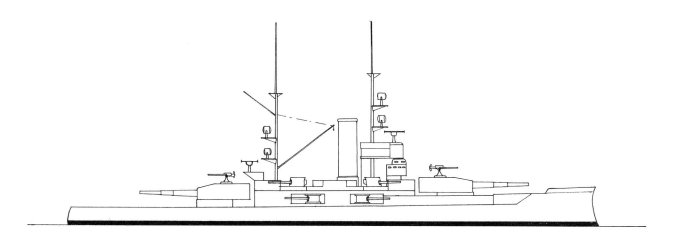

Niels Juel
This is how Niels Juel *was supposed to have been completed, with Krupp 305mm guns in two turrets fore and aft. As it was, the First World War ensured that she was finished as a kind of unsatisfactory amalgam between a light cruiser (6in guns) and a slow coast defence ship (CMP)*

armour of 8.7–6.1in (195–155mm), plus 7.5in (190mm) on the turret faces provided respectable protection.

Compared to *Peder Skram* with its very low freeboard, the original concept of *Niels Juel* was of a vessel armed with two single 305mm (12in) guns from Krupp. Laid down in Copenhagen Naval Dockyard in September 1914 just as the First World War broke out, *Niels Juel* was a true victim of the conflict in the sense that she could not in the event be completed to her original design. With very slow construction of the vessel continuing during the war despite the lack of any likely armament in the short term, it was scarcely surprising that the ship as completed was by far the most unsatisfactory and unbalanced of all the coast defence ships.

In 1922, eight years after *Niels Juel* was laid down, Sweden's Bofors finally received a contract for the main armament, which comprised of ten 150mm. These were fixed in curious positions, with a pair at the bow next to each other, a pair at the stern with X-turret superfiring over Y-turret, and the balance divided three on each beam, mounted in rather odd barbettes. Speed was just 16kts, far below her Swedish coast defence contemporaries, and armour was no improvement on *Peder Skram*: the gunshields were only 2in (50mm) thick and the conning tower armour, at 6.7in (170mm), was even less than *Peder Skram*'s 7.5in.[3]

Niels Juel was completed in 1923, her dimensions being 90m x 16.3m x 5m (295ft 3in x 54ft 6in x 16ft 5in). She was reconstructed several times, but as a hybrid between a light cruiser and a coast defence ship she was for all practical purposes useless. It was no surprise therefore that the Danes, unlike their Norwegian and Swedish neighbours, chose to emulate the Finns and designed new coast defence ships during the 1930s, which would have far better suited their needs had they been built.

As it turned out, both *Peder Skram* and *Niels Juel* had eventful careers during the Second World War, first in brief moments of tragic glory in 1943 while flying the Dannebrog

(the Danish ensign) and then in the service of Hitler's Kriegsmarine.

De Zeven Provincien

There were six coast defence ships in service with the Dutch fleet in 1914, of which five had been launched between 1900 and 1906. They were the three vessels of the *Koningen Regentes* class (*Koningen Regentes*, *De Ruyter*, *Hertog Hendrik*), and the later, but similar derivatives *Marten Harpertzoon Tromp* and *Jacob van Heemskerck*. The last of the earlier coast defence ships, *Piet Hein* (launched in 1894), was finally discarded in 1914.

The newest coast defence vessel in the fleet in 1914 was *De Zeven Provincien*, laid down at Amsterdam Dockyard in 1908, launched the following year and completed in October 1910. This ship had been built following the realisation that the Netherlands' colony in the East Indies was somewhat more vulnerable now that Japan had defeated Russia and the British had withdrawn their battle squadron from the region.

With a normal displacement of 6,530 tons, *De Zeven Provincien* could make 16kts (16.27kts on trials) courtesy of her eight Yarrow boilers. Her armament of two single 280mm (11in) 42.5cal was substantially more imposing than the 240mm (9.45in) 40cal guns of the other coast defence ships. Her belt armour protection though was still comparable to her predecessors, at 150–100mm (5.9in–3.9in), as was her turret armour of 248mm (9.8in). Secondary armament of four single 150mm (5.9in) 40cal was barbette-mounted below the weather-deck, while the lighter anti-torpedo boat battery comprised ten 75mm 40cal and four 37mm. Dimensions were certainly compact 101.5m w, 103.5m oa x 17.1m x 6.2m (333ft wl, 339ft oa x 56ft 1in x 20ft 4in), with a short bow.

The Netherlands' plans to build a somewhat more

powerful fleet to defend the East Indies, leading to ever stillborn proposals for battleships or battlecruisers, had their roots in the request for funding for the first of four larger 7,600 ton coast defence ships in 1912. With a speed of 18kts (10,000ihp), they were to be far more worthwhile propositions than *De Zeven Provincien*, with the armament of a respectable pre-dreadnought: four 280mm (11in) 45cal, ten 4.1in (105mm) and three torpedo tubes. Their belt and turret armour would have been as on *De Zeven Provincien*.

As it turned out, these vessels was deemed inadequate for the task and attention shifted to the benefits of acquiring five dreadnoughts of the British-designed *Espana* type. As a result the original scheme to buy coast defence ships was rejected by the States General and the Minister of Marine resigned. The issue was then forced into the limbo of a Royal Commission which in 1913 recommended the construction of, *inter alia*, no fewer than nine 14in-armed battleships.

Nothing came of this, of course, as the plan was quite beyond the Netherlands' finances. The First World War imposed great strains on the Dutch economy and the country was never able to acquire capital ships after the conflict's end. It is hard to avoid the conclusion that had the Netherlands stuck to the original plan, the four 11in-armed coast defence ships would have been far better than nothing and could have proved a very useful adjunct to the handful of cruisers built after the war for the East Indies' defence. They might even have been able to sink a Japanese ship or two in 1942.

As it turned out, *De Zeven Provincien* was sent east in 1921, suffered a serious mutiny in February 1923, which was only ended when a Dutch seaplane bombed the forecastle. She was laid up in 1933, but the most dramatic – and tragic – moment of her career, in 1942, was yet to come.

Miniature Dreadnoughts – The Espanas

Mention should also be made of one dreadnought battleship class, the smallest ever built, which seems to have been strongly influenced by the example of smaller coast defence ships.

Spain's three *Espana* class battleships – built locally to a British design using British-supplied materials – represented another way to approach the same challenge facing the lesser powers but which only built coast defence ships. It was therefore no accident that after first considering coast defence vessels, the *Espana* concept was regarded by the Dutch as the next most plausible, and affordable type of capital ship.

These three battleships – *Espana*, *Alfonso XIII* and *Jaime I* – were first planned according to the Spanish Naval Law adopted on 7 January 1908 which laid the foundations of a new navy after the disaster of the Spanish-American War in 1898 in which the Spanish fleet was so roundly defeated. Designed by a British consortium comprising Armstrongs, John Browns and Vickers, the *Espana*s were built from 1909 to 1921 in a new shipyard, specially created for the purpose at El Ferrol by Sociedad Espanol de Construccion Naval.

With a displacement of 15,700 tons (normal), very compact dimensions (133.9m x 24m x 7.9m), and a four shaft steam turbine powerplant developing 15,500shp for a maximum speed of 19.5 knots, these were unprepossessing ships with an unusual arrangement for their flush deck-mounted main armament of eight 12in (305mm). Two twin turrets were arranged fore and aft, leaving the other pair of turrets diagonally offset on either beam. The casemated secondary armament of twenty 4in (102mm) was arranged conventionally for the period and two 3pdrs and two Maxim machine guns were also carried. Belt armour of 8–4in (203–101mm) was modest by comparison with some other dreadnoughts, and was slim, extending only 1.4m below the waterline and 0.6m above it, although turret and barbette protection at 8in for the turrets and 10in for the barbettes was reasonable.

The *Espana*s' size was dictated not only by cost, but also by the restricted length of Spanish docks. Construction of *Jaime I* was extremely protracted because of the First World War, as essential materials and some guns could not be delivered during the conflict. *Espana* herself ran aground in

Espana
No apology is needed for the inclusion of this vessel in this volume: the Espana*s were the smallest dreadnoughts to be built and owe far more to coast defence preoccupations than to illusions about ocean-going warfare. The drawing shows* Espana *in 1914; she was wrecked on an uncharted Moroccan reef in August 1923 (CMP)*

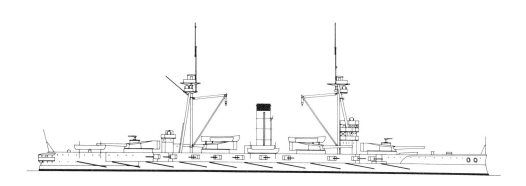

August 1923 near the Moroccan coast during the Riff War and had to be abandoned after some guns and materials were salvaged. *Alfonso XIII*, under her new name, *Espana*, joined the Nationalist side during the Civil War and was sunk by a mine in April 1937. *Jaime I* joined the Republican side, was badly damaged during the conflict and was scrapped in 1939. Both the latter vessels had also seen service during the Riff War.

Opinions about these battleships vary. Breyer is blunt and says the attempt to combine dreadnought armament with the size of a pre-dreadnought was a failure, because this 'was no doubt achieved but at the expense of staying power. The *Espana* class thus proved to be the smallest, but also the weakest, type of capital ship in the world'.[4]

Preston is more generous, implying that Breyer misses the point somewhat: 'Contemporaries sneered at these, the smallest dreadnoughts to be built, but they were a sensible design for Spain's needs. With no obvious enemies, Spain required battleships for prestige and coast defence, and for such purposes the *Espana* class represented a much better investment than the large Swedish coast defence vessels, or the Brazilian *Minas Gerais* class Dreadnought, which were their nearest equivalents'.[5]

Whether the issue of obvious enemies coloured Spanish perceptions or not, the spectacle of a host of greater powers around Spain arming themselves to the teeth with dreadnoughts during the frenetic building race before the First World War was always likely to have unnerved any Spanish government, hence the construction of these vessels did make a good deal of sense. They are also important in the context of Spain's subsequent naval history, as the facility built to construct them, at El Ferrol, remains the centre of Spanish naval shipbuilding today. That Spain is today a not insignificant naval power can be traced back directly to the decision to build the *Espana*s.

1 William Hovgaavd, *Modern History of Warships* (London, 1920), reprinted by Conway Maritime Press (London, 1971). Hovgaard points out that: 'the primary as well as the secondary battery of the Swedish ship is exactly twice as powerful as in the Dutch ship'.

2 Daniel G Harris, 'The *Sverige* Class Coast Defence Battleships', *Warship 1992*, Conway Maritime Press (London, 1992), pp80–98 for a thorough description of these vessels. See also *Conway's All the World's Fighting Ships 1906–1921*, (London, 1985), pp355–9.

3 *Conway's All the World's Fighting Ships 1906–1921*, ibid., pp351–2.

4 Siegfried Breyer, *Battleships and Battle Cruisers 1905–1970* (London, 1973), pp323–5.

5 Antony Preston, 'Alfonso XIII', *Purnell's Illustrated Encyclopaedia of Modern Weapons and Warfare* (London, 1978), p83.

CHAPTER 7

Coast Defence Ships in the First World War

AN EASY ASSUMPTION ABOUT the state of the forces specifically assigned to coastal defence in 1914 is that this was a role beneath the dignity of the major blue-water fleets. But during the First World War this discipline was by no means the exclusive province of the pure coast defence fleets of Scandinavia and the other lesser powers which managed to stay out of the conflict.

Moreover the practice of transferring older and slower tonnage to the guardship role of coastal or harbour defence to extend their usefulness was by now well established. Some older coast defence ships had also been retained, either in their original role or to perform much more humble, but nonetheless useful tasks, several for example serving as depot ships.

The fleet lists of the major powers involved in the conflict still included a fair sprinkling of survivors of the great coast defence shipbuilding boom of the quarter century preceding *Dreadnought*'s completion. That most were discarded and no more were built by these countries after *Dreadnought* was merely a recognition of reality. With so many pre-dreadnought battleships suddenly relegated to technical obsolescence, despite their age, there was no shortage of relatively modern, powerfully armed vessels, in some cases less than 10 years old, which could be assigned to coast defence as required. But, as the First World War also demonstrated, the pre-dreadnoughts could still be very useful in an offensive role, as the Allies demonstrated in the Dardanelles Campaign.

The borrowing of coast defence ship design concepts, and ships, to provide offensive vessels for use against enemy coasts – for instance the construction of monitors by Britain and Italy – provided a neat turn of fortune for the idea of putting big guns on relatively small ships.

Many of these vessels, to say nothing of pre-dreadnoughts and purpose-designed coast defence ships, were armed with 12in (305mm) guns or smaller. Yet the seeming invincibility of the more heavily armed super-dreadnoughts was such that the 1919 edition of Brassey's Naval Annual confidently stated that 12in guns had no place in naval warfare,[1] a statement which eliminated many vessels built only a few years before. The actions of numerous battleships, coast defence ships and monitors with armament of this and smaller calibres surely places at least a question mark against so sweeping a statement, especially since some smaller calibres, modified to fire at higher elevations, could reach farther than the 20,000 yards (18,288m) of 12in.

Britain

The Royal Navy's use of monitors in an offensive role against both the Central Powers after 1914 and the Axis after 1939 has been excellently described by Ian Buxton, although his statement that it was 'strategically unsound for a major power to build coast defence vessels' is, at the very least, debatable, given the German attacks on British east coast ports in 1914.[2] These mortified the Admiralty – and public opinion – and required the very public despatch of vessels to defend England's exposed shoreline. Thus Beatty's battlecruisers were moved from Scapa Flow to Rosyth, incidentally allowing them to be swiftly committed to the action at the Dogger Bank in 1915.

Several aspects of the coast *offence* monitors are relevant to the story of coast defence ships. Most of these monitors were fitted with big guns taken from redundant or obsolete battleships, calibres including 15in, 14in and 12in, although some had 9.2in and 6in, the latter including weapons mounted on ex-Brazilian river monitors, taken over when their customer could not pay for them. (This was because of a collapse in rubber prices which badly damaged Brazil's economy, ironically because of competition from Britain's Malayan colony.)

All these vessels shared certain basic characteristics: they were cheap and easy and fast to build. They generally had very good stability, necessary for vessels fitted with armament far heavier than might usually be fitted to craft of these displacements, and they were capable of absorbing considerable punishment from shore batteries. Their draughts were shallow – just 10ft for the 14in-armed monitors to allow them to operate close inshore – yet their seagoing ability had to be good enough to transit quite long distances in the open ocean. Underwater protection against mines and torpedoes was rightly deemed essential, explaining why the ex-Norwegian coast defence ships were so dramatically modified to meet this requirement. Finally, they were simple: generally just consisting of the hull, a basic tripod mast with a control top, one funnel and an absolute minimum of

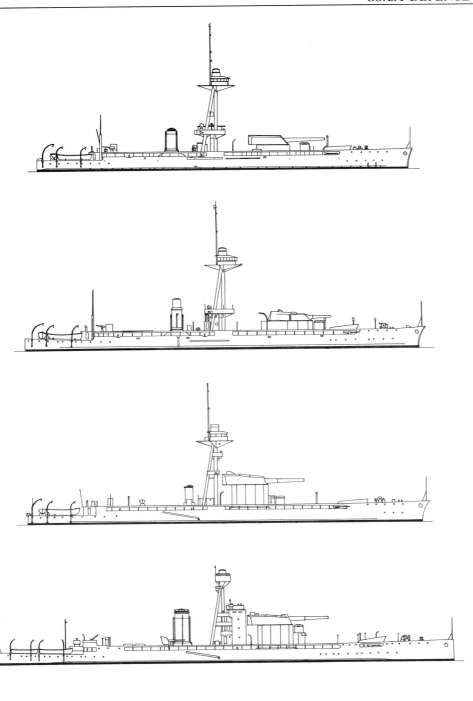

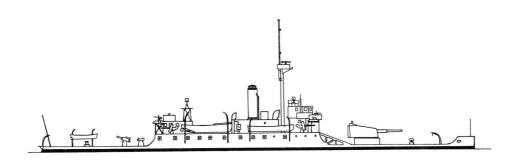

Roberts
The Abercrombie *class monitor* Roberts *(shown as completed) was a rush solution to a sudden need: the urgent requirement for a shore bombardment capability against the Belgian coast. Armed with US Bethlehem Steel-provided 14in guns in a single raised turret forward, the 6,150 ton* Roberts *had the characteristics of some coast defence ships, but with an offensive purpose in mind. Four of the class were built in 1914–15 (CMP)*

General Craufurd
Eight Lord Clive *class monitors were built in 1915, armed with twin 12in guns taken from* Majestics. *This is* General Craufurd, *in 1915 (CMP)*

Marshal Soult
Marshal Soult *(shown as completed) was the more fortunate ship in this two vessel, 15in-armed monitor class, as* Marshal Ney's *MAN diesels were notoriously unreliable; the Vickers 8-cylinder engines on* Soult *were more reliable (CMP)*

Erebus
Another 15in-armed monitor was the RN's Erebus *(seen as she was in 1916), which with* Terror *was to supplement the* Marshal Ney *class for Gallipolli duties. However she never got beyond Dover during the war (CMP)*

Javary
Brazil ordered three river monitors from Vickers at Barrow, but could not pay for them when the economy collapsed because of a fall in rubber prices. The ship and its sisters were taken over by the Royal Navy and Javary *was renamed* Humber.

Humber
Seen here in Royal Navy service is the former Brazilian river monitor Javary, *taken over from her builder Vickers in 1914 and renamed* Humber, *under which name she performed valuable duties in the Mediterranean (CMP)*

Hagen
Together with the other Siegfrieds, Hagen *was reconstructed around 1900 by being lengthened and reboilered, with an extra funnel. After reconstruction, displacement was up from 3,691 to 4,158 tons. She is seen here in 1910. (CMP)*

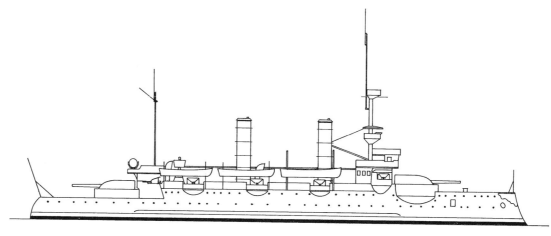

other impedimenta, although some vessels were later fitted with secondary armament and high angle AA guns as well.

In all, no less than forty-two monitors of various types served with the RN between 1914 and 1965, including two coast defence ships which were being built for the Royal Norwegian Navy in 1914.[3] Originally named *Nidaros* and *Bjorgvin*, these had been ordered from Armstrong-Whitworth in 1913 and were basically improvements on the *Norge* and *Eidsvoll* ordered from Armstrong's in 1899, but with a more powerful 9.45in 50cal (240mm) armament. Renamed *Gorgon* and *Glatton* respectively on their purchase from the Norwegians (for £370,000 each), Armstrong's was tasked in January 1915 to finish them quickly, but to a modified design.

As the main guns and the secondary battery of four 5.9in (150mm) 50cal were not RN standard, these were all relined to 9.2in (234mm) and 6in (152mm) respectively, allowing existing shells to be used. The main guns' elevation was increased to 40 degrees, allowing them to achieve what Buxton notes was the 'remarkable' range of 39,000 yards (35,660m) using special ammunition. The designed tertiary battery of six 3.9in (100mm) mounted in the superstructure were replaced by more accommodation and both submerged 17.7in (450mm) torpedo tubes were also discarded, to be replaced by large anti-torpedo bulges. High angle AA armament comprising two 3in (76mm), four 3pdr Vickers on *Glatton* and four (*Glatton*) and two (*Gorgon*) 2pdrs was also added. A dozen double bottom tanks were altered to carry

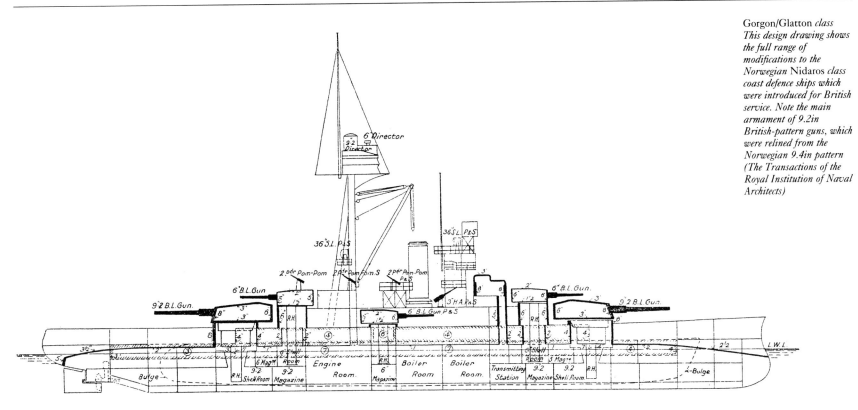

Gorgon/Glatton *class*
This design drawing shows the full range of modifications to the Norwegian Nidaros *class coast defence ships which were introduced for British service. Note the main armament of 9.2in British-pattern guns, which were relined from the Norwegian 9.4in pattern (The Transactions of the Royal Institution of Naval Architects)*

Glatton
Seen here shortly before her tragic loss at Dover in 1918 is Glatton, *formerly the Norwegian-ordered coast defence ship* Bjorgvin, *but fitted for RN service with bulges for better stability, a larger bridge and fighting top (CMP)*

fuel oil to increase the range of these coastal combatants. Side armour protection ranged from 7in to 3in (179–76mm), deck armour from 1in to 2.5in (25–64mm), while the turrets had 8in (203mm) protection for their fronts and 6in (152mm) for their sides respectively, the barbettes having 8in for the 9.2in guns and 6in for the 6in guns. The conning towers had 8in side armour.

Construction of these vessels was delayed by the re-assignment of shipyard personnel to other more pressing duties and as a result neither were ready before 1918 – and at a substantially greater cost than expected by their original Norwegian customer. Displacement had also risen from the designed 4,807 tons to some 5,705 tons (*Gorgon*), deep displacement for *Glatton* being 5,746 tons. Twin shaft triple expansion 4,000ihp engines gave these ships a top speed, as designed, of 15kts, although neither ever achieved that, *Gorgon* making 13kts on trials (and 14kts in action), while *Glatton* made 12.5kts. Preston records the endurance of the class as about 2,500 miles at 10kts.

Gorgon had a short, but busy, war service between 26 July and 15 October 1918, hurling the last shells of the war fired by monitors against the Belgian coast, escaping German shore fire on 14 October at an unexpected, and unprecedented, 14kts. *Glatton*'s career was somewhat shorter. She finally left her builders on 9 September 1918, and was in service for just a week before she was lost in tragic circumstances on 16 September in Dover harbour, when a magazine of 6in shells overheated and ignited. Buxton records that the combustible material which caused this disaster was probably newspaper stuffed in an insulation space – not cork as stated by the Court of Enquiry. *Glatton* was torpedoed on Admiral Keyes' instructions in order to prevent an explosion in her after magazine causing unacceptable damage to Dover.

The RN had no use for *Gorgon* after the war, although she was first employed to try to discover the cause of *Glatton*'s fate. Thereafter she was offered back to the Norwegians, who could not take her because the anti-torpedo bulges added by the British had increased her breadth, which meant she could no longer be docked at the Norwegian naval dockyard at Horten. Argentina and Peru made enquiries about a purchase, and Romania came closer to one – apparently for the asking price of £60,000 – but in the event *Gorgon* was never sold, instead being used for various experiments and trials until broken up in 1928.

Most of the monitors built by the British were put to offensive use for much of the time against targets on the occupied Belgian shoreline, or in the Dardanelles, or in the Adriatic, or elsewhere, but some were used for coastal defence. Just as these vessels were designed to be expendable in the last analysis, so they were also useful for coastal defence against more formidable adversaries.

Havelock was a monitor armed with 14in American guns which had been made available to the British at the outbreak of war when they were no longer allowed to the Greek battleship *Salamis*. First sent to the Dardanelles, *Havelock* returned to Britain in April 1916 and was assigned to the defence of Lowestoft after the German Navy's raids on England's east coast. Other monitors used in defensive roles included four smaller 6in armed vessels – *M.22*, *M.29*, *M.31* and *M.33* – all converted into minelayers after the war.

Also used for coastal defence were several of the nine old *Majestic* class battleships, armed with 12in 32cal guns.[4] In the cases of *Hannibal*, *Magnificent*, *Mars* and *Victorious* the guns were later transferred to new coast offence monitors. *Hannibal* served as a guardship at the Humber and Scapa Flow in 1914, as did *Illustrious* between 1914 and 1916 at Loch Ewe, Lough Swilly, the Tyne and the Humber. *Jupiter* was another Humber and then Tyne guardship in 1914; *Magnificent* did the same at Scapa Flow and so did *Mars* and

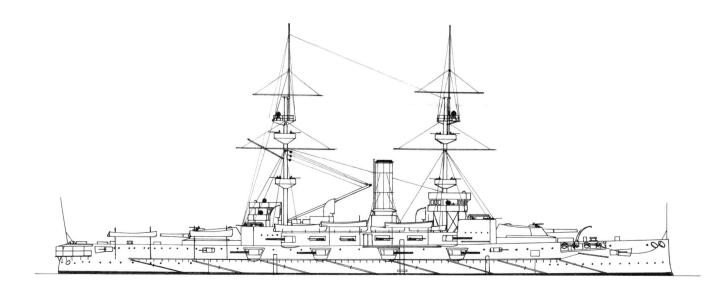

Majestic
Majestic *was the name of class of pre-dreadnoughts built between 1893 and 1898, some of which performed harbour/coast defence duties during the First World War. She is seen here as she was in 1908 (CMP)*

Victorious at the Humber, all three performing these unglamorous, though vital, roles in 1914–15.

Of the 12in-armed *Canopus* class, *Canopus* herself served as guardship at Cape St Vincent and then Port Stanley in the Falkland Islands in 1914, even firing a few salvoes at Von Spee's squadron. She also landed some 12pdr guns for local coast defence, at least one example of which is believed to have survived there. *Glory* served as a guardship in the West Indies in 1914 and at Archangel and Murmansk in 1916, while *Goliath* served as guardship at Loch Ewe before a short, though distinguished final part to her career as a bombardment vessel off the Belgian coast, then as one key component in the bombardment of the light cruiser *Königsberg* in the Rufiji river in East Africa in November 1914, and finally as a bombardment vessel again in the Dardanelles, where she was sunk in May 1915.

Of the 10in-armed *Triumph* class, *Swiftsure* served in the defence of the Suez Canal from November 1914 to March 1915 when she moved to the Dardanelles, while three 12in-armed *King Edward VII* class 'intermediate dreadnoughts' – *Britannia*, *Dominion* and *Hindustan* – were sent to the Nore in early 1916 to guard the Thames estuary. This role was also performed by none other than *Dreadnought* herself, from May 1916 until March 1918, when she was based at Sheerness.

Germany

The German High Seas Fleet expended an enormous effort to present the most serious of all challenges to the Royal Navy's power at the outbreak of war, with a ready fleet of thirteen dreadnought battleships, plus the four *Königs* just being completed and four battlecruisers. Yet the Germans also took coastal defence seriously and eight elderly vessels built for the task were still performing that role in the Baltic. These were the six *Siegfried* class ships laid down between 1889 and 1893 (*Siegfried, Beowulf, Frithjof, Heimdall, Hildebrand* and *Hagen*), and *Odin* and *Ägir*, laid down in 1894 and 1895 respectively.

When laid down, the *Siegfried*s displaced 3,691 tons light and 3,750 tons fully loaded and *Odin* and *Ägir*'s displacements were similar. But around 1900 all these vessels were reconstructed by inserting a new section amidships plus new boilers. The *Siegfried*s' displacement had now risen to 4,100 tons (4,158 tons full load) while the final two ships now tipped the scales at 4,150 tons (4,224 tons full) and also had twin funnels as opposed to the *Siegfried*s' original single stack. (Preston records different displacements after reconstructing: 4,058 tons normal and 4,225 tons maximum, with *Ägir* and *Odin* displacing 4,119 tons and 4,292 tons respectively.)

All these ships were still armed with three 9.4in 35cal guns, mounted in two barbettes forward and one aft with 8in (203mm) armour protection. Other armament had changed however. In 1914 this consisted of ten 88mm, six 1pdrs and four machine guns, plus three submerged 17.7in torpedo tubes. As designed they carried only eight 88mm, but *Siegfried* in particular carried much more underwater armament at six 13.8in (350mm) tubes. The others carried four tubes, except *Odin* and *Ägir* with their three larger 450mm tubes. The *Siegfried*s, which could make 14.5–15kts, had varying armour protection. Jane's reported in 1914 that 'the first two' vessels had 8.5in (216mm) nickel belt protection, but only amidships, while the others had complete belt compound armour protection ranging from 9.5in to 6in (241–152mm).[5]

At the outbreak of war, the *Siegfried*s were mobilised to form the High Seas Fleet's 6th Squadron, with which they served until 31 August 1915, when their crews were reassigned. The ships served out the rest of the war as pure coast defence ships in 1915–16, or as accommodation ships, though *Beowulf* was used as a practice U-boat target. Preston records that *Odin* had already been reassigned to coast defence in 1914. In June 1919 they were all stricken. However, the *Odin*s were not scrapped, but were sold for use as merchant ships.

The two ships of the *Wörth* class – *Wörth* and *Brandenburg* – had been completed in 1893 to an unusual design in which of the three *en echelon* twin 11in turrets, the amidships turret carried guns with shorter, 35cal barrels as opposed to the 40cals of the other two. Other armament of these 10,060 tons (normal) ships comprised eight 88mm, a dozen 37mm and six 450mm torpedo tubes. Though assigned to the 5th Squadron in the Baltic in 1914, they were reassigned to coast defence in 1915, serving as accommodation ships from 1916. They were broken up in 1919–20.

France

The great French coast defence fleet of earlier years no longer existed by 1914, by which time the emphasis had belatedly switched to the construction of dreadnoughts, four of which were ready by the war's outbreak. But three purpose-designed coast defence vessels still survived, while a fourth was thought to be no good for anything else than coast defence but had a surprisingly active 'Indian summer' of a career. These were *Bouvines* and *Amiral Tréhouart*, completed in 1896 and 1894 respectively and now serving as submarine depot ships; *Styx*, a 1,767 ton vessel completed in 1892, and *Requin*, a remarkable survivor of a class of four 7,214 ton (normal) battleships which had been completed in 1885. *Bouvines* and *Tréhouart* displaced over 6,500 tons and were not stricken until 1920 in the case of the twin-funnelled *Bouvines* and 1922 in *Amiral Tréhouart*'s case.

Despite their new role, for which they were well suited given their low freeboard aft, they retained their full armament of two 305mm (12in) 45cal, which were equipped for high angle fire, plus eight 3.9in and sundry smaller weapons. Top speed was still 16.5–17kts. It is worth mentioning that although the *Bouvines* class were rated as coast defence ships, their heavy armament has been attributed to an intended operational role as offensive vessels for use against the German coast.

Meanwhile *Styx*, of the *Achéron* class and armed with one 275mm (10.8in) 28cal and one 140mm (5.5in), was originally classed as an armoured gunboat, although its size certainly justified its later classification as a coast defence vessel. *Styx* was stricken in 1919 and broken up.

Requin's wartime career, despite her considerable age, was very impressive. Originally armed with two single 420mm (16.53in) guns in open barbettes, with a secondary armament of four 100mm (3.9in), two (or four) 3pdrs and sixteen 1pdr revolver cannon, *Requin* had been rearmed with two single 275mm (10.8in) and eight new 100mm quick-firers. Her original four 355.6mm (14in) torpedo tubes were removed and she was also reboilered before the war with twelve Niclausse boilers and her funnel arrangement was altered from four in two pairs abreast to two on the centreline. *Requin* had been a gunnery school hulk around 1908 and from August to November 1914 was stationed at Bizerta for local defence, being moved to Egypt in December to help protect the Suez Canal. There she remained until used for the bombardment of Turkish-occupied Gaza in November 1917. She was broken up in 1920.[6]

Finally, the experimental battleship *Henri IV*, completed in 1902 to a very unusual Emile Bertin design, was still in service in 1914 and was a guardship at Bizerta until February 1915. She was notable for her forward 275mm gun turret above shelter deck level and her superimposed 140mm (one of seven) aft. She later went to the Dardanelles and then served in the reserve, then in the eastern Mediterranean and finally in Taranto as a depot ship before being stricken after the war and broken up in 1921.

Italy

None of Italy's purpose-designed coast defence ships still served in 1914, but some old battleships had been reassigned to the role. The best-known was *Dandolo*, the second of the famous *Duilio* class turret ships laid down in 1873 and completed, after more than nine years, in 1882. These vessels had the distinction of being both the first ocean-going battleships to go to sea without sailing rig and also the battleships with the heaviest gun armament of the time. These weapons were Armstrong-built muzzle-loading (436mm) 17.2in 20cal leviathans, weighing 100 tons and firing 1,905lb shells, albeit only once every 15 minutes.

These guns were, however, removed before the turn of the century, to be replaced by four 10in 40cal. The latter,

together with seven 152mm (6in), five 120mm (4.7in), sixteen 57mm and eight 37mm (later reduced to two) provided a still considerable punch for such an old vessel, which could still make over 15kts. Armour protection (steel) consisted of an amidships 546mm (21.5in) belt plus 254mm (10in) Harvey armour on her turrets.

After serving as a floating oil tank at Brindisi at the outbreak of the war under the name *GM.40*, *Dandolo* spent the years from 1915 to 1918 on coast and local defence duties at Brindisi and then Valona, only being decommissioned in January 1920.

Another Italian vessel with a distinguished history and which was given a coastal defence role during the war was the battleship *Italia* which, together with its sibling *Lepanto*, for some time constituted the fastest and largest warships in the world. *Italia* had been substantially modified before the war, the six distinctive funnels being reduced to four, while the single mast gave way to a pair. Displacement should thus have been reduced somewhat from her original 13,678 tons normal, although Jane's recorded her displacement in 1914 at 15,654 tons. Shortly before the war, she was serving as the main vessel operating specifically in defence of the key naval base of Taranto, but in June 1914 she was removed from the navy list. She was also recorded as serving as a torpedo schoolship in 1914. Removal from the navy list was not the end though, for on 20 March 1915 *Italia* was towed to Brindisi to serve as a floating battery in the outer harbour until 16 December 1917, when she was formally recommissioned in the Navy as a 'first class auxiliary'.

At that time *Italia* was still armed with four 432mm (17in) of 26cal and 27cal, having dispensed with seven or eight old 150mm (5.9in) 26cal, four 120mm (4.7in) and some thirty-two smaller guns. Armour protection was limited: there was no armour belt, but there was 76mm (3in) deck protection and a 483mm (19in) steel redoubt on her upper deck for the main armament. She ended her navy days in November 1921, but not before serving, *inter alia*, as an armed cereal carrier (two 120mm) and as a ship assigned to Italian State Railways.

Also serving as a floating battery during the war was *Re Umberto*, another battleship which took a long time to build, finally completing after almost nine years in 1893. With a normal displacement of 13,673 tons and a main armament of four 342.9mm (13.5in) 30cal, supplemented by eight 152mm 40cal and fourteen 120mm, *Re Umberto* had already been removed from the navy list by the war's outbreak, although by the time Italy entered the war she had been reinstated (on 9 December 1915), serving as a floating battery at Brindisi from March 1916 to November 1917 and then at Valona until April 1918. Her armour protection comprised 356mm (14in) for her barbettes and a more modest 110mm (4.33in) amidships belt, finally being extensively modified as an assault ship for the planned major raid on Pola, which did not take place because of the war's end. For this purpose, her armament was altered to eight 3in, several 240mm trench mortars, plus cutters and saws for use against harbour defences. Another vessel of the same class which saw service as a harbour defence ship at Brindisi from November 1917 was *Sardegna*, for which purpose she was modified to an armament of the four 13.5in, four 76mm 40cal and two AA machine guns. She moved to the defence of Taranto in July 1918.

Another former front-line battleship reassigned to coast defence was the 11,027 ton *Andrea Doria*, launched in 1885, completed in 1891 and originally armed with four 17in (432mm), two 6in, four 120mm and two 355.6mm torpedo tubes. A depot ship at Taranto at the war's outbreak, she was converted to a floating battery for harbour defence at Brindisi from April 1915, under the new name *GR.104*. After the war she served as a floating oil tank until being broken up in 1929.

Although they were not strictly speaking classic coast defence vessels, either as purpose-designed ships or converted battleships, mention must be made of a motley collection of small craft built, or converted, specifically for the defence of Venice in the face of the Austrian and German offensive during October and November 1917. These included unpowered floating batteries and barges. Although some vessels, like the *Brondolo* class gunboats, were of pre-war construction, others like *Capitano Sauro* was a former Austrian gunboats with a 120mm 40cal main armament. The tiny *Ape* class gunboats were built for canal work and managed to pack in a 76mm 17cal Army gun, plus eleven 6.5mm machine guns on 30–50 ton displacements.

Finally, Italy, like Britain, also built purpose-designed monitors for coast offence tasks, the 381mm (15in)-armed *Faa di Bruno* and *Alfredo Cappelini* putting their guns to extensive use at the 11th Battle of the Isonzo for instance. Smaller craft of this type were fourteen other monitors all displacing between 95 and 570 tons, armed with 15in, 12in, 7.5in and 6in guns.

Austria-Hungary

The Hapsburg fleet was always the 'cinderella' of the empire's military, both because of Vienna's continental preoccupations and also because, after the creation of the dual monarchy in 1867, Budapest had a say in naval expenditure. Thus it was no accident that the Empire's first proper turret ships were small vessels designed specifically for coast defence. These three vessels, the 5,547 ton *Monarch* class (the others being *Wien* and *Budapest*), were all built between 1893 and 1898 and despite their diminutive size they shipped four Skoda 240mm (9.45in) 40cal, six Skoda 150mm (5.9in) 40cal, two 76mm 18cal plus fourteen assorted 47mm/3pdr quick-firers (ten Skoda L/44s and four Hotchkiss L/33s). They also carried two 450mm (17.7in) torpedo tubes, above-water and

mounted at the bow and stern. Capable of making 17.5kts they were faster than most vessels of the genre. Armour protection consisted of 270–220mm (10.6–8.7in) belt and 250mm (9.8in) on the turrets. These vessels laid up at the war's outbreak and were recommissioned in 1916 as the 5th Division at Cattaro. Thereafter they counted as useful elements of the small Hapsburg fleet, led by this time by a quartet of dreadnoughts of the *Tegetthof* class.

Monarch suffered a mutiny on 1 February 1918 at Cattaro harbour and from April she served as the accommodation ship at the submarine base there. In 1920 *Monarch* was handed to the British as a war prize and was scrapped in Italy. *Wien*'s war came to an end when she was detached, with *Budapest*, to the defence of Trieste and was then sunk in the Gulf of Trieste on 10 December 1917 by the Italian motor torpedo boat *MAS 15* under the command of the legendary Luigi Rizzo. *Budapest* was decommissioned in March 1918 and then served as an accommodation ship at the Pola submarine base. She was then converted for an intended coastal bombardment, which did not take place, with the installation of a 380mm (15in) 17cal howitzer in place of her forward turret. Like *Wien*, she was transferred to the British and scrapped in Italy.

Both the coastal barbette ships *Erzherzogin Stephanie* and *Erzherzog Rudolf* were still in service in 1914, though the former had been reduced to serving as an accommodation vessel for the mine warfare school. *Rudolf* passed the war as a coast defence ship in Cattaro Bay. They were scrapped in 1926 and 1922 respectively. *Rudolf*, dating from 1887, was still armed with three old 305mm and six 120mm.

Finally, still in service during the First World War were several very old centre battery ships built during the 1870s, most of which had latterly served as harbour defence vessels in the years preceding the First World War. The centre battery ship *Mars* was built as the *Tegetthof* between 1876 and 1881 and from 1897 served as the harbour guard ship at

Rudolph
Relegated to coastal defence duties during the First World War was the venerable Austro-Hungarian ironclad barbette ship Rudolph, *seen here in a drawing by 'J.H.', circa 1880 (GPH Collection)*

Pola. Armament consisted of six old 240mm Krupp and five old 6in; protection was provided by a 368mm (14.5in) iron belt. The vessel was renamed *Mars* in 1912 to release her name for the lead ship of the new Austro-Hungarian dreadnoughts.

Mars had a close shave at the beginning of November 1916 when an Italian MAS boat carried to Pola by a mothership attacked the Austro-Hungarian vessel in the harbour after a daring, nail-biting approach. The two torpedoes fired at the vessel did not explode however and the next day, *Mars*' crew found the MAS boat which was nevertheless able to make its escape. Given up to Italy after the war, *Mars* was scrapped in 1920.

For the record, other such vessels still in service during the war were the repair ship *Vulkan*, formerly the *Prinz Eugen* until its conversion, plus the *Feuerspier*, formerly the *Erherzog Albrecht* until it was renamed in 1908. Handed to the Italians after the war, it became the hulk *Buttafuoco* until it was broken up in 1947. Also still in service during the war were the *Custoza* and *Kaiser Max*. These vessels served as tenders, floating barracks and hulks and, apart from *Feuerspier*, all were scrapped in 1920–21.

Russia

After the disaster of Tsushima where three coast defence ships were sunk or captured, the Russian Navy could no longer afford to build a mixed fleet of vessels for both fleet actions and coastal defence. Thus the only large warship formally assigned to a coast defence role in the Russian fleet in 1914 was the Black Sea fleet's *Georgi Pobiedonosets*, a barbette ship of the line which originally displaced between 11,000–12,000 tons[7] and was now a port guardship at Sevastopol (where she had been built between 1889 and 1894). She was originally armed with six 305mm (12in) 35cal in three twin turrets, plus seven 152mm (6in) 35cal and smaller guns variously reported as either eight 12pdrs or eight 3pdrs, plus ten 1pdrs. Her compound armour protection consisted of 406–203mm (16in-8in) belt and 305mm (12in) redoubt. As a port guardship, her armament was reduced to just the eight 6in plus a few anti-aircraft 3pdrs. The ship raised the Ukrainian flag in April 1918, was captured by the Germans at Sevastopol the following month and in November surrendered to the British, who handed her over to Wrangel's White Russian fleet in September 1919. After the Russian civil war, she was sold in 1924.

Her sister ship *Sinop*, built in Sevastopol between 1883 and 1890, was also still in service, although in this case in the more humble, but equally useful role of a mine barrage breaker or 'mine bumper' for the Battleship Brigade in 1914, for which she was fitted with a special bulge. Her armament was reduced and torpedo tubes removed during the war, during which she operated in a coastal defence role.

Sinop was disarmed at Sevastopol in June 1917, flew Ukrainian colours from April 1918, was captured by the Germans in May and by the British in November, who wrecked her machinery on 6 May 1919 to prevent her use by the Bolsheviks. *Sinop* was broken up in 1922.

United States

It was with a huge collective sigh of relief that the United States Navy finally escaped the shackles of a Congressionally-imposed coastal defence role during the 1890s. But the dearth of orders for ocean-going ironclads following the Civil War and the preoccupation with innovative subterfuges like the 'great repairs' which allowed new monitors to replace old ones with the same names led to a situation where the USN had to construct a proper battleship force from scratch.

This the Americans did with great gusto. They were anyway able to reap the benefits of a strengthening economy which, by 1916, was crucial to sustaining Britain's faltering war effort. But in 1914, when ten dreadnoughts were in USN service with four more building, America still possessed a sizeable coast defence force. It is probably also fair to include in this category one ship which the Americans identified as a second-line battleship. This was *Iowa*, completed in 1897. Armed with four 12in and eight 8in guns, this vessel displaced 11,346 tons and was not much larger than three ships still in service which were openly identified as 'coast line battleships' – the *Indiana* class, completed in 1895–6.

This trio had been given major refits between 1905 and 1908. Armed with four 13in and eight 8in, these 10,288 tonners had an 18–15in (457–381mm) belt amidships, which was stronger than *Iowa*'s 14–11in (356–280mm) belt. During their refits, eight Babcock engines had replaced the *Indiana*s' original cylindrical boilers. At 17kts, they were anyway not good for much more than coastal defence any more, but nevertheless the *Indiana*s represented a very interesting intermediate stage between the pure coast defence ship of the Scandinavian navies and the later predreadnoughts of the US fleet like *Alabama* and *Maine* which, like two of the *Indiana*s (and *Iowa*), were all built by Cramps.

Interestingly, *Iowa* was renamed *Coast Battleship No 4* on 29 March 1919 and was the first radio-controlled target ship used in a USN fleet exercise, eventually falling victim to 14in shells. Also on 29 March, *Indiana* and *Massachusetts* were renamed *Coast Battleships No 1* and *No 2* respectively, and were sunk or scuttled as targets in 1920 and 1921. Meanwhile *Oregon* – renamed *Coast Battleship No 3* – was moored as a monument at Portland, Maine, from 1925 to 1942 when work on breaking up the ship was interrupted to

allow her to be used as an ammunition hulk for the recon-quest of Guam in 1944.

Other than this quartet, the USN still had nine monitors in service in 1914. These were the four 12kt ships of the *Ozark* class (*Ozark*, *Tonopah*, *Talahassee* and *Cheyenne*), laid down in 1900 and 1901, which displaced 3,356 tons full load. Their freeboard, like the other monitors, was a matter of inches.

Tonapah's role in 1914 as a tender to the Atlantic Fleet's Submarine Division must have seemed rather appropriate. At any rate, disembarking from a submarine to such a tender would have been easy and *Tonopah* would not be the

first monitor to excel in this role even though, like all the *Ozark*s, she still shipped two 12in and four 4in guns. More-over, in keeping with the demands of the age, *Talahassee* at least had been refitted with wireless by 1914. The other monitors still in service were the somewhat larger *Monterey*, *Monadnock*, *Terror*, *Miantonomoh* and *Amphitrite*, laid down between 1876 and 1891 – all still armed with four 10in and two 4in or 6pdr guns and capable of 12–14.5kts. Most of the monitors were sold between 1920 and 1923.

Three of the USN's monitors were on loan to the Naval Militia in 1914. These were *Amphitrite*, *Cheyenne* and *Ozark*, serving with the Louisiana, Washington State and District

Chicago
The US cruiser Chicago *served the Massachusetts and then the Pennsylvania Naval Militia in a coast defence role during the First World War. Built as a barque-rigged vessel, she was rebuilt in 1895–98, with new pattern 8in 45cal and 5in 40cal (GPH Collection)*

of Columbia Naval Militias respectively. The Naval Militia, as its name might suggest, performed a supporting role to the US Navy and, as such, many of the thirty-two mostly rather unprepossessing vessels serving in 1914 were providing a coast defence capability of sorts. This little fleet included ships like the old cruiser *Chicago*, built between 1883 and 1889, and the torpedo boats *Mackenzie* and *Somers*, built in the late 1890s, besides converted yachts of dubious combat utility. But whatever their individual failings, all were useful for coastal surveillance and policing.

Japan

Across the Pacific, Japan, with the Battle of Tsushima behind it, was a major naval power with established blue water credentials – four dreadnought battleships and battlecruisers in service in 1914, plus two 'semi-dreadnoughts'. Yet the memory of the conflict with Russia was still fresh and Vladivostok was close. Thus, not only were five old vessels classified as coast defence ships but, remarkably, the Japanese had seen fit to raise one of them from the dead.

This was *Tango*, formerly the Russian 11,354 ton battleship *Poltava* of the *Petropavlovsk* class, sunk in action against the Japanese at Port Arthur on 5 December 1904 after sustaining serious damage at the Battle of the Yellow Sea on 10 August that year. She was raised by the victors of that conflict in 1905. Laid down in 1894, at her loss *Poltava* still shipped her original armament of two twin 12in (305mm) 35cal Obuchov guns, plus a dozen 6in (152mm) 45cal. It is not clear how many of her previous battery of forty smaller guns had survived her sinking. Renamed *Tango*, she was rearmed by the Japanese: 47mm and 37mm guns were removed and new 3 pdrs and 1 pdrs fitted. One account says identical replacements for some of her 6in were provided[8] and another[9] says six Model 41 3.14in (80mm) were added, while her four above-surface 18in (456mm) torpedo tubes were kept but her two submerged tubes were removed. *Tango* also carried a 16–15in (406–381mm) Harvey belt and her maximum speed was now 17kts, adequate for the coast defence role the Japanese had assigned to her and half a knot faster than under her previous owner.

The Japanese reboilered *Tango* at Maizeru and, in place of her former vertical triple expansion engines generating 11,250ihp, she now could apparently only manage 10,600hp after reboilering with sixteen Miyabara large tube boilers and the extra speed can only have been due to her lower displacement in Japanese hands, at some 11,000 tons or 10,960 tons.[10] In 1916 *Tango* was returned to Russia, now an ally in the First World War, was renamed *Tchesma* and served in the White Sea until being hulked at Murmansk by Western intervention forces. The ship was finally scrapped by the Soviets in 1923.

The most prominent of Japan's other vessels classified as coast defence ships in 1914 was *Fuji*, her last and most recent such ship to have been laid down (in 1896) and among the last British-built battleships of the Japanese fleet. Built as a class of two battleships by Thames Iron Works at Elswick (her sister *Yashima* sank after hitting a mine in 1904), this ship could not make much more than 15kts by 1914, although she made 18.5kts on her first trial and *Yashima* even made 19kts. This explained her relegation to the coast defence role in 1910, in which year she was also reboilered with ten Miyabara boilers. Armament mainly consisted of four Japanese Model 41 12in 40cal which replaced the 12in Armstrongs in 1910, ten 6in 40cal, sixteen 12pdrs and five 18in torpedo tubes (four submerged).

Fuji's main 18–14in (457–357mm) Harvey belt was 7ft 6in (2.29m) wide and 230ft (70.1m) long, 5ft 6in of which was below the waterline, the lower edge being 8in thick. The main armament had 250 degree firing arcs and Jane's reported frankly in 1914 that the torpedo tubes were 'early pattern Elswick' and 'cannot deliver at speeds above 14kts'.[11] At 12,300 tons, *Fuji* was large to be now classed as a coast defence unit, though lighter than her previous normal displacement of 12,533 tons. But the Japanese were nothing if not realistic in most naval matters and the relegation to coast defence was sensible enough. A fine ship and a Tsushima veteran – she fired the battle's last salvo – *Fuji* spent the First World War on training duties at Kure and was eventually disarmed as a hulk training ship, certainly in 1922–23 if not sooner as Preston intimates (op.cit., p.184).

Training was definitely an appropriate use for Japan's three other coastal battleships, all of them prizes seized during the Russo-Japanese war. *Iki*, the eldest, had been laid down in 1889 as the barbette ironclad battleship *Nikolai I* of the *Imperator Alexander II* class. She was Admiral Nebogatov's flagship of the Third Division of Admiral Rozhestvensky's doomed fleet at Tsushima. Captured after the battle, she was repaired and refitted from July 1905, after which she displaced 9,672 tons. This was up from her original 9,500 tons in Russian service before her 1898–1900 refit; this was itself somewhat greater than her designed displacement of 8,440 tons. *Iki* had an armament of two outdated 12in 40cal and a dozen 6in – her original eight 6in 35cal, plus four Japanese or Armstrong model 6in 45cal installed as replacements for the original Russian secondary battery of four 9in 35cal. There were also twenty lighter guns and, compared to most coast defence ships, a heavy above-water battery of six 14in torpedo tubes. *Iki* was designed to make 15.9kts. Her armour protection comprised 14in-4in (357–101mm) belt, 2.5in (64mm) for the deck, 10in (254mm) on the turret. *Iki* was stricken in 1915, in which year she was sunk as a target.

The other two Russian coast defence ships captured after Tsushima were *Admiral Senyavin* and *General Admiral Graf Apraksin*, which were renamed *Mishima* and *Okinoshima* respectively. These were similar 4,200 ton, 16kt ships laid down in 1894 and 1896 respectively which differed in the number of their main armament, four guns (two twins) in the case of *Mishima* and three (a twin and a single aft) in the case of *Okinoshima*. There is, however, some disagreement over their calibre, some accounts describing these as 10in (254mm) 45cal and others as 9in (228.6mm) 45cal.[12] Complicating matters further, Jane's in 1914 said *Mishima* had four 9in and *Okinoshima* three 10in. *Mishima* had two twin 9in 45cal turrets as opposed to *Okinoshima*'s twin 10in 45cal forward and single 10in aft.

Otherwise both ships had four Armstrong 4.7in 45cals at the quarters (replacing similar Russian weapons), *Mishima*'s superstructure being somewhat larger than its sibling's though both arrangements were of about the same length. One account says two 4.7in were added by the Japanese.[13] *Mishima*'s original 47mm and 37mm guns were replaced by four 3.1in Armstrongs and two 50mm Yamaguchi and her four 18in torpedo tubes were removed (Jane's in 1914 described both ships' tertiary armament as ten 3pdrs, a dozen 1pdrs plus the torpedo tubes). A 10–4in (254–101mm) belt originally protected this pair amidships (again Jane's differs,

recording their belt protection as ranging from 8–10in), with 8in (203mm) protection on the turrets. All the Japanese coast defence ships in 1914 were recognisable for their twin funnels and fairly high but lean masts, with minimal or no fighting tops.

Turkey

One vessel of the Ottoman fleet curiously identified by Jane's in 1914 as a coast defence battleship was an extraordinary survivor, although by this time she was actually a torpedo training ship at Istanbul. She was the 2,362 ton casemate ironclad *Muin-I-Zafer*, built by Thames Iron Works between 1867 and 1870 and rebuilt by Ansaldo between 1904 and 1907. She emerged from this reconstruction armed with four Krupp 152mm (6in) 40cal, six 76mm (3in), ten 6pdrs and two 1pdrs. In 1914 Jane's quoted her 'best recent speed' as 12kts: she had been reboiled in 1906. Her armour protection still ranged from 152mm to 76mm (6–3in) iron to protect her battery, the main 152mm guns being

Fuji
The venerable British-built battleship Fuji, *shown here in a lithograph from* The Engineer *in 1897, served as a coast defence vessel in the Imperial Japanese Navy during the First World War (GPH Collection)*

mounted at the vessel's quarters. However, when she became a training ship, four 76mm and eight 6pdrs were removed and finally all guns were removed in 1916–17, after which she continued to serve as a torpedo school ship until 1920, then as a barracks ship and finally as a submarine depot ship from 1928 to 1932, when she was decommissioned.

The coast defence role was also performed by the aged German-built battleship *Torgud Reis* (10,013 tons normal), armed with four 280mm (11in), two 40 cal and two 35 cal, plus six 105mm and, from 1912, six 88mm. Her sibling *Barbaros Hayreddin* was sunk on 8 August 1915 by the British submarine *E 11* in the Sea of Marmara. Both vessels had defended the Dardanelles coast against the Greeks in December 1912 and January 1913 in the First Balkan War and both landed guns for coastal defence during the First World War.

Portugal

Of the lesser powers which entered the conflict, most had coast defence preoccupations, but Portugal, which declared war on Germany in March 1916, was more concerned with protecting trade with her African colonies. However, before the overthrow of the monarchy, the 1907–08 naval programme had provided for the construction of two coast defence ships of the Argentine *Libertad* type (the design of which dated from 1890), plus sundry protected cruisers, destroyers and submarines – a scheme quite beyond Portugal's slender finances. Thus in 1914 Portugal's flagship was still the venerable *Vasco Da Gama*, launched in 1876 by Thames Iron Works for the defence of Lisbon and completely reconstructed and lengthened by Orlando in Genoa from 1901 to 1903. In this refit her original armament of two 10.2in (260mm) gave way to two 8in (203mm) 40cal on side sponsons, a single 5.9in (150mm) 45cal aft, plus one 12pdr forward, four 9pdrs and six 3pdrs. The whole armour belt was renewed (9–4in: 229–101mm) and the main guns were protected by 10–6in (254–152mm) on the sponsons and turrets. Her normal displacement accordingly rose from 2,384 tons to 2,972 tons.

Greece

The Greeks entered the war on the Allied side in controversial circumstances in June 1917, at which time the small Hellenic fleet still included three 4,885 ton coast defence ironclads of the *Hydra* class built from 1889. All were rearmed with five 150mm (5.9in) 45cal quick-firers in 1908–10, after having been earlier rearmed in 1897–1900 with new lighter guns: one 150mm (3.9in) 50cal, eight 9pdrs, four 3pdrs and ten 1pdrs, and two 355mm (14in) submerged

torpedo tubes and one above-water 14.55/15in tube (sources vary). These ships served with distinction during the First Balkan War at the seizure of Lemnos in October 1912. Further modernisation had been proposed during the Greek naval programme of 1911, as suggested by a British naval mission, but this proposal was overtaken by events. The old ironclads were seized by the French on 19 October 1916 together with the rest of the Greek fleet at the culmination of a crisis between the Allies and Greece over the latter's sympathies. After performing the coast defence role in 1917–18, all the *Hydra*s served as gunnery and navigational training ships until they were broken up in 1929. Also, the two US-built battleships *Kilkis* and *Lemnos*, although the largest and most potent units of the Greek fleet, were used for coast and harbour defence duties from 1916 to 1918.[14]

Brazil

Brazil declared war against the Central Powers in October 1917, dispatching a squadron of cruisers and destroyers to operate off north-west Africa. Still in service were the two old coast defence battleships *Marshal Deodoro* (formerly named *Ypiranga*) and *Marshal Floriano*, built between 1896 and 1901. Both of these 3,162 ton, La Seyne-built vessels were still armed with two Armstrong 9.2in (233.6mm) and four Armstrong 4.7in (120mm) 50cal quick-firers.[15] *Deodoro* was sold to Mexico in 1924 and renamed *Anahuac*, being discarded in 1938. *Floriano* was stricken in 1936. It should be mentioned that a design concept was drawn up for a so-called 'improved *Deodoro*' class after the turn of the century. This would have been armed with two 12in (305mm) and four 8in (203mm), all in single turrets, and would have been faster than the 15kt *Deodoro* and could have been the basis of Armstrong's 6,000 ton 'armourclad' Design No.365.[16]

1 Antony Preston, *Battleships of World War I* (London, 1972), p10.

2 Ian Buxton, *Big Gun Monitors* (Tynemouth, UK, 1978), p11.

3 Buxton, op. cit., the ex-Norwegian ships are discussed in Chapter VI, pp94–100.

4 *Conway's 1906–1921*, op. cit., pp7–8 for details of the uses to which *Majestic* and *Canopus* class pre-dreadnoughts were put during the war. See also Preston, op.cit., pp99–102 for the *Majestic* and *Canopus* classes, and p108 for the *Triumph* class, p111 for the *King Edward VII* class, and p113 for *Dreadnought*.

5 Fred T Jane, *Fighting Ships* (London, 1914), p128.

6 See Preston, op.cit., pp30 & 36 for details of *Requin* and *Henri IV*.

7 Different tonnages are offered by different sources and may relate to *Georgi Pobiedonosets*' condition at different times in her career. *Conway's 1906–1921*, op. cit., p294, says she displaced 11,940 tons; *Conway's 1860–1905*, op. cit., p178, puts her actual displacement in the range 11,032–11,396 tons, and her designed displacement at 10,100–10,280 tons; 11,230 tons (11,410 tonnes) full load are the figures quoted by Gibbons, op. cit., p122; 10,250 tons is the figure

offered by Jane's, op. cit., p357 and could well be a more or less accurate estimate of her condition after the removal of some of her armament, like torpedo tubes, although the addition of mine bulges would have added some weight.

8 Gibbons, op. cit., p142.

9 *Conway's 1906–1921*, op. cit., p226.

10 For the latter figure, see ibid.; all other accounts consulted cite the former.

11 Jane's, op. cit., p229.

12 See *Conway's 1906–1921*, op. cit., p226 for reference to 9in 45cal, but other accounts which refer to 10in 45cal are: Grove, op. cit., p15 and *Conway 1860–1905*, op. cit., p181.

13 *Conway's 1906–1921*, op. cit., p226.

14 Preston, op.cit., p165, although *Conway's 1906–1921* makes no reference to this.

15 There has been some debate over these vessels' armament. George A Gratz, answering a query in *Warship International No.3*, 1994, published by INRO Inc., Toledo, Ohio, says they were armed with two 9.2in Armstrongs, four 4.7in Armstrongs, six 57mm Nordenfeldt guns, and had no torpedo tubes. Gratz refutes suggestions that they were armed with torpedo tubes, as stated by Preston (op.cit., p24) and *Conway's 1860–1905* (op.cit., p407). These sources respectively state that they were equipped with 14in and 18in tubes. Preston says they carried howitzers, which Gratz refutes, and four 6pdrs and two 1pdrs; *Conway's* says they carried six 6pdrs.

16 George A Gratz, separate letter in *Warship International*, ibid, pp221–225.

CHAPTER 8

The Last Classic Coast Defence Ships

AFTER THE FIRST WORLD WAR, several countries were either still very interested in acquiring coast defence ships, or were to acquire them for the first time as the most affordable route to recognisable capital ships.

In Siam's case, the initial pair of vessels acquired from Britain suited her limited needs well, although the later – and larger – pair bought from Japan were too small for the armament carried. Finland pursued a logical enough route and the *Väinämöinen* class remain impressive examples of what could be achieved on a small hull, although it remains curious that the Finns did not try to equip the two vessels with slightly heavier guns, such as the Bofors 283mm (11.09in) of Sweden's earlier *Sverige* class, the last pair of which were completed after the war in 1921–22.

Sweden herself looked at the acquisition of more coast defence ships before the Second World War, but none were built. Another Scandinavian country which seriously considered a major overhaul of its coast defence fleet and which produced some very interesting designs was Denmark. Some of these concepts would have been as impressive as the *Väinämöinen* class, had they been built.

Another country which took a sober look at coast defence as an alternative strategy to keeping alive any hopes of an ocean-going fleet was Germany. Some powerful coast defence units were considered in the early 1920s. The extraordinary story of how these very lengthy deliberations eventually led to the construction of the 'Panzerschiff' (Armoured Ship) *Deutschland* shows that there is a direct lineage between this vessel and its sisters and the coast defence ships of more modest fleets.

It would be tempting, but wrong, to consider the usefulness of the vessels described below only in terms of their eventual war records. The Finnish vessels had busy careers, although one met an early end in 1941. Siam's second pair of coast defence ships, though probably too small for ocean warfare, should have been able to destroy the French squadron in 1941. There is every reason to believe that, while the Germans pounced on the Danish fleet in 1943, had any vessels been built to the intriguing designs considered by Denmark in the 1930s, they would have been gratefully accepted by the Kriegsmarine – had they managed to get their hands on them.

Finnish Lions and Siamese Twins

With names rooted in Finland's mythology, the two 3,900 ton (standard) coast defence ships *Väinämöinen* and *Ilmarinen* were the most impressive of the genre built anywhere after Sweden's *Sverige* class.

These ships were the result of a parliamentary vote at the end of the 1920s for a modernisation of the newly independent country's small navy, which also called for four submarines, motor torpedo boats and other craft. The brief emphasis on naval shipbuilding in the late 1920s and early 1930s was to be overturned by the army during the 1930s, but the navy which sported the ensign with the golden lion crest was nonetheless an impressive force by the winter of 1940 when it suddenly had to face the might of the Soviet Union.

Väinämöinen and *Ilmarinen* were extraordinarily compact vessels which had been designed by the Netherlands' Ingenieur-Kantoor voor Scheepsbouw (IvS). Ordered in August and September 1929 respectively from Finland's Crichton-Vulcan yard at Turku, they were launched on 28 December 1930 and 7 September 1931, and were completed in 1932 and 1933.[1]

Armament, virtually all supplied by Bofors, comprised two twin 254mm (10in) mountings fore and aft, and four twin 105mm (4.1in) dual-purpose guns, exposed to the rear, in B and X positions and also amidships port and starboard. The 254mm guns had an elevation of 50 degrees and fired a 495lb (225kg) shell. Some photographs also show the amidships 105mm (4.1in) twin mountings replaced by single unshielded guns[2] of an unknown nature, but it is probable that they were British-pattern 4in (102mm) as guns of this calibre equipped the *Hämeenmaa* and *Klas Horn* class sloops. Lighter AA armament initially comprised four Bofors 40mm and two 20mm, later to increase to eight and more 20mm during the Second World War.

Protection was not exactly on the heavy side, with side armour of 55–50mm (2.2–2in), deck armour of 20mm (0.79in), 100mm (3.9in) on the turrets and 120mm (4.7in) on the conning tower. The dimensions were a compact 93m x 16.9m x 4.5m (305ft 1in x 55ft 5in x 14ft 9in), with ice-breaking bows, a vital feature for a navy protecting a coast

Väinämöinen *class ship*
Seen during construction,
the Väinämöinen *class*
ships' layout looks modern
65 years after her
construction. Design was
by IvS, a Netherlands firm
with an interesting history,
and relationship with the
rearming German
Reichsmarine (CMP)

which was ice-bound for half the year. These twin-shaft, 6,000bhp vessels could make a stately 15–16kts, courtesy of their Germania diesels and Leonard electric drive. Given their limited role, this class could economise on fuel oil, of which just 93 tons were carried. Crew numbers ranged between 320 and 411.

The wartime career of this class is discussed in Chapter 9, but some general points should be made about their design. Speed was certainly modest, given the top designed speed of *Sverige* at 22.5kts and 23.2kts for its follow-ons *Drottning Victoria* and *Gustav V*. The main armament also had a lower calibre than that of the main potential enemy, the Soviet Union, whose Baltic Fleet battleships of the *Gangut* class were each armed with three triple 12in. As it turned out, the Finnish ships never had to take on the Soviet battleships.

The complement also seems to have been rather large,

given the expected efficiency of the oil-fired powerplant, when one considers that the substantially larger and much more heavily armed Swedish coal- (later oil-) fired ships had crews of just 443 for *Sverige* and 427 for her sisters.

Ilmarinen also needed an escort, in the shape of Sweden's *Drottning Victoria*, during its journey to and from Britain for King George VI's 1937 coronation review. This was because, according to a Swedish officer on board the Swedish vessel, *Ilmarinen* had poor seakeeping qualities. She had after all been built for Finland's shallow coastal waters – not the open sea.[3]

Nevertheless, the two Finnish ships were remarkable for their clean lines, well-disposed secondary batteries and for what they showed was possible on a relatively small hull. The Danes were later to take the *Väinämöinen* concept to its logical conclusion in Projects A and B of 1936 and Project E

Ratanakosindra
More an armoured gunboat than a coast defence ship, the Ratanakosindra *class nevertheless merits inclusion in this volume because it gave inspiration to the much larger* Sri Ayuthia *class. Built by Elswick in 1924–25, armament of two 6in and four 3in was good for her size and displacement (1,000 tons full load) (CMP)*

of 1939. The Siamese Navy was to learn the wrong lesson though, accepting even smaller vessels in their *Ayuthia* and *Dhonburi*, which cut too many corners. As it turned out, Finland's coast defence ships had a busy war, although *Ilmarinen*'s career was cut short by a mine in September 1941.

Siam, renamed Thailand (literally 'the land of the free') by the nationalist government of Marshal Phibun in 1939, acquired two classes of coast defence ships in the 1920s and 1930s, of which the latter pair in particular had eventful careers, while the first pair were very long lived.

It is indeed a pity that the Thai government did not see fit to preserve either *Ratanakosindra* or *Sukhothai*, the two Armstrong-designed 'gunboats' ordered in the 1920s. The former survived until the 1960s and the latter the 1970s, yet these relics of a bygone coast defence era were disposed of. Although classified as armoured gunboats in some accounts, in others they are properly regarded as coast defence ships, albeit the smallest of the genre built in the twentieth century.

Ratanakosindra was ordered from Armstrong in 1924 and laid down at Elswick on 29 September of that year, launched on 21 April 1925, and completed in the following August. *Sukhothai* was ordered from Vickers Armstrongs in 1928 (after the companies' amalgamation), laid down in December, launched on 19 November 1929 and finished by December 1930. Their raised forecastles meant that they were somewhat more seaworthy than their beamy, monitor-like appearance might suggest at first glance.

Displacing 886 tons standard and 1,000 tons full load, these twin shaft vessels were powered by a pair of Yarrow boilers giving 850ihp and a speed of 12kts. Interestingly they carried slightly more oil, at 96 tons, than the much larger and more ambitious *Väinämöinen* class. Armament was presentable for such small craft: two 6in (152mm) and four 3in (76mm) AA, all singles, the 6in having their own armoured turrets, with 2.5in (64mm) protection, shared by the

barbettes. Belt armour was 1.25–2.5in (32–64mm), the conning tower had 4.75in (121mm) and the decks had 0.75–1.5in (19–38mm). Dimensions, at just 174ft x 37ft 1in x 10ft 9in (53.04m x 11.3m x 3.28m), were tight. A 9ft rangefinder on the fighting top and two searchlights completed the fit of these interesting and ultimately successful vessels.[4]

Success was not, however, to be the hallmark of their much larger successors, *Sri Ayuthia* and *Dhonburi*, the smallest truly ocean-going coast defence ships built in the twentieth century at 2,265 tons.[5] Laid down by Kawasaki at Kobe in 1936 and launched on 21 July 1937 and 31 January 1938, they were completed on 16 June 1938 and 5 August 1938 respectively. These vessels marked the high point of Marshal Phibun's rearmament programme, which also included the *Taksin* class cruisers and *Puket* class torpedo boats (also sometimes classified as destroyers) ordered from Italy, and the Japanese-built *Tachin* class sloops and *Sinsamudar* class coastal submarines. All this was ordered during a wave of nationalism partly directed at repossessing lost territories from the French and British, an astonishing aim for a country with only a tiny merchant fleet and which faced no further claims on its territory.

With dimensions of 251ft x 47ft 4in x 13ft 8in (76.5m x 14.43m x 4.17m) and a complement of 155, these ships had a compact, boxy appearance with a centralised rangefinder and conning tower. Two twin 8in (203mm) and four single 3in (76mm) AA on the shelterdeck amidships, and four single 20mm (not 40mm as one account has it) made up the armament – remarkable for such a small vessel. Belt armour was 2.5in (64mm), turrets and barbettes 4in (101mm) and decks 1in–1.5in (25–38mm). Twin shafts were driven by MAN diesels developing 5,200bhp for a speed variously described as 15.5kts or, by Buxton, 16kts. Fuel oil provision was again better than *Väinämöinen*, at 150 tons, but the Thais had a much longer coastline to defend.

These ships had short, if dramatic careers, both being beached or left in the shallows after the battle of Koh-Chang with the Vichy French fleet on 16–17 January 1941. *Ayuthia* was raised but was lost in the 1951 revolution. Their stories during and after the Second World War are described in the next chapter.

Denmark's post-war options after Niels Juel

The ship with the distinguished name *Niels Juel* which flew the Dannebrog ensign from 1923 was in every respect an unsatisfactory and rather weak coast defence vessel, as the understanding of the concept was then understood in Scandinavia.

Because the First World War had prevented delivery of her planned main armament of two Krupp 305mm (12in), eight 120mm (4.7in) and two 75mm, this 4,100 ton (standard) ship was completed instead with ten Bofors 150mm

Dhonburi
Japanese-built, Dhonburi *(seen here in 1938), was one of a pair of coast defence ships which were savaged by the Vichy French fleet in January 1941 at Koh-Chang. They are generally thought to have been too small for the job, but still they ought to have been able to deal with their weaker French opponents (CMP)*

Väinämöinen
Built at Crichton-Vulcan at Turku in 1930, Väinämöinen *was perhaps the classic coast defence ship, at least in terms of her concept, though her seakeeping in the open ocean was inadequate (National Maritime Museum)*

Danish coast defence ship concepts
Denmark designed some fascinating coast defence ships during the 1930s, although unfortunately none were built. This view shows (top), a not so good 1933 idea for a coast defence ship with the primary armament aft, and (bottom), a far more practical May 1936 concept for what is effectively a development of the Väinämöinen *class, with two twin 250mm and three twin 150mm (GPH Collection)*

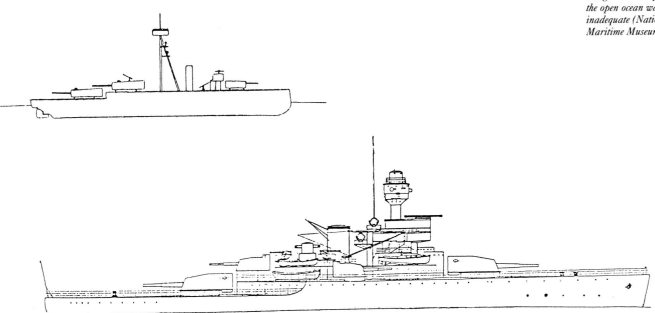

(5.9in) 45cal, all in single mountings of which the forward pair were alongside one another, giving the vessel a distinctly ungainly appearance. *Niels Juel*'s 16kt speed meant that she could not even benefit from her lighter armament with a few more knots to chase away anyone who might threaten Danish neutrality – which was far from being a remote possibility.

After all, the British had built the light battlecruisers *Courageous*, *Glorious* and *Furious* for possible Baltic operations which might have involved the violation of Danish neutrality, while after Versailles the German Reichsmarine played at least one wargame in which Denmark was a presumed enemy (see following discussion of German designs of the 1920s and footnote 13).

Not that a better defence capability would have mattered to most people in Denmark at the time. Grateful for having been spared the horrors of the First World War, most Danes were not of a mind to take defence very seriously. The Danes did very little to bolster their small navy during the inter-war years, even considering a proposal in 1924 to scrap the navy and manage with just a coastguard. Hence the German Reichsmarine files include a reference to one Danish essay from 1926 titled 'Fleet or Sea Police',[6] one of many indicators of Germany's far from academic interest in Danish naval policy, a continuation of pre-war preoccupations (see below). The Danes gained from Germany's defeat with the return to Denmark of parts of Schleswig, originally lost to Prussia in 1864, which voted for Danish rule after a referendum.

Although *Niels Juel* was refitted with more AA guns in the 1930s to beef up her initial secondary armament of four 57mm 30cal and two 450mm torpedo tubes, she never had a very active career until the Second World War when she was captured by the Germans – of which more later. Otherwise, only six new torpedo boats and five submarines were commissioned between the wars, though another submarine and a minelayer were being built in 1939. Besides *Niels Juel*, Denmark retained the three old coast defence ships of the *Herluf Trolle* class and the even more ancient *Skjold*, launched in 1896.[7]

But although the Danes were not very defence-minded, this did not prevent the Danish Navy from considering several designs for new coast defence ships which include some of the best ever designed.[8]

The first idea, dating from 1933, is something of a curiosity in that the main 240mm (9.45in) armament was in two twin turrets aft (X turret superfiring, with its own roof-mounted open twin 75mm AA mounting), with a twin 150mm secondary mounting forward and two more open twin AA mountings (larger than those on X turret) abreast a rangefinder with 225mm (8.6in) protection. This was forward of a single funnel which itself was forward of a tall tripod mast, recalling the criticised mast arrangement of *Dreadnought*. Side armour protection was 8.6in over the main

turrets and their magazines, otherwise being 5.9in, including the forward secondary turret.

This oddity was passed over, but in 1936 the Danish Navy was again considering replacements for her existing coast defence fleet and this time the ideas were much more realistic. Five designs were considered. The first proposal, in May 1936, was Project A, with a standard displacement of 5,730 tons and a speed of 20kts. Armament would have been two twin 254mm (10in), with a strong secondary armament of three twin 150mm – two abreast the single funnel and the third in X position aft. Three twin 40mm – two port and starboard immediately aft of the funnel, with the third forward of the aft 150mm mounting – made up the main AA armament, supported by two twin 25mm Madsens atop the two twin 150mm abreast the funnel.

With 1,830 tons more displacement than the slower Finnish 10in-armed *Väinämöinen* class which, to some extent at least, seems to have been its inspiration, Project A would still not have been quite a match for the German *Deutschland* class with their 280mm guns. Perhaps it was the awareness of this which led to the slower 18kt Project B of October 1936, in which the main armament was upgunned to two twin 280mm, while secondary armament was changed to eight 120mm – four twins. Displacement was slightly greater than Project A, at 5,775 tons.

A lighter proposal was the 4,600 ton Project C of the following month, November 1936, in which speed was up to 21kts, though armament was altered to two twin 203mm; secondary armament was the same as Project B, with eight 120mm. An additional armament feature, though, was a pair of 533mm torpedo tubes. A very similar 1936 concept (the month is not known), was Project D, a 4,000 tonner with only six 120mm and no torpedo tubes but otherwise the same gunnery as Project C.

The final Danish coast defence design of the 1930s was Project E of August 1939. This constituted a return to the Project A concept and was identical in displacement, speed and armament except that the three twin 150mm were replaced by four twin 120mm dual-purpose weapons. This modification would have made the concept by far the best of the Danish coastal battleship ideas of those years, in that its anti-aircraft protection would have been much the most modern. Although detail on the lighter AA armament of Projects B to E are not available, it is known that all might have carried weapons of 40mm, 25mm, 20mm and 8mm calibre.

Unfortunately for Denmark, none of these concepts were built, although given the Danes' impossible position in 1940 and their curious position until 1943 as a nominally independent country under actual German occupation, there is little any Danish coast defence ship could have done, except fight a last battle with bravery – much as *Niels Juel* did in 1943 before she was captured.

Sweden

Another Scandinavian country which looked again at the possibility of building new coast defence ships after the First World War was Sweden. She already possessed three impressive coast defence battleships in the shape of the three *Sverige* class vessels commissioned between 1918 and 1922. She also had eleven older coast defence ships after the First World War, reduced to five *Oscar II* and the four *Äran* class ships by the outbreak of the Second World War. These vessels, with the exception of the *Äran* class ship *Wasa*, were all modernised between 1939 and 1941 with tripod masts and stronger AA armament, just as the *Sverige* class themselves had undergone significant modification and modernisation in the period 1926–39.

In this case, the changes varied for each vessel in the class, although all had new tripod masts and substantial bridge superstructures added. They also were changed from coal- to oil-firing and a pair of 152mm guns were removed to make way for 40mm AA. In 1926, 1933 and 1939 *Sverige* was altered substantially and had her forward funnel reconstructed into a curious 'S' shape to keep smoke clear of the fighting top, while in 1930 and 1938 *Gustav V*'s funnels were modified by trunking them into a single funnel for basically the same purpose. *Drottning Victoria* was modernised in 1927, 1935 and 1941, but retained her original funnel arrangement.

During the 1930s, there was a growing understanding in Sweden that some form of rearmament was necessary because of the rise of Nazi Germany and the 1936 Defence Law allowed for stronger armed forces. Plans for two new coastal battleships were accepted by parliament and money for these and other vessels was voted in 1937, 1938 and 1939, but, despite this, none of these ships were started.[9]

Coast defence force majeure? Germany's choices after 1918

The naval restrictions of the Versailles Treaty were intended to prevent Germany from ever putting proper capital ships to sea again. The 10,000 ton limit on replacement tonnage for the eight pre-dreadnoughts of the *Deutschland* and *Braunschweig* classes allowed to the Reichsmarine (two of them in reserve) was decreed with the express purpose of obliging Germany to retreat to the perceived ignominy of coast defence.

At a time when the victors were settling on 35,000 ton limits for maximum battleship displacements under the Washington Treaty, it must have seemed to Germany that she had no worthwhile options open to her other than coast defence (although the Washington Treaty's displacement definitions benefited Germany in that the English ton, equivalent to 1,016kg, was used, officially allowing her the slight flexibility of an additional 160 tonnes). Furthermore,

while there was no explicit limitation on the calibre of the main armament of replacement tonnage permitted to Germany, the Germans eventually realised that the Allies would object to anything over 11in – the armament of Germany's remaining pre-dreadnoughts. Even so, they nonetheless considered 12in and even 15in armament for some of the designs drawn up during the 1920s.

That at length Germany managed to produce the Type C design for the Panzerschiff 'A' later named *Deutschland* – a true high-seas combatant – was certainly a great credit to the inventiveness of her Marineleitung designers, but the road to what was dubbed in Britain the 'pocket battleship' was by no means an easy or straightforward one. The long drawn out, and interrupted, design process was extremely interesting for the number of sketch designs produced for various concepts which were intended to square an apparently impossible circle for the Weimar navy. These included several fascinating coast defence ship designs.

The scuttling of the High Seas Fleet at Scapa Flow and the seeming absoluteness of British naval mastery after 1918 led the German Navy to exclude Britain from its list of potential naval enemies after Versailles, which were henceforth deemed to be France and Poland. In 1920, the German naval staff – the Marineleitung – under Admiral Paul Behncke's leadership, therefore identified the ten French battleships of the *Danton*, *Courbet* and *Provence* classes as the benchmark against which any new German combatant had to be measured.[10]

The French warships had all been completed between 1911 and 1915, with standard displacements between 18,850 and 22,189 tons, and speeds ranging from over 19kts to 21kts. Main armament calibres varied from 305mm (12in) to 342.9mm (13.5in). Thus they already outclassed the slower pre-dreadnoughts allowed to Germany after Versailles and, after 1921, they were likely to receive further enhancements during refits because of the Washington Treaty's limitations on the construction of new tonnage.

The German Navy's efforts to discover a solution to the problem of designing viable replacement warships of 10,000 tons can be divided into two periods. The first search for answers lasted from 1920 to 1923 and was ultimately judged

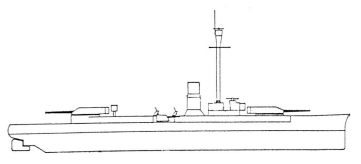

German coast defence ship concept
This view shows the first, basic monitor-type vessel under consideration by the Reichsmarine before it was rejected in favour of more seaworthy types (GPH Collection)

unsuccessful; the second lasted from 1924 – when Vice-Admiral Hans Zenker succeeded Behnke – to 1927 when he ultimately chose the Type C design which became *Deutschland*.

The first coast defence concept (Entwurf [Design] II/10) was armed with two twin 381mm (15in) turrets fore and aft, two twin 150mm (5.9in) turrets port and starboard amidships, and two single 88mm AA mounts aft of the single funnel. Also included were two underwater 500mm torpedo tubes.

This design (dimensions 124m x 21.4m x 6.8m: 406ft 10in x 70ft 3in x 22ft 4in) was to be powered by twin shaft turbines developing 25,000shp providing a top speed of 22kts. Side armour and command tower armour was up to 200mm (7.9in), while deck armour of 30mm (1.2in) was planned. The concept was regarded as too weak, with low endurance and survivability, and accordingly variations with stronger armour and weaker armament, and greater length and beam, were also examined. None of these proved adequate – partly because the requirement was to be able to fight French cruisers – and accordingly German designers turned to another concept, which became the cruiser-like Design I/10 with eight 210mm (8.3in) in four twin turrets, but a very weak secondary armament of just four single 88mm AA on the centreline, although the torpedo armament, four twin 500mm tubes, was a little more respectable for the time. Top speed from the 80,000shp twin-shaft turbines would have been 32kts, while side armour would have been 80mm (3.1in), conning tower up to 100mm (3.9in) and deck 30mm (1.2in); dimensions were 176m x 18.8m x 6.5m (577ft 5in x 61ft 6in x 21ft 4in). But this design was also considered inadequate when pitted against the possible opposition, in the shape of French battleships. This was where the work of 1920–23 was left, to await the efforts of Admiral Zenker, the new Marineleitung chief, and his staff.

But it is worth briefly considering how Design II/10 would have compared to her Baltic contemporaries had she been built. For one thing, her armament would have been substantially more powerful than any other coast defence ship in the region such as Sweden's 283mm (11.09in)-armed *Sverige* class, as well as any French or, for that matter, Russian battleship. Her speed would also have been either faster or comparable to local coast defence designs, though *Sverige* was half a knot faster.

Where Design II/10 would have fallen down, though, would have been in the required speed to chase the French cruiser squadron which was expected to assist the Poles in the event of war with Germany. The Marineleitung understood that Article 7 of the 1921 Franco-Polish military pact, pledged France to both defend Poland's small coast, and land French troops to aid the Poles in the event of war with Russia – or Germany. The promised French naval squadron was to consist of two armoured cruisers, four cruisers, four destroyers, three submarines and one minelayer.[11]

The uncertainty facing Reichsmarine planners was partly dictated by Germany's strategic dilemmas. The tasks facing Germany were deemed to be: (a) to hinder an enemy landing, for which all important points between Schleswig-Holstein and the Oder were either completely unprotected or had scarcely any defences; (b) the establishment of naval mastery in the Baltic and the maintenance of links between Germany's harbours west of the Polish corridor and those in East Prussia (besides keeping those harbours themselves open), as well as the protection of links between Germany and north European states; (c) the protection of economically important trade in the North Sea.[12]

The possible conflict scenarios for which the Marineleitung were planning in 1922–23 included a Russian-Polish conflict in which Russia declares war and France helps Poland. Britain and Denmark are neutral, but because Germany refuses to allow French troops to march through the country to Poland's aid, Germany is forced into war. Another scenario in a 1923 wargame envisaged Germany fighting against France and Denmark, incidentally explaining the interest shown by the Marineleitung in Danish naval plans.[13]

The Marineleitung's 1928 retrospective on the factors which led to the adoption of the Type C vessel as Panzerschiff 'A' refers to Germany having faced the insoluble problem of a 10,000 ton displacement restricting her to 'a "coastal monitor" of the kind like our former armoured gunboats of the '90s of the foregoing century'. Such a vessel anyway 'scarcely came into question' as far as the Marineleitung was concerned, because Germany's existing old battleships and their 280mm guns had to face, in the largest French battleships, 13.5in-armed vessels.[14]

The stalemate reached among the designers led to the abandonment of design work in 1923, the discussions only resuming in the following year when Vice-Admiral Zenker took over at the Marineleitung. As before, initially only two options were considered: a shallow-draught coast defence monitor and a cruiser. For the former, a strong armament and armour protection was considered necessary, while the cruiser could be weaker in both respects, but faster. Both were considered inadequate and work on the apparently impossible, a miniature battleship, commenced instead. No further details of the coast defence monitor concept have emerged, except perhaps by implication in that it was not regarded as having carried the argument forward much beyond Design II/10.

The diminutive battleship which was to follow, however, was somewhat more impressive, but was still in effect a very heavily armed coast defence ship. The main armament of Design II/30 of 1925 comprised three twin 305mm turrets, one fore and two aft, the latter in an asymmetrical superfiring arrangement with the raised superfiring turret to port and the stern turret to starboard. This curious arrangement may have had the main purpose of buying a few more degrees firing arc; there seems no other point given that the superfiring arrangement could easily have been achieved on the same hull length (132m: 433ft 1in) with both turrets on the centreline. (Dimensions were otherwise 22m x 6.5m.)

The principal advance of Design II/30 on the previous concepts was, for the first time, the proposed adoption of diesel engines in a triple-shaft 24,000shp arrangement which would have provided a speed of 21kts. All later sketch designs for the future armoured ship were to include diesels. Armour protection was generally as good as that of the explicitly coast defence Design II/10, with side and conning tower protection up to 200mm (7.9in), and 25mm (1in) deck armour. Where Design II/30 was undoubtedly weak was in its secondary armament, which was to comprise only three 105mm AA guns on the centreline and two underwater 533mm torpedo tubes.

Next came Design IV/30 which was intended to resolve II/30's problem of secondary armament. All three 305mm turrets were now placed forward, with two twin 150mm turrets aft and three 105mm AA. The drawback though was that this meant limiting side armour to 180–160mm (7.1–6.3in).

An attempt to rectify the problem of all the main fighting power being concentrated forward, á la *Nelson* and *Rodney*, was made in the following Design V/30 in which two triple 305mm turrets were placed fore and aft, with secondary armament of six 150mm and three 88mm AA. This permitted side armour of 200mm (7.9in) and a conning tower protected by 200mm. Both designs IV/30 and V/30 assumed the same triple shaft diesel arrangement as Design II/30.

All the above designs in this second sequence of the Marineleitung's new capital ship concepts under Zenker's leadership were carefully considered. Design II/30 was judged the 'least unfavourable', but none satisfied endurance requirements and were therefore rejected.

The next idea, considered at a meeting of the naval staff on 15 May 1925, was to take Design II/30, but fit it with two twin 305mm which, because it now seemed they might achieve a rate of fire of one per barrel every 25 seconds, would enable the vessel to achieve the required endurance while retaining considerable combat power. This approach led to Designs VI/30 and VII/30, in which the two twin turrets were mounted fore and aft in VI/30 and both forward in VII/30. Both designs had four 150mm, in two twin turrets (both positioned aft amidships in VII/30), and twin 88mm mountings, three in VI/30 and two in VII/30. In both designs, armour protection was (250mm) 9.8in throughout and the triple-shaft diesels would have made 21kts.

However, because it was felt that the Allies might object to the proposed 305mm armament, two more concepts, Design I/28 and II/28, were also drawn up in which the main armament was 280mm, mounted in triple turrets in I/28 and twins in II/28 (two turrets aft). Other armament comprised four 150mm (two twins), and six or four (Design II/28)

88mm. Armour protection, however, differed somewhat between the two concepts. Design I/28 had 240mm (9.4in) side armour and turret and conning tower armour of 250mm (9.8in), whereas all of Design II/28's proposed armour was limited to 230mm (9.1in).

Although the Reichsmarine knew that time was now pressing for a decision on the first replacement for the oldest pre-dreadnought (the Versailles Treaty stipulating that these ships could be replaced 20 years after their launch), the Marineleitung was no nearer a decision in 1925.

Two more designs were now drawn up. The first, Design I/35, was recognisably a monitor-type coast defence ship. One triple mounting forward of a new calibre, 350mm (13.65in), four 150mm in two twins aft, with two pairs of 88mm AA amidships gave this vessel an appearance not unlike some of the British shore bombardment monitors of the First World War. Four underwater 533mm torpedo tubes completed the armament fit. Top speed from the twin-shaft, 16,000shp diesels was to be a stately 19kts, while armour protection was good: 300mm (11.8in) side and main mast protection, 350mm (13.8in) for the command positions and 30mm (1.2in) for the deck. Dimensions were not dissimilar to the coast defence Design II/10 at 126m x 21m x 7.2m (413ft 5in x 68ft 7in x 23ft 7in). Had it been built, I/35 would have offered the clearest possible signal that Germany had no great seagoing pretensions any more, but this was in 1925 an unresolved issue.

The second design in this sequence, Design VIII/30, was more akin to a cruiser, though still not fast enough. Two twin 305mm fore and aft and six 150mm positioned amidships port and starboard, with the third twin aft made up the main armament; the rest was made up of six 88mm in three twins centreline amidships, plus two underwater 533mm torpedo tubes. Triple-shaft diesels generating more than twice I/35's power at 36,000shp still only provided a top speed of 24kts. Side armour of 180mm and main mast and conning tower protection of 180mm was another sign that this concept was neither fish nor foul. Dimensions were 141m x 20.2m x 7m (46ft 7in x 66ft 3in x 23ft).

The hope that the first steel for the replacement ship might be cut in 1926 was abandoned after the decision was put off in August 1925 for another year. It was by then blindingly obvious to Zenker and his staff that a fundamental decision had to be made. What did Germany want: an ocean-going ship with cruiser-like qualities, the best feasible armament and thin armour; or a slower, heavily-armed vessel with strong armour for European waters?

The issue was now seemingly decided by an assessment of the 1926 fleet manoeuvres, which were deemed to have shown that the cruiser-battleship was what was needed. Thus Designs I/M 26 and II/M 26 emerged, recognisable for their similarity to the design which became *Deutschland*. Two triple 280mm fore and aft and eight 120mm AA (two amidships and two on the centreline aft), made up the armament. Speed was now well up to 28kts, courtesy of 54,000shp diesels and, like the later *Deutschland*, armour protection was limited to 100mm throughout. Dimensions were 188m x 20.7m x 5.5m (616ft 10in x 67ft 11in x 18ft 1in). Design II/M 26 differed only in that six 37mm AA were added, and the aft tower was raised.

However, after the issue came so close to a resolution, Zenker changed his mind again and opted for a more conservative approach. The discussion drifted on, amid much further argument, but by 11 June 1927, yet another four designs had been put before Zenker, from which a winner was eventually chosen. These were: Type A, an 18kt coast defence ship with four 381mm and 250mm armour protection; Type B1, a variant on A with six 305mm; Type B2, the same as B1 but with 200mm armour and hence a higher 21kts speed; Type C, – the winner – with six 280mm, 100mm armour and a speed of 26–27kts.

The vessel which was eventually built closely to this design, Panzerschiff 'A' or *Deutschland*, was officially stated to have been designed for a displacement of 10,000 tons, but of course turned out somewhat heavier at 11,700 tons standard despite the weight-saving advance of electric-arc welding. *Deutschland*'s one great advantage over some of its expected opposition was that its 280mm guns' range was 35,000m as against, for example, the 23,000m range of the 305mm guns of the *Voltaire*s.[15] Secondary and tertiary armament comprised eight single 150mm and, initially, just three 88mm, although AA armament was to be substantially beefed up with 105mm and numerous 37mm and 20mm. The vessel was later renamed *Lützow* to avoid the humiliation of losing a ship with Germany's very name.

Consideration of some of the source material at the Militärarchiv in Freiburg does provoke the thought that perhaps some of the questions asked by the Marineleitung in the early 1920s were artificially skewed to deliberately lead to the adoption of a design such as *Deutschland*. More effective coast defence designs than those considered were certainly feasible, as much smaller vessels like the Finnish *Väinämöinen* were to demonstrate in principle a few years later. That said, Design II/10 would have been a fearsome opponent in the Baltic, and even a match for its presumed French opponents.

Therefore Panzerschiff 'A' need not necessarily have emerged as a fully-fledged commerce raider, unless the intention was always to construct an ocean-going warship – which it certainly was by 1927. As Breyer says, the objective was simply to produce 'a ship of great fighting and staying power capable of engaging French battleships with some prospect of success'.

The building of the vessel was certainly a major political issue in Germany in the late 1920s, pitting left against right. One Social Democrat (SPD) slogan in the 1928 elections was 'Food not Panzerkreuzer' (Armoured Cruiser), while newspapers of the period also indicate the heat of the debate. Thus 'Die Rote Fahne' (The Red Flag) on 14 August 1928, derisively referred to one occasion attended by 'the armoured cruiser-Cabinet', while an article in *Deutsche Tageszeitung* on 11 August 1928 was simply titled 'the embarrassing armoured ship'. It must indeed have seemed an embarrassment, given the length of the design's gestation.

But the type was certainly not an embarrassment in combat, as it took to the limits the idea of a diminutive capital ship which – according to the orthodox view of modern naval historians was essentially a fast, powerfully-armed cruiser. That it was born out of a lengthy deliberative process which had also looked closely at the other way of achieving a quart in a pint pot – by designing a slower, but powerfully-armed and well-armoured coast defence ship – has been all but forgotten since the Second World War.

Deutschland was always classified as either an 'armoured ship' (Panzerschiff) or, by the British, as a 'pocket battleship' or, in the opinion of more recent commentators, merely a very well-armed cruiser. Yet it is hard to resist the temptation to see the *Deutschland* as merely a larger and faster *Sverige* – the coast defence battleship concept exploited to its ultimate extent, with the speed and range, but without so much of the armour.

One question arises: what might have been possible had *Deutschland*'s designers ditched the 150mm battery and opted instead for, say, four or more twin dual-purpose guns of, say, 105mm? Weight saved could then have been used for extra armour over the vitals without sacrificing either speed or endurance. A later example of the Panzerschiffe, *Admiral Graf Spee*, might then have perhaps been better placed to deal with her dogged British pursuers in the South Atlantic in December 1939. It is just conceivable that with a slightly more resilient vessel Captain Langsdorff would have got the upper hand and not have met his end in such a sad and ignominious suicide in Montevideo, after suffering the indignity of scuttling his ship within sight of port.

Admiral Scheer
The design of the German pocket battleship Admiral Scheer, *seen here as she appeared at the end of her career in 1945, drew on work which commenced over 20 years earlier with coast defence concepts as a starting point (CMP)*

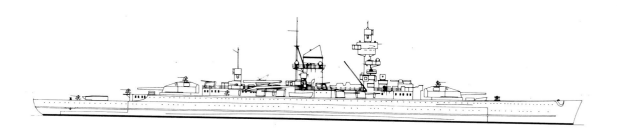

This is not so improbable as it may seem. Although anti-aircraft fire control had a long way to develop until the Second World War, the Finns understood this well enough in 1929 when *Väinämöinen* and *Ilmarinen* were laid down with a secondary armament of four twin 105mm AA. The guns were supplied by Bofors, which, to complete the irony, had received secret Reichswehr funding in the 1920s to develop Germany's future gunnery – which included just such a 105mm AA mounting.

1 For English-language references to the Finnish ships' histories, see Ian Buxton, 'Coast Offence and Defence Vessels' p.78, in *The Eclipse of the Big Gun* (London, 1992), and *Conway's All the World's Fighting Ships 1922–1946* (London, 1987), pp.363–364.

2 Visa Auvinen (ed.), *Leijonalippu Merella, Satakunnan Kirjateollisuus Oy* (Pori, Finland, 2nd Edition, 1983), p.8 & pp.52–4 & p.65 on.

3 Daniel G Harris, 'The *Sverige* class coastal defence ships', *Warship 1992* (London, 1992), p.94 & footnote 15, p.98.

4 *Conway's 1922–1946*, ibid, pp.410–411 for discussion of both classes of Siamese coast defence ships.

5 See *Conway's*, ibid, and Buxton, *op. cit.*, p.78. Certain details are also taken from an unpublished French account of the battle of Koh-Chang by Dr J Billiottet, Médecin en Chef Honoraire and former Médecin Major on board the aviso *Amiral Charner*, which took part in the battle. The account is available in: *Documents Séparés – Cols Bleus No 1169 13 Février 1971 – La Victoire Navale de Koh-Chang*, Musée de la Marine, Paris. This account differs from the accepted view in recording the Thai ships' AA armament as being of 80mm and 20mm calibre. One Danish account (see footnote 8 below for reference), records 88mm guns on p.449.

6 1926 Denkschrift (essay) 'Flaade eller Søpoliti' (Navy or Sea Police) der danischen Seeleutnantsgesellschaft, prepared by Korvetten Kapitän Andriano. RM 8/135 (Band I), Militärarchiv, Freiburg.

7 For general discussion of Danish coast defence ships and the Danish fleet between the wars, see Buxton in *The Eclipse of the Big Gun*, *op. cit.*, pp.71–8, and *Conway's 1922–1946*, ibid, pp.381–384.

8 R Steen Steensen, *Vore Panserskibe 1863–1943* (Copenhagen, 1968), pp.446–51 & footnotes pp.145–60 for very interesting material on domestic and foreign coast defence ships and designs of the period.

9 *Conway's 1922–1946*, *op. cit.*, pp.368–9 & Daniel G Harris, op.cit. pp.80–98.

10 Discussion of German replacement capital ship designs after Versailles draws principally on three sources: Gert Sandhofer, 'Das Panzerschiff 'A' und die Vorentwürfe von 1920 bis 1928', *Militärgeschichtliche Mitteilungen* Vol.I/68, Militärgeschichtlichen Forschungsamt (Germany, 1968), pp.35–62; Siegfried Breyer, *Battleships and Battlecruisers, 1905–1970* (London, 1973), pp.285–91; *Conway's 1922–1946*, ibid. pp.218–22 & pp.227–8.

11 'Denkschrift über Panzerschiff 'A' ', Der Militärische Wert der Panzerschiffneubauten, Reichswehrministerium Marineleitung A II 795/28; Berlin, 2–10–1928, p.3. Militärarchiv, Freiburg.

12 Ibid, p.2.

13 RM 20/999 AIa-XV-1 Kriegspiele 1922–23 for the Russian-Polish war, and RM 20/1000 A1a-XV-2 for the 1923 wargame pitting Germany against France and Denmark. Militärarchiv, Freiburg.

14 'Denkschrift über Panzerschiff 'A'', p.3. para 5.

15 Ibid, p.4.

CHAPTER 9

A Brave Swansong: The Second World War

A SURPRISING NUMBER OF classic coast defence ships managed to survive until the Second World War. A few, such as the Finnish and Thai ships, were of recent or relatively recent construction, but most were aged, had undergone several refits or had served in more modest roles.

Most countries retained such coastal artillery as seemed appropriate, although by now only a few nations had well defined conceptions of a network of interlocking shore-based and offshore coastal defences. This discipline was to undergo an enforced renaissance with the creation of Hitler's much vaunted Atlantic Wall, although it did the defenders of Fortress Europe little good in the end. Yet, as is argued below, D-Day did provide perhaps the classic coast defence opportunity, one which was missed not so much because the defenders lacked the resources, but because their organisation was, thankfully for the Allies, woefully inadequate and mis-directed.

The stories of some of the battles and engagements in which coast defence ships were involved show clearly that the oldest vessels, like the Norwegian ships, had little chance, but it would be wrong to assume that the outcome of the Battle of Koh-Chang between the Vichy French and the Thais was entirely inevitable. Rather, what was missed on that occasion was an opportunity to demonstrate that coast defence ships could still do their job. In this instance it seems Thai fire control of their 8in guns was bad; had their ranging been better, Vichy's isolated naval triumph might not have been so emphatic. It is notable that, unlike the careers of many earlier coast defence ships, a great deal more is known about the combat and service records of some of their successors during the Second World War, and these are presented below.

Even when they ceased to perform their original function, many coast defence ships continued to perform useful roles, although not always in the hands of their original owners, for example as anti-aircraft (AA) ships or even as blockships. Several other coast defence ships survived the conflict and it is a great pity that none were preserved for posterity in something like their original guise.

Sweden

In Sweden's case, the three refitted *Sverige* class coast defence ships continued to perform a useful deterrent role during the Second World War, with the Soviet Union as the main presumed enemy after 1938. The Swedish Navy still possessed in 1939 the older coast defence ships of the *Oscar II*, *Äran*, *Dristigheten*, *Oden* and *Svea* classes.

The defensive strategy of the Swedes before 1941 was to use all three vessels together as the knock-out blow to an invasion fleet, with the first line of defence being provided by submarines and mines, with a second line of destroyers and the aircraft-carrying cruiser *Gotland* performing a reconnaissance function. The presumed enemy was either Russia's two Baltic fleet battleships of the *Marat* class, armed with 305mm (12in) guns, or any of Germany's three 280mm (11in) armed *Deutschland* class Panzerschiffe. These vessels' capabilities were such that Swedish thinking as to their use changed from the concept of waiting in the shallow channels to dealing with the enemy in the open sea, even at night. This required the building of escorts and in time the *Sverige* class became the second tier of defence behind the cruisers and destroyers. In the late summer of 1944, Harris records that a German naval force was spied which was thought to be threatening Sweden or Åland. The Germans turned away and it is apparent that they held the *Sverige* class in high regard and their destruction was regarded as an essential precursor to any invasion of Sweden, as was actually considered in 1943. By this time, this class had their original 283mm and 152mm main and secondary armament, plus a standardised AA fit of four twin 75mm, six twin 40mm, four twin 25mm and three 20mm singles.[1]

Perhaps with Sweden's example in mind, Russia felt sufficiently impressed by the smaller Finnish *Väinämöinen* to take it as a war prize and retain it in service until the end of the 1950s. In 1946, a Russian naval journal publicly expressed its respect for the *Sverige* class, further indicating how this type of vessel remained relevant in the minds of many naval thinkers. The *Sverige* class went to the breakers after the war.

Denmark and Norway

The story of the Danish and Norwegian coast defence ships during the Second World War is certainly a story of considerable, albeit hopeless bravery. When Hitler struck north he wanted to ensure access to Swedish iron ore, which the British equally wanted to deny him. Both courses of

action involved violating Norwegian neutrality. According to the German logic therefore, securing that ore for Germany meant gaining control of Norway and taking Norway also meant that Denmark had to be occupied.

The British and French had meanwhile dreamed up a quixotic plan to assist the Finns in their struggle against Russia, which had attacked Finland in the winter of 1939. That assistance was to be provided via a route crossing Norway and Sweden. At the same time, a landing in Norway – at Narvik – would allow the Allies to put a stop to the trade in iron ore from mines in northern Sweden. The stage was therefore set for a violent end to the 'phoney war' on 9 April 1940.

Denmark was seized quickly on that day, with negligible loss of life and a passable pretence by the Germans that the invasion had been intended as a 'peaceful' takeover. The Danish Navy had been ordered not to fire unless fired upon, even though the German ships sailing through the Great Belt – Danish waters – had been clearly seen. Neither the two surviving Danish coast defence ships, *Niels Juel* or *Peder Skram*, nor the navy's other ships, were even seized by the Germans. Like the country, the Danish Navy was to remain nominally independent of the Germans until 1943,

although they forced the Danes to 'lease' six torpedo boats to the Kriegsmarine in January 1941.

However Denmark increasingly resisted its status as a *de facto* occupied country and in August 1943 the Danish government refused to hand over captured resistance fighters to German forces. On 29 August the Germans tried to disarm and capture all Danish forces. The Danish Army had already been forced out of Jutland into Sjaeland and Funen. According to orders, twenty-seven Danish Navy vessels were blown up or scuttled in Copenhagen Dockyard and at least four others were scuttled elsewhere.

The most modern Danish coast defence ship, *Niels Juel* (which had been refitted with a pole mast and modern AA guns in 1936), was attacked by the Luftwaffe in August 1943 and was beached in Isefjord at full speed. But this did not result in her total loss, and she was refloated by the Germans, who from 1944 used her as the training ship *Nordland*. In this condition her ten main 150mm (5.9in) guns were removed and emplaced as coastal artillery, while she then received three 105mm, three 37mm, sixteen 20mm and four 8mm AA guns and machine guns. Bombed at Eckenfsrde near Kiel on 3 May, 1945, she was finally used as a refugee vessel for officers and their families – a sad end.

Niels Juel
Niels Juel *as she appeared before the war, showing clearly her large 5.9in battery. The Danes conceived far better designs in the 1930s to supplant her (National Maritime Museum)*

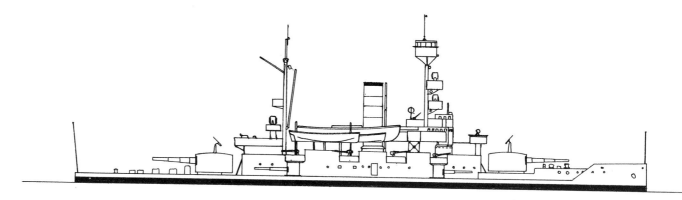

The older coast defence ship *Peder Skram*, launched in 1908, was one of those ships to have been successfully scuttled in 1943, but the Germans nevertheless raised her and used her as the AA battery *Adler* until she was bombed in April 1945. Her original AA armament had been substantially altered during the 1930s with the reduction in the 75mm battery and the addition of at least four 40mm plus some 20mm. As *Adler*, the Germans added AA guns and removed the secondary 150mm (5.9in) guns, using them ashore. Salvaged after the war, *Peder Skram* was towed to Denmark and was broken up at Odensee on 1 May, 1949.

After the war, Denmark learned one lesson though: surrender to an enemy is now a criminal offence there. If Denmark's coast defence ships were swiftly overcome by history, their Norwegian counterparts put up a real fight – or tried to.

Writing of the Norwegian coast defence ships *Norge* and *Eidsvold*, the historian Francois Kersaudy records that Norway's commanding admiral had 'affectionately dubbed them "my old bathtubs"'. Most of the rest of the navy was in the same condition, though the two old coast defence ships had still been refitted with an additional two 76mm high angle AA, plus two 20mm cannon and two 12.7mm and four 7.92mm Colt AA machine guns. The navy did not often leave port after 1918 because of an economy drive, Norway's ports being protected by copious, though obsolete, coastal artillery.

For instance, the Oscarsborg fortress in the middle of Oslo fjord was protected by, amongst others, a 19th-century Krupp cannon. The Agdenes fortress at the mouth of Trondheim fjord was garrisoned by a company which had only received 48 days' training a decade before. Several batteries had skeleton crews or none at all. At Bergen fortress, rusty batteries were undermanned and had not fired a shot for 20 years and most of the shells were defective. Narvik's shells were modern, but Kersaudy records that 'there were no cannons to fire them: several batteries had been sent there in 1912, but they were never mounted for lack of funds'.[2]

Indeed, the Norwegian historian Johan Waage records that this was attested to by the Germans. At the outset of their invasion of Norway on 9 April 1940, the Germans landed troops from the destroyers *Anton Schmidt* and *Hans Lüdemann* in the approaches to Narvik, who sure enough found the expected concrete gun emplacements, but with no guns.[3]

Yet, on paper, the coastal defences at Narvik, and at every other strategically significant point on the Norwegian coast, were adequate. Documentary evidence available in Germany shows that the Kriegsmarine took the potential threat seriously and had performed an in-depth analysis of what was known of the Norwegian defences.[4]

The large number of guns, howitzers and torpedo batteries, to say nothing of minefields, for which Norway had at least made plans, could have significantly influenced the course and perhaps even the outcome of the campaign, had all these defences been ready, manned and properly equipped on that fateful April morning. With the full benefit of hindsight, an effective intelligence, communications and mobilisation system, even by 1940s standards, might have enabled these same defences to have had a far greater impact on events than proved to be the case.

Indeed, as it turned out, the response in some threatened areas was moderately swift. Colonel Sundlo, commander of Norwegian troops at Narvik, had already been ordered to resist any forces attempting to land early that morning. As for Commodore Friedrich Bonte, commander of the German destroyers, he was not going to fire unless fired on, although he and his superior, General Dietl, had very clear orders to smash any resistance proffered.

Kriegsmarine historian Cajus Bekker records that early in the morning at Narvik's Ofot Fjord the visibility was poor with driving snow.[5] At 0410 a warning of eight warships in the fjord, signalled by radio on the 600m band from an outbound Norwegian craft, was ignored. Waage records that two small Norwegian patrol vessels in the fjord, *Michael Sars* and *Kelt*, were ordered by the Germans to return to Narvik after the destroyer *Dieter von Roder* fired a couple of 37mm shots astern of the little craft, which were only armed with 47mm guns. Norwegian shore batteries at the narrows between

Ramnes and Hamnes did not fire. Three destroyers, the command vessel *Wilhelm Heidkamp*, plus *Georg Thiel* and *Berndt von Arnim*, now approached Narvik harbour.

Captain Per Askim, commanding the two Norwegian coast defence ships in the Ofoten division, had already been ordered to resist an attack on Narvik and both Dietl, commanding the land forces committed to the operation, and Bonte were under no illusions that had the Norwegian coast defence ships immediately opened fire, the *Wilhelm Heidkamp* at least would not have stood a chance. *Eidsvold* now fired a shot across *Wilhelm Heidkamp*'s bow and ordered her to heave to. This order was complied with and Commodore Bonte sent over a boat to the *Eidsvold* with an officer, Lieutenant-Commander Gerlach, who passed on an order to surrender to the captain of the Norwegian ship, Lieutenant-Commander Willoch. He refused, angrily saying that his honour would not allow him to do that. What passed between Gerlach and Willoch was now being relayed by radio to Askim in *Eidsvold*'s sister ship, *Norge*, which was in Narvik harbour. Willoch told Gerlach he needed 10 minutes to ask for orders – with hindsight a fatal error – and later told him that he had been ordered to fight and Gerlach had to return to his ship. This Gerlach did in a boat which was flying a white flag. *Eidsvold*'s guns were now trained on the German destroyer. Despite flying the white flag, Gerlach then fired a red starshell indicating danger, effectively inviting *Heidkamp* to fire. According to Bekker, *Heidkamp* then got under way, Gerlach's boat removed itself from the line of fire and either two (according to Bekker) or four (Waage) torpedoes fired from the *Heidkamp* struck the *Eidsvold* at a range of just 250m, breaking her apart amidships. Waage says the *Heidkamp* had already been ordered to clear torpedo tubes and that the destroyer had indeed been waiting for a signal as to whether the Norwegians meant to fight. *Eidsvold* sank in seconds and there were just eight survivors. Bonte's distaste for all this is on record. He even asked Dietl before firing: 'Do we have to do this?'.

Norge now engaged *Berndt von Arnim* which had tied up, along with the *Thiele*, at Narvik. The destroyer returned fire 'with all weapons' and Bekker says that Askim continued the fight 'with no regard for the fact that his shells were exploding behind the German vessel in Narvik town', an account which Waage seems to support when he writes that the second salvo 'seemed to coincide with the explosion of the shells on land'. *Norge* was eventually hit by the sixth and seventh torpedoes fired by *Berndt von Arnim*, earlier torpedoes having missed. Waage records that the torpedo tubes' firing gear had been iced up and first had to be cleared and therefore the *Arnim* had initially opened fire with guns. Despite this, *Norge*'s fire was ineffectual, partly because the snow had made it impossible to lay the guns accurately and partly also because the gun crews were struggling with the 'old-fashioned gun-laying mechanism'. *Norge* had avoided the first five torpedoes fired because Askim

Norge
The 4,165 ton Norge *was the third of Norway's quartet of coast defence ships, and, like the preceding lighter* Harald Haarfagre *class, was armed with two single 8.2in, though secondary armament of six 5.9in 46cal was an improvement on the previous class. She is seen here on her speed trials in 1900 and was little changed when she met a brave end at Narvik on 9 April 1940 (Frank Abelsen)*

sensibly ordered *Norge* to go about to avoid them, demonstrating that the 'old bathtub' was not so sluggish a vessel as has been inferred.

Nearby ships rescued ninety-seven survivors from the two coast defence ships, but Norwegian naval historian Frank Abelsen records that 276 had died with them, 101 on *Norge*. Another account records eight survivors from *Norge* and ninety-seven from *Eidsvold*.[6] The 'self-sacrificing resistance of the Norwegian Navy had shattered the fiction of a 'peaceful occupation',' Bekker says. This is correct enough although it is quite clear that the Germans had been ordered to ruthlessly crush any resistance which might have been offered.

What observations can be made about this one-sided engagement? Yes, it was true that the local coastal artillery was notional rather than real and *Eidsvold* and *Norge* were very old ships, 'bathtubs' even. But had Willoch not entered into a parley, had the orders to Askim to resist an attack been executed from the very outset, it is not inconceivable that *Wilhelm Heidkamp* and the *Bernt von Arnim* at least might have been overcome by the Norwegian ships' guns. It did not all go Germany's way that morning though, the heavy cruiser *Blücher* sailing up the Oslofjord, straight into a hail of fire from a 1908-vintage Krupp cannon. The vessel sank and still threatens Oslo at the time of writing, as oil seeps from the wreck.

Although *Eidsvold* and *Norge* had been lost in tragic circumstances, Norway's two other former coast defence ships, the older *Harald Haarfagre* and *Tordensjold*, survived the onslaught and were impressed by the Germans to serve as the AA ships *Thetis* and *Nymphe*. Both had been reduced

Eidsvold
Another victim of the German destroyers at Narvik on 9 April 1940 was the luckless Eidsvold, *sister ship to* Norge. *Her forward starboard 5.9in (better protected than the 4.7in secondary guns of the earlier* Harald Haarfagre *class, can be seen clearly abreast the bridge (Frank Abelsen)*

in 1939 to service as unarmed accommodation and depot ships at the Norwegian naval base at Horten. In March 1941, they were rebuilt as floating AA batteries, *Nymphe* joining Marine-Flakabteilung 41. *Thetis* meanwhile served as the 'listening post' for the battleship *Tirpitz* in Kafjord, at Alta near Tromso during 1943–44. Both ships had been rearmed by the Germans with six 105mm, two 40mm and no less than fourteen 20mm Flak, with new open platforms for the heavier AA armament. In 1945 the Germans tried to run *Nymphe* aground during its transfer back to the Norwegians and she sank at Moldora, being salvaged and scrapped at Stavanger in 1948. *Thetis* however, served again in the Norwegian Navy as an accommodation vessel in 1946–47. Details of the AA armament provided by Abelsen differ somewhat from another account which incorrectly lists seven '102mm', two 40mm and nine 20mm; the AA fit of *Eidsvold* and *Norge* above is provided by Abelsen.

The Netherlands

The most recent Dutch coast defence ship to be built, *De Zeven Provincien*, became a gunnery training ship in 1936 with a reduced armament. Converted from coal to oil (with 1,100 tons of oil fuel), five of her eight boilers were removed and in 1936 she was renamed *Soerabaia* (also rendered sometimes as *Soerabaja*) and thereafter served in the Dutch East Indies. Her condition was somewhat changed from her original state. *Soerabaia*'s displacement was down from 6,530 tons (normal) to 5,644 tons, accounted for partly by the removal of her forefunnel and the reduction in her secondary armament from four to two 150mm (5.9in) 40cal, plus two 76mm, six 40mm AA and six 12.7mm AA, the latter now being standard Dutch AA armament – as fitted to the

new Dutch East Indies flagship, the cruiser *De Ruyter*. Her speed was still 16kts.

After the Japanese attack in December 1941, *Soerabaia* was detailed, together with a transport vessel, to take 650 Dutch and Australian troops of the 'Sparrow Force' from Koepang in Dutch Timor to Dili in Portuguese East Timor to improve its security. Bombed by the Japanese Naval Air Arm on 18 February 1942, *Soerabaia* was scuttled in the port after which she had been named, although surprisingly the Japanese raised the hulk and used it as a blockship in 1942–43. Despite the earlier transport of 'Sparrow Force', the Japanese still landed all over Timor on 20 February, taking the island.

Two older Dutch coast defence ships in home waters which survived until the Second World War were *Jacob van Heemskerk*, which was renamed *Ijmuiden* in 1939 after the commissioning of the new light cruiser *Jacob van Heemskerck*, and the older *Hertog Hendrik*. *Ijmuiden* served as a guardship with her original heavy armament of a pair of 240mm (9.45in) 40 cal, but with other armament reduced to two 40mm AA. Scuttled in May 1940, she was later raised and towed to Kiel for conversion in 1944 into the floating German AA battery *Undine*, in which condition she was recaptured at Wilhemshaven at the end of the war. In 1948 the Dutch recommissioned her as the accommodation ship *Neptunis*, remaining in service until the mid 1970s.

Another coast defence ship to serve the Germans was the 5,000 ton *Hertog Hendrik*. She had been converted into a training ship in 1924 with the removal of her after 240mm 40 cal turret and was further modified in 1928 to carry a pair of seaplanes. From 1939 she very briefly served as a coastal battery at Vlieereede, appropriately being renamed *Vlieereede*. She was decommissioned in the November of that year, was captured by the Germans the following May and was sunk in an RAF air raid in the following month. The Germans yet saw fit to refloat her in October 1940, converting her at Antwerp into the floating AA battery *Ariadne*. Remarkably, she survived the war and served under her original name of *Hertog Hendrik* as a Dutch Navy accommodation ship until 1972.

Finland

The Finnish coast defence ships *Väinämöinen* and *Ilmarinen*, the most recent classic coast defence ships to be built in Europe, both saw action against the Soviet Union during the Second World War, although *Ilmarinen* fell victim to a mine early on in the conflict. Armed with two twin Bofors 254mm (10in) 45cal mountings which fired a 225kg shell, and secondary armament of four twin 105mm 50cal AA and smaller 40mm (four) and 20mm (two to eight) AA, these diesel powered vessels were apparently not excellent seaboats (see the previous chapter) but, for what they were,

(*Left*) Thetis, *ex-*Harald Haarfagre
The former Norwegian Navy coast defence ship Harald Haarfagre *was taken by the Germans in 1940, renamed* Thetis, *and refitted as a useful AA ship. Here she is seen at Tromso. (Frank Abelsen)*

Nymphe, *ex-*Tordenskjold
Another German war prize was Norway's coastal battleship Tordenskjold. *She was renamed* Nymphe, *served in an AA role and is seen here following a German attempt to scuttle her at the conclusion of the war in 1945 (Frank Abelsen)*

remained remarkable examples of how compact armament arrangements could be provided for on small (3,900 ton) hulls. They certainly provided the inspiration for the abortive Danish coast defence ship designs of the 1930s.

Both vessels formed a 'fleet in being', deterring amphibious landings during the Winter War against Soviet Russia in 1939–40, and faced bomb attacks on Christmas Day 1939 and also in January 1940 at Turku. Both ships also saw action in the later and longer war with the same enemy between 1941 and 1944.

In September 1941, both *Ilmarinen*, under the command of Commander Göransson, and *Väinämöinen*, under the command of Commander Koivisto, had formed an Armoured Ship Division under Captain Rahola which was escorting ten patrol boats, a German minelayer (*Brummer*) and twelve other vessels in a mixed Finnish-German force during the seizure of Ösel island in the Baltic. But, on 13 September, *Ilmarinen* was suddenly sunk by a floating mine off Hangö, with the loss of thirteen officers and 258 men, during the 'Nordwind' feint operation which comprised part of the seizure of Ösel.

After this, the most grievous single loss to the Finnish Navy during the Second World War, efforts were taken to preserve *Väinämöinen*, although she continued to provide fire support during the balance of the conflict, notably during operations against the Russians in July 1942. During this time, she was given a zig-zag camouflage and received enhancements to her AA armament, including eight 20mm, up from the original two. A portside chute was also fitted, seemingly for the rapid disposal of shell cases from her forward twin 105mm mounting. Ceded to the Soviet Union in 1947, *Väinämöinen* was renamed *Vyborg* and served with the Soviet Navy until 1958, being broken up at Leningrad in 1960.[7]

Thailand

The Battle of Koh-Chang in February 1941 saw the Vichy French Navy inflict an extraordinary defeat on the Thai fleet, in so doing savaging the two modern Japanese-built coast defence ships *Dhonburi* and *Sri Ayuthia*. The engagement took place as the dramatic culmination to what had been sluggish though bitter conflict which had begun in late 1940 and which, though it was exploited to the full by the Japanese, had its roots in the troubled relations between France and Siam, as it then was, since at least the mid nineteenth century.[8]

Koh-Chang is remarkable for several reasons, besides its particular relevance to this narrative. It was the only French naval victory of either World War conceived and executed by French forces entirely alone and without even the implied support of an ally. That it was a Vichy victory and one which nonetheless failed to nullify Thai aggression against French Indochina – as the Japanese reversed the usual dictum of 'to the victor the spoils', forcing the French to give back previously annexed territory to the nationalist Thai regime – perhaps explains why so little is known of it.

Still, it was an extraordinarily audacious enterprise, as the old French light cruiser *Lamotte-Picquet* and four sloops or 'avisos', *Amiral Charner*, *Dumont d'Urville*, and the older *Marne* and *Tahure* sailed in secret from Saigon in January 1941 to pounce on the unsuspecting modern Thai fleet at the anchorage of Koh-Chang on the morning of the 17th of that month. This Thai flotilla comprised not only the previously described Japanese-built coast defence ships *Dhonburi* and *Sri Ayuthia* with their four 203mm (8in), four 76mm (3in) and four 40mm AA, but also the small Italian-built destroyers, or rather torpedo boats, *Chonburi*, *Songhkli* and *Trad*, all armed with six 18in (456mm) torpedo tubes plus three 76mm and two 20mm AA.

The French group could muster as offensive armament the eight 152mm (6in) and twelve 550mm torpedo tubes of *Lamotte-Picquet*, plus three 137mm (5.4in) on *Amiral Charner* and *Dumont d'Urville* and two guns of the same calibre on *Tahure* and four 100mm (3.9in) on *Marne*. The French group also had three seaplanes, two of which played a key role in establishing the positions of the Thai ships in missions on the morning of 16 January.

Extraordinarily perhaps, the Thais were not only thus

Battle of Koh-Chang
One of the Thai fleet's
hapless destroyers burns in
the distance after being hit
by French fire at the Battle
of Koh-Chang on 17
January 1941, in which
two Thai coast defence
ships were sunk or beached
(Musée de la Marine,
Paris)

warned of the French approach on the following morning, but also opened fire first with their 8in guns from the two coast defence ships. The French cruiser replied with its somewhat less powerful guns, and its torpedoes, sinking all three closer Thai torpedo boats, though *Trad* was later salvaged and repaired. Captain R Berenger, the commander of *Lamotte-Picquet*, proceeded to skilfully and speedily man-oeuvre his weaker cruiser closer to the Thai ships. *Dhonburi* was hit by what has been described as a lucky strike on her fighting top which killed her commander and officer of the watch. She, like *Sri Ayuthia*, was forced to beach and *Dhonburi* later sank under tow after being refloated after the battle. *Sri Ayuthia* was similarly refloated, was repaired in Japan, but met an ignominious end at the hands of Thai Army artillery during the revolution on 3 July 1951.

It is certain that *Sri Ayuthia* was struck by at least one of three torpedoes fired by the French cruiser. The battle, which began with the Thai coastal battleships opening fire at 0614, lasted until an abortive Thai air attack on the

French ships at 0858. It is apparent from one crude map of the engagement that the French vessels enjoyed, and exploited, full tactical freedom of movement, whereas the Thai ships seem to have been stunned by the speed of their opponents and their skill at manoeuvering between the islands of the picturesque anchorage.

Dhonburi at least, though, is recorded as having fired until the end, although at times both she and her sibling were at an apparent disadvantage in only being able to bring one of their two turrets apiece to bear on their opponents. But one French account suggests the Thai 8in fire fell short, whereas the 6in fire of *Lamotte-Picquet* was far more accurate, even at 12,000m. The impression given by French accounts of the battle is of two none too nimble whales being harried by a swarm of orcas. At least twenty men died on *Dhonburi*, losses on *Sri Ayuthia* not being known, and it seems many of the Thai sailors involved in the battle survived.

As a postscript, there were two surviving ships in the

Gustav V
Gustav V is seen here in 1934, with additional AA armament and appeared essentially like this during the Second World War (National Maritime Museum)

Thai coast defence fleet after Koh-Chang, the previously described British-built diminutive coast defence ships *Ratanakosindra* and *Sukhotai*, still in use until the 1960s and 1970s respectively.

Italy

Although Italy did not possess any classic coast defence vessels, she nonetheless decided to reconstruct her armoured cruiser *San Giorgio* specifically as a coast defence ship in 1937–38 at La Spezia. Converted to oil with eight boilers and 1,300 tons of fuel, her four funnels were reduced to two with caps. Smaller topmasts and an altered tertiary armament of four twin 100mm (3.9in) 47cal and seven twin 13.2mm AA cut *San Giorgio*'s weight to 9,470 tons standard and 11,500 tons full load. During the war she served as a floating AA battery at Tobruk, with an additional pair of 100mm and six twin 20mm mountings. She was scuttled there on 22 January 1941 as the first British offensive neared the port.

Otherwise, the First World War-era monitor *Faa di Bruno*, which had been stricken in 1924, was nevertheless redesignated *GM194* by the Italian Navy and was used as a harbour defence vessel in Genoa from 1940 until the Italian surrender in 1943.

Russia

The Soviet Union's fleet of 'guardships' (Storozhevoi Korabl), generally lightly armed vessels which might have been described elsewhere as sloops or corvettes, performed what was essentially a coastal protection role, although obviously they were not armed with heavy guns. They stand apart from classic escort vessels in that the early Soviet conception of the guardship was as a vessel supporting, rather than escorting the 'mosquito' fleet of torpedo boats and submarines which were the new Soviet Navy's main lines of coastal defence.

First of the genre were the eighteen *Uragan* class guard-

ships authorised under the 1926 programme and launched between 1929 and 1935, the first surface warships to be built under the then new Soviet government. Displacing only 450 tons standard (619 tons full load), the *Uragan* class was armed with two 102mm (4in) or 100mm (3.9in) 56cal, three 13.2mm machine guns, three 450mm torpedo tubes and 30–48 mines, though later AA armament was improved with the incorporation of three 45mm and/or 37mm AA as well as depth charge throwers and rails. With a bad reputation owing to their poor construction, the *Uragan*s provided many lessons which were made good in the succeeding *Yastreb* class, of which eight were built, followed by the dozen *Albatross* class vessels. Both classes had been authorised under the third five year plan and were launched between 1940 and 1944.

The *Yastreb* class, displacing 906 tons standard (1,059 tons full load), and the *Albatros* class (920 tons) had standardised armament of three 100mm 56 cal, four or six 37mm and six or eight 12.7mm AA, three 450mm torpedo tubes and 20 mines. Much faster than the 23kt *Uragan*s, at 31kts and 24kts respectively, the *Yastreb* and *Albatros* class were effectively torpedo boats or small destroyers, although they suffered in not possessing anti-submarine armament and in the curious positioning of two separate 100mm mountings *en echelon* aft.

Russia also took as reparations the previously mentioned Finnish coast defence ship *Väinämöinen* in 1947, renamed *Vyborg*, as well as the far, far older German *Hessen* in 1946, which interestingly was classified by the earlier Reichsmarine as a coast defence ship. A *Braunschweig* class pre-dreadnought completed in 1905 and armed, by the 1920s, with four 280mm, fourteen 6.7in, four 88mm AA guns and even four 500mm torpedo tubes, the 14,167 ton *Hessen* had been converted into a radio-controlled target in 1935–36, with four automatic oil-burning boilers which raised output to 18,000ihp and top speed to 20kts. Renamed *Tsel* by the Soviet Union, her postwar career and fate is not known.

Hessen's refitted state is nonetheless very interesting, as her designed speed, courtesy of her three-shaft 17,000ihp coal-fired engines was 18.25kts. Given the refits which the

Yastreb
The Soviet Navy guardship Yastreb *(seen as she was in 1945) is typical of a genre which might properly be considered as escorts. However they were not used as such, but in a classic coast defence gunboat role, albeit with inadequate armament (CMP)*

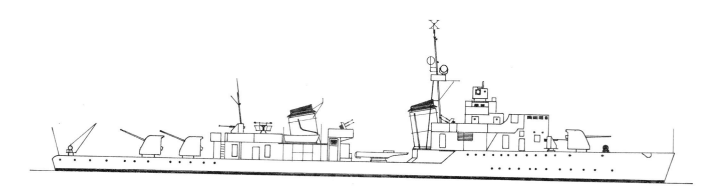

later German pre-dreadnoughts *Schliesien* and *Schleswig-Holstein* were given, when two of their three funnels were trunked into one and secondary armament was significantly altered, it is perhaps worth considering how other older coast defence battleships might have benefited from more extensive refits.

After all, the Italians had already shown the way with their extensive refits of the *Conte di Cavour* and *Andrea Doria* class battleships. The factor mitigating against this of course was the fact that most coast defence ships were so elderly as not to be worth rebuilding, but there were a few candidates, such as the *Sverige* and *Väinämöinen* classes.

A Note on D-Day

Perhaps the definitive coastal defence opportunity was provided on 6 June, 1944, when the Allied armies descended on Normandy. Field Marshal Rommel had correctly estimated that the battle would be won, or lost, on that first day of the opening of the second front – and by the water's edge.

That the Germans lost, and how, is known well enough, but it remains remarkable that despite Allied air and naval supremacy, the Germans retained sufficient forces in the general area of the assault to have inflicted far more serious damage on the Allies than was actually achieved.

In the area of the landings on D-Day, the Germans had twenty-nine major coastal artillery batteries, with a total of 125 guns (with three more in another battery under construction) of calibres ranging from 210mm to 100mm. In addition, there were numerous smaller so-called 'resistance nests' with smaller guns, such as 75mm, 47mm, 37mm and static turrets taken from captured French tanks. Some of these resistance nests were particularly well camouflaged and provided nasty surprises for the Allies on the day. The six infantry divisions (one technically an airborne unit) and the single tank division immediately available to the Germans on the Normandy coast were, on paper at least, a match for the 50,000 Allied troops taking part in the initial invasion, although the latter clearly had the advantage of surprise and being able to choose their precise landing zone.[9]

That one of the five Allied landing beaches, Omaha, almost turned into a major defeat, is a matter of record. The losses of the US 5th Corps' 1st and 29th Divisions reached almost 6,000 casualties by the evening of D-Day. It seems probable that the entire enterprise might have failed, despite air and naval superiority, had similar casualties been suffered on the other four landing beaches of Utah, Gold, Juno and Sword. It is also essential to remember that the Germans critically damaged their own ability to react to any landings by the limitations imposed by Hitler on the armoured reserve's freedom of movement.

At sea, the German Navy's strength was negligible by comparison with the immense Allied armada, though some of the latter's ships had some very lucky escapes indeed. Thus the Germans' 5th Torpedo Boat Flotilla, comprising *T28*, *Möwe* and *Jaguar*, engaged British forces covering the invasion off Sword beach on the night of 6–7 June, sinking the Norwegian destroyer *Svenner* and narrowly missing the British battleships *Warspite* and *Ramillies* and the headquarters ship *Largs*. Other Allied losses that night included the *LST715* and one LCT, though the attacking S-boats (E-boats) suffered the loss of two boats on British-laid mine fields. Another unknown Allied destroyer was missed that night by an S-boat's torpedoes.[10]

Further losses were of course inflicted on the Allies in subsequent days, but on the key day, the Allied forces' fleet of eight battleships, twenty-two cruisers, ninety-three destroyers, 229 escorts, 200 minesweepers, 360 smaller vessels and no less than 4,222 landing craft carried out their task almost unscathed. The Germans' performance was of course not aided by the fact that only two FW190 fighters put in an appearance for the Luftwaffe on D-Day itself, all of the other immediately available fighters having been withdrawn to French airfields deeper inland.

As in Norway in 1940 (see footnote 4), the Germans did not lack for shore-based artillery. Some of the emplacements withstood very heavy Allied air and naval bombardment. For example, east of Sword beach, the Merville battery's 100mm guns continued to fire until the end of July, despite 1,000 bombs being aimed at it, of which only fifty actually hit it, and only two of them on a bunker.[11]

Much has been made, perhaps too much, of the allegedly poor quality and morale of some of the many non-German troops employed by the Wehrmacht on the Normandy beaches – Ukrainians, Cossacks and the like – but it still does not explain the German defeat, nor does it explain how close the Americans came to complete disaster on one beach.

What does seem clear though, is that had the German Navy's own early warning system of Sicherungsboote, or patrol vessels, been better organised; had the still considerable number of U-boats on Kriegsmarine strength, to say nothing of the twenty-two immediately available S-boats on that morning, been properly employed on the day, then Allied naval losses would have been far more grievous than they were. If ever there was an occasion where an effective coastal defence at sea might have had a key bearing on events, then this was it. Had naval units still available to the Germans been properly used and had the Luftwaffe not withdrawn some 150 fighters from proximity to the immediate area of the landings, aircraft which could have at least contested Allied air superiority, then D-Day's outcome might have been very different. Yet, with hindsight, there is still little doubt that the Allies would have pressed on regardless of the casualties – unless these had been so terrible that withdrawal was safer than battling on. Given that the Allies had prepared enormous reserves of men and material to launch their second front, it is hard to even consider how the venture would have been completely abandoned, though a German defensive success on D-Day would surely have further delayed the eventual Allied victory.

1 Daniel Harris, *Warship 1992*, op.cit.

2 Francois Kersaudy, *Norway 1940* (London, 1991), pp10–12 for Norwegian naval 'preparations', such as they were.

3 Johan Waage, *The Narvik Campaign* (London, 1965), pp55–65 for the engagements between the invaders and *Eidsvold* and *Norge*.

4 The considerable notional strength of the Norwegian coastal defences at several key locations – with the critical exception of Narvik – is recorded in *Der Zweite Weltkrieg im Kartenbild – Band 2. Die Besatzung Dänemarks und die Erproberung Norwegen* by Klaus-Jürgen Thies, a volume accessible at, and drawing on documents from, the Militärarchiv in Freiburg. This states (p57) that the Oskarsborg fortress, which accounted for the *Blücher*, had, at Kaholm, one 305mm gun (all the following artillery are guns unless otherwise stated), plus three 280mm and six 57mm. Elsewhere strength was as follows: at Kopaas, three 150mm; Husvik, two 57mm; Haaoe had four 280mm howitzers and ten 120mm, plus a torpedo battery with three 450mm tubes. At Kristiansund (p86), the Odderoen battery had four 240mm howitzers, two 210mm, six 150mm and two 65mm; the Gleodden battery had three 150mm and two 65mm. Bergen (p103) had three 210mm at the 1st battery at Hellen, three 240mm howitzers at the 2nd at Sandviken, while the 3rd battery at Kvarven had three 210mm, three 240mm howitzers, and one torpedo battery. At Trondheim (p107), the Brettingnes battery had two 210mm, three 150mm and two 65mm, the Hysnes battery had two 210mm, two 150mm and three 65mm, while the Hambara battery had two 150mm.

5 Cajus Bekker, *Hitler's Naval War* (London, 1974), Chapter 2, 'Norwegian Gamble', pp96–166; see pp101–13 for Bekker's description and assessment of the loss of the *Eidsvold* and *Norge* (pp102–3) and the *Blücher*.

6 J Rohwer and G Hummelchen, *Chronology of the War at Sea 1939–1945: The Naval History of World War Two* (London, 1992 – 2nd Edition), p16. Frank Abelsen's alternative figures, and information, are provided in his authoritative *Marinens fartoyer 1939–1945 og deres skjebne: Norwegian naval ships 1939–1945* (Oslo, 1986). For information on *Eidsvold*, *Norge* and also *Harald Haarfagre* and *Tordenskjold*, see pp14–15 and pp289–90 respectively.

7 The wartime careers of *Ilmarinen* and *Väinämöinen* are taken from Rohwer & Hummelchen, ibid., pp84–5, and *Leijonalippu Merellä*, op.cit., pp53–4 & pp68–70.

8 For background on the conflict, see George Paloczi-Horvath, 'Thailand's War with Vichy France', *History Today*, March 1995, pp32–9. Sources for the Battle of Koh-Chang, all available at the Musée de la Marine, Paris, are: Guy Pellon, *La Victoire Navale de Koh-Chang*, Cols Bleus No 1169, 13 February 1971; Jacques Pordal, *Marine Indochine*, Bibliothéque de la Mer, Amiot-Dumont (Paris 1953), Chapter 2, 'La Victoire de Koh-Chang'; J Billiottet, former Médecin Major on board the aviso *Amiral Charner*, a short unpublished postwar account of the battle.

9 Karl-Heinz Schmeelke and Michael Schmeelke, *German Defensive Batteries & Gun Emplacements on the Normandy Beaches: D-Day June 6 1944* (Atglen, Pennsylvania, 1995).

10 Rohwer and Hummelchen, op.cit., pp280–84 for a detailed account of vessels involved on both sides during D-Day and in the area of the landings up to 30 June 1944.

11 Schmeelke & Schmeelke, op.cit., p18.

CHAPTER 10

Forts and Integrated Coastal Defences to 1945

A BRIEF SURVEY OF shore-based coastal defences between 1850 and 1945 shows that from relatively early on in the age of the shell-firing ironclad, that is from the 1880s, it was understood that the best coastal defences might involve an integrated network comprising not only coast defence ships, but also torpedo boats, minelayers and shore-based guns. What is noteworthy about the entire period though is the way in which certain simple lessons which are hardly taxing to the intellect are never learned.

As the new weapons technologies became more reliable during the nineteenth century, notably the shell gun, new elements of the coastal defence mosaic could be put into position, chiefly the controlled minefield, the shore-based torpedo battery and, somewhat later, maritime attack aircraft, armed with bombs, torpedoes and mines. The success of mine warfare during the Russo-Japanese War and the First World War lent support to the 'jeune école' views of many naval strategists that modest defensive means, properly furnished and organised, could theoretically overturn the seemingly overwhelming strategic advantage possessed by a great naval power. For example, of the eight battleships lost to mines during the First World War, three were lost to a single small minefield laid by a single Turkish minelayer.

The culmination of all these efforts to develop coherent coastal defences was seen during the Second World War, when it became apparent that a defender had to control all the dimensions of combat operations in order to stand a chance of defeating any serious assault on a coast, while the attacker similarly had at least to have the edge at sea and in the air if the first wave of any invasion force was to survive long enough to establish a proper foothold.

These absolute rules of the necessity for the advantage in attack or defence became even more apparent during sundry fights to the death at the water's edge, whether on Omaha beach during D-Day, or at Iwo Jima and many other Pacific islands where the Japanese demonstrated that they really did mean what they said about being willing to lay down their lives for their Emperor. The defender lost tactical control of a battle on those occasions when at least a temporary beachhead could be firmly established in just a day or two, as during Operation Overlord. If, on the other hand, the defender contained the invader on the beachhead, as at Gallipoli, even if he lost the immediate battle, an

enterprise could be made expensive enough to force an eventual evacuation.

The Salerno landing and the succeeding battle showed how the eventual outcome of an amphibious attack could be placed in doubt for weeks, especially when, as on this occasion, a strategic blunder over Italy's political status after its surrender was compounded by a serious tactical error in delaying a shore bombardment. With the lessons of Salerno in mind, the Allies tried another assault at Anzio. But, like Salerno, this proved to be a very good example of how an energetic defence could contain a beachhead, for months in this instance.

Conversely, without air superiority and at least temporary control of the cross-Channel sealanes, there was never any

15in Gun
This 15in gun was installed by the British at the Wanstone battery in Kent. (Tom Hornshaw)

6in Gun
British coastal defence of the First World War included a variety of weapons, including this 6in Mk VII. (Mrs D Russell)

realistic prospect of success for Operation Sealion, the German plan for the invasion of Britain. Where this scheme so singularly failed in its conception was in the inability of the German Army and Navy to resolve their disagreement over whether to land on broad or narrow fronts, but either way was unrealistic without at least local air superiority.

Despite the apparent edge possessed by the properly trained, provisioned and organised attacker, throughout the period under consideration effective integrated coastal defences posed a serious inhibitor to even the best equipped great powers. The lesson of the Dardanelles campaign in particular was that lucky defenders exploiting favourable geographical circumstances could upset many preconceived offensive equations of the amount of force, and the quantity of particular assets, required to achieve given amphibious objectives.

Nineteenth-century Lessons

Lessons in coastal defence of various kinds were provided by several conflicts during the nineteenth century. Long before the advent of the armoured steam-powered warship, the experience of battles before and during the Crimean war, at Sinope on Turkey's Black Sea coast and in the Baltic, the necessity of an integrated coastal defence was apparent.

At Sinope in November 1853 at the outset of the conflict over Russia's demand for right of protection over the Sultan's Christian Orthodox subjects, a Turkish squadron of ten frigates and corvettes found itself cut off by a marauding Russian force of six ships-of-the-line and two frigates. The 'battle' was a slaughter, lasting some two hours in which the wooden Turkish vessels were shattered by the Russian warships' spherical explosive shells, after which the Russian squadron set about the destruction of Sinope harbour and its fortifications. There were at least nine separate batteries of Turkish coastal guns at Sinope, but these seem to have had no effect on the outcome of this violent encounter, which was to spark the British and French decision to aid Turkey, war being declared on Russia in March 1854.

The most important lesson of this one-sided battle for coastal defence was the need for vigilance: one does not leave a fleet at anchor waiting for the enemy to suddenly arrive. Surprisingly, that lesson, the need for pickets, was still not learned when, almost a century later, an outnumbered and outclassed Vichy French squadron surprised and destroyed a Thai fleet at Koh-Chang. However, the lesson was not lost on the British, who in 1863 constructed forts in the sea off Portsmouth. These circular constructions were armed with no less than twenty-five 10 in (254mm) and twenty-four 12.5 in (317.5mm) rifled muzzle-loaders in two tiers. Complimentary shore-based defences, the Portsdown Forts, were given the nickname 'Palmerston's Follies' after the Prime Minister of the day. These forts could engage landward, as well as seaward threats, and the former feature earned these forts some uninformed criticism.[1]

The relevance of the Crimean War to this study is two-fold. From the damage caused to *Albion* by shore-based guns at the outset of the bombardment of Sevastopol, to the British interruption of Russia's supply network in and around the Sea of Azov, the command of the littoral was shown to depend on a meaningful defence against explosive shells, and thus was born the idea of the French and British floating batteries. They showed, as at Kinburn in the case of the first three French floating batteries (*Dévastation*, *Lave* and *Tonnant*), that coastal offensive action against a determined defender was feasible, even when the shore-based guns were firing on the floating batteries at practically point-blank range. It should be pointed out though that the Sevastopol fortress, re-equipped with shell-firing guns, gave a particularly good account of itself in October 1854, the fortress only falling to the Allies in September 1855 after a landward assault.

At the Sveaborg fortress in Russian-occupied Finland in August 1855, the Allied fleets engaged the position in a manner which was to become *de rigeur* for the next century and a half: they started the engagement with a sweep for mines for the first time in warfare. The subsequent engagement between the attackers and defenders, conducted at a range of around 2,000m (2,187 yards), resulted in the destruction of twenty-three Russian ships. There was of course a lesson in reverse to be learned from all this, one which was not lost on the classic coast defence navies of the latter half of the nineteenth century.

By the 1860s, the shell-firing ironclad was a reality, as the American Civil War showed, with coastal offence and defence forming a major element of the conflict between the Union and the Confederacy. This was centred upon the Union's efforts to blockade the Confederacy, preparatory to land battles in which the rebels' strength could be seriously put to the test against an emergent industrial superpower. The first coastal defence engagement of the war, the Confederate attack on Fort Sumter in Charleston Harbour in South Carolina, was an attack on a Union enclave in Confederate-controlled territory in which the fort's garrison of eighty-four men, with rations for only a few days, stood little chance. Attempts to relieve the garrison were beaten off and the fort was bombarded by fifty guns from 12 April 1861 until its surrender two days later. The obvious twentieth-century parallel is with Singapore, attacked from landward by the Japanese.

Certainly, the most significant coastal defence engagement of the war was the Battle of Mobile Bay in August 1864 in which Admiral Farragut succeeded in not only capturing four Confederate warships during the battle itself, but also in capturing soon after the two key Confederate fortresses at Fort Gaines and Fort Morgan which guarded

the entrance to Mobile Bay. Farragut's success, which involved four new Union monitors (*Chickasaw, Manhattan, Winnebago* and *Tecumseh*) plus fourteen other warships, had come about despite the formidable threat of 'torpedoes' (mines), particularly those near Fort Morgan. *Tecumseh* fell victim to one of the new 'infernal machines'.

Eighteen years later, at Alexandria in Egypt during the conflict with Arabi Pasha, the British provided another object lesson in the defender's need to prevent, if possible, a bombarding fleet from getting close enough to tackle a fort head on. At Sevastopol, the issue was decided by a landward attack, but at Alexandria, as at Sinope, the recently strengthened defences of the nine forts and four independent batteries proved to be no match for the assault. The eight battleships and several gunboats of Admiral Sir Frederick Seymour's fleet reduced the Egyptian defences,

firstly at a range of about two miles, and then at a closer range as the defenders' fire abated, with landing parties finally being sent in to demolish any surviving guns, which by then had been abandoned. The Egyptians had failed to provide proper infantry support to prevent just such an eventuality.[2]

In the following decade's Sino-Japanese War, the risk of close-range assault on important harbours did not encourage the Chinese to be more careful with their defensive preparations at Wei-hai-Wei. Here, the lack of rapid-fire medium calibre shore-based guns and torpedo nets enabled Japanese torpedo boats to close in and torpedo the Chinese Navy's Vulkan-built flagship, the armoured turret ship *Ting Yuen*, on 5 February 1895. The vessel sank in the shallows the next day. The same conflict was notable for the Japanese use, in the Battle of the Yalu Sea, of their coast defence

Attack on Sidon
An indication of the threat of close bombardment came with Commodore Charles Napier's attack on Sidon (Acre) in the Levant in 1840. Seen here are, from the left, Gorgon, Thunderer, *a Turkish 20-gun corvette, the Austrian corvette* Guerriera, Wasp *and* Stromboli *(GPH Collection)*

*Bombardment of Odessa
The explosion of the
Imperial Russian mole
during the bombardment of
Odessa by British and
French warships on 22
April 1854 concentrated
minds on the issues
involved in coastal defence
and offence in the mid-
nineteenth century.
Bombardment vessels
needed to be capable of
receiving as well as giving
punishment. Forts needed
to be better protected
against a close-range
adversary (GPH
Collection)*

ships *Matsushima*, *Itsukushima* and *Hashidate*, unusual vessels armed with a single 12.6in (320mm) 38cal which, contrary to popular Japanese opinion at the time, failed to strike any Chinese vessels during the battle because of the main armament's malfunctions and slow rate of fire.[3]

The Spanish-American War of 1898 and the Battles of Santiago and Manila Bay provided further eternal lessons for the discipline of coast defence. In the former case, the lesson was simple. Do not let your fleet to be bottled up behind a narrow harbour entrance, allowing your enemy to concentrate his forces on the harbour's shore-based defences. In this case, the four armoured cruisers and other vessels of Spain's Admiral Pascual Cervera had slipped past American patrols to enter Santiago, which the US Navy's Admiral William Sampson then proceeded to blockade by 1 June. A failed American attempt to block the channel to the harbour with the collier *Merrimac* was followed by a comic opera misunderstanding in which a US Army landing force, instead of capturing Morro Castle and three gun batteries, proceeded to attack Santiago, but without success. But the

blockading force included the battleships *Iowa*, *Indiana*, *Oregon* and *Texas*, plus the armoured cruiser *Brooklyn*.

Cervera was now ordered by the Spanish command in Havana to take his ships out of Santiago and what followed was a disaster for Spain. One by one the four armoured cruisers were ravaged and forced to run aground, while two destroyers were also sunk, none of these vessels being able to manoeuvre properly for firing positions. In any case, the Spanish vessels, armed with guns ranging from 11in (279mm) to 8in (203mm), were outgunned by the American vessels' 12in (305mm) and 13in (330mm) guns.

In the Battle of Manila Bay, the Spanish coastal guns failed to hit Admiral Dewey's American ships entering the bay, where a substantially inferior Spanish flotilla comprising one cruiser and sundry other craft, some wooden-hulled, was waiting. These were savaged by the Americans' four cruisers and supporting vessels, the interesting point being that the Spanish shore batteries, at Manila, whose fire proved inaccurate, were not to be shrugged off. These comprised, four 240mm (9.4in), four 150mm (5.9in), four

140mm (5.5in) and two 120mm (4.7in), and should by rights have inflicted more damage.

Twentieth Century – The Same Lessons

The Russo-Japanese War opened with another Japanese surprise attack. Plainly the Russians had digested the example of Wei-hei-Wei. The strike on Port Arthur on 8 February 1904 was spectacular in intent, but failed to do much damage, causing only reparable harm to two battleships and a cruiser. But here the Russians missed an opportunity to take their fleet out to engage the Japanese, who tried and failed to sink blockships on 23 February. Again the Russians failed to take the initiative until the appointment of a new commander, Admiral Makarov, who briefly raised morale before being killed when his flagship *Petropavlovsk* was sunk by a Japanese mine on an sortie from Port Arthur in April.

This was the first capital ship loss to a mine in this war, showing that mines now had offensive as well as defensive uses, though in the latter application the Russians also proved adept, sinking the Japanese battleships *Hatsuse* and *Yashima*. The subsequent Japanese victories at the Battle of the Yellow Sea and the Battle of Tsushima, while momentous, had little impact on coast defence thinking, except that the Russian use of their coast defence ships of the *Admiral Ushakov* class at Tsushima and their resultant fate probably persuaded many countries not to commit such vessels to a battle alongside larger and more sophisticated brethren, not that these made much difference to the Russians.

But the abiding lesson of this conflict was how mines can benefit the weaker protagonist. In the First World War, the Gallipoli campaign provided a textbook example not only of shore-based coastal defence and shallow-water mine warfare, but also of how not to conduct a coastal bombardment.

The British had been involved in many such actions in the nineteenth century, but, after Fisher's appointment in 1904 as First Sea Lord, little attention was paid to the mechanics of a modern bombardment. The result was that the 15in-armed superdreadnought *Queen Elizabeth* had only armour piercing shells to engage the Turkish defences at Gallipoli in March 1915, but not the high explosive shells which were actually required. *Queen Elizabeth* was supported by various British and French pre-dreadnoughts, whose guns proved adequate for the task, but *Queen Elizabeth*'s guns had also not been calibrated well enough to ensure success against the Turks, as shown on 5 March in the duel with the five 14in (355mm) and thirteen 9.4in (240mm) guns covering the Narrows.[4] The rate of fire was slow and spotting by the attendant seaplanes was poor. On 18 March, *Queen Elizabeth* was firing from a range of 14–17,000 yards (1,280–1,554m), but was yet hit by five 5.9in (150mm) shells

and only managed to take out one shore-based gun. In this engagement, the so-called 'big push', the French battleship *Bouvet* was the first victim of a tiny Turkish minefield of just twenty mines laid by the minelayer *Nusret*, the other victims being the battleships *Inflexible* and *Irresistable*. The main Turkish minefields and intermediate shore batteries remained intact after this costly assault.

Though *Queen Elizabeth* drove off the Turkish capital ships *Torgud Reis* and *Barbaros Hayreddin* on 26 April, the day after both of the latter had begun shelling the British landing, the overall lesson of Gallipoli was that if mines cannot be swept because the minesweepers cannot be afforded protection, and if bombarding ships cannot close to accurately strike coastal guns, then the outcome can be a stalemate in which other means need to be found to resolve the issue. In this case, troops were landed for a landward assault, but Turkish resistance ground the Allies down until a furore over the campaign's conduct obliged the Allies to withdraw after a terrible, and ultimately pointless sacrifice. In a later age, air power would probably have decided the issue one way or another at an earlier stage, but Gallipoli remains an impressive example of what integrated fixed coastal defences and warships can achieve against a theoretically superior opponent.

The Second World War

The bloodiest conflict in human history opened with a coastal defence engagement, when the old pre-dreadnought German battleship *Schleswig-Holstein* fired on the Polish fortress of Westerplatte on the Hel peninsula on 1 September 1939. An attack by a naval assault company was beaten off on that day and despite further naval, air and land attacks, the fort held out until the very end of the Polish campaign, the garrison of the Hel fortress surrendering on 1 October. During the campaign, a Polish destroyer, a minelayer and shore-based 5.9in (150mm) guns beat off an attack by, *inter alia*, the destroyer *Leberecht Maas*. Polish vessels in the area which did not escape were eventually sunk or captured. Yet as late as 12 September, three Polish minesweepers managed to lay a minefield south of Hel, and on the same day the German old minesweeper *Otto Braun* was hit by Hel's artillery.

The reason for mentioning this particular one-sided episode is that, compared to other hopeless engagements such as those in the Spanish-American War, the Poles held out for what was, with hindsight, a surprisingly long time, tying up German troops, ships and aircraft which could have been used elsewhere. Similarly, later in the same war, the Germans delivered the same lesson to the Allies, holding out at some French ports for months after the rest of the German Army had been swept from the hinterland. In itself, the decision to hold out seemed pointless, but there is no question that it tied up Allied forces which could have been used elsewhere. In any case, as Tobruk showed, some coastal fortresses and their landward defences, can change hands more than once in the same war.

The Norwegian campaign, with the brave fight at Narvik by the Norwegian coast defence ships *Eidsvold* and *Norge* and the lamentable failure to properly provision many forts, is described in its full context in Chapter 9, but again some general points can be made. The fixed coast defences, when manned and properly provisioned, were very dangerous. Even though Norwegian plans entailed the use of rapidly called-out reservists to man the forts, the loss of the German cruiser *Blücher* to Norwegian defences in Oslo fjord demonstrated that despite being outnumbered on land and at sea, the Norwegian fortresses could have caused far worse damage to the invader.

Everything went right in the Oslo fjord on the night of 8–9 April 1940, from the watchfulness of the Norwegian minelayer *Olaf Tryggversson* noticing the German ships and opening fire forthwith, to the alertness of the 11in (280mm Krupp) gunners at the Oscarsborg fortress, who proceeded to fire on the *Blücher*, eventually sinking her. The cruiser *Lutzow* was forced to retire, the light cruiser *Emden* was struck and the torpedo boat *Albatros* was badly damaged. Oslo fell later in the day, but to airborne troops, and only later did German troops land from the sea. Norway has learned the lessons from the previous conflict and a very impressive coastal defence system has been in place in that country for some fifty years now.

Operation Sealion, the German plan to invade Britain in 1940, was singularly ill-conceived in a number of respects and had little chance of success without air superiority, since the German Navy which was to cover the landing force had suffered grievously in the Norwegian campaign and the German Army was not only exhausted after the French campaign, but had absolutely no experience of the kind of amphibious assault proposed. In any case, it is not generally appreciated that besides a large navy, Britain had also amassed a considerable coastal defence force, in the shape of 153 batteries of coastal artillery by the second half of 1940.[5]

Across on the other side of the world, the fortress was a major element in the defensive plans laid by both the Americans and the British. Thus the Americans took the coastal defence of key points in the Philippines seriously and accordingly several fortresses were constructed in Manila Bay. Corregidor was the largest, with fifty-six mortars and guns, some on 'disappearing' mountings. The most remarkable fort in the Philippines was Fort Drum, originally El Fraile Island, which had been completely reconstructed with tunnels, accommodation and magazines, a 25–36ft (7.5–11m) thick concrete shell, and four 14in (355mm) guns in two twin turrets. The island that became more of a man-made structure and the other forts held out against the Japanese until May 1942, providing further examples of how forts can hold out while contiguous territory is lost.

At Singapore, the British strengthened a naval base, but the guns there could not affect the course of the campaign across the straits in Malaya, and this doomed the base. In any case, certainly in the instance of some of the 9.2in (233.6mm) guns at Singapore, there were only thirty rounds for each gun available to engage the Japanese. Few meaningful lessons therefore can be learned either from the fate of Singapore or the American actions in the Philippines, other than the general point about continued resistance holding up ships and troops which could be used elsewhere.

At Salerno and Anzio, at Guadalcanal and elsewhere in the Pacific, and finally in Operation Overlord, D-Day, the Allies demonstrated a greater mastery of amphibious warfare than ever shown before. Specially-designed vessels for such landings in the form of landing craft, combined with a coherent understanding of the absolute necessity of obtaining co-ordinated tactical control of the battle on land, sea and in the air, ensured eventual success.

But at Anzio in Italy in 1944, the Allies also learned that a vigorous defender with a clear-cut objective, in this case one of containing, rather than eliminating, a beachhead, could achieve impressive results, even without the benefit of air superiority. The Japanese showed even greater determination in their fanatic defence of numerous islands in the Pacific. On D-Day at Omaha beach, the price of Allied errors in navigation was a couple of thousand casualties in one day and the risking of one of the Allied beachheads and, therefore, the whole operation.

But in all these operations, where the defender could not contest control of every dimensions of an operation, then the medium term outcome would be grim. It would take new technologies to upset the new absolute rules of coastal defence in which the advantage seemingly always lies with the attacker.

1 Martin Brice, *Forts and Fortresses* (London & Oxford, 1990), p143.

2 Richard Natkiel & Antony Preston, *Atlas of Maritime History* (London, 1986), p125.

3 Jiro Itani, Hans Lengerer, Tomoko Rehm-Takahara 'Sankeikan: Japan's Coast Defence Ships of the *Matsushima* Class', *Warship 1990* (London, 1990), pp51–3.

4 John Campbell, *Warship Monograph 2, Queen Elizabeth Class* (London, 1972), 50pp.

5 Peter Schenk, *Sea Lion – The German Invasion of England 1940* (London, 1990), p146ff.

CHAPTER 11

Design Considerations

AN EXAMINATION OF SOME of the most important classic coast defence ships of the period 1860 to 1945 shows that there were certain common characteristics among these vessels, depending on the period. As coast defence ships became the key elements of the fleets of many of the smaller naval powers, the drive to standardise armament calibres and powerplants created some patterns which remained enduring features of many of these countries' fleets.

The requirements were more or less common to most of the countries which operated coast defence ships. These vessels were moreover acquired, with the notable exceptions of France, Russia, Brazil and Argentina, in the context of tight public purses unable to afford true battleships. Moreover these countries, with the above exceptions and one or two others, had no real requirement for an ocean-going battlefleet. They simply required a mobile adjunct to their existing coastal artillery which would be capable of providing some protection to key points along a coastline and take their positions in a coastal defence web also involving destroyers, torpedo boats and minelayers, as well as coastal artillery, controlled minefields and shore-based torpedo batteries.

The basic *modus operandi* of most of the organised coast defence fleets, in which coast defence ships formed part of a coherent whole and were not simply acquired for prestige, involved the facility to drive away hostile fleets, whether cruisers, especially armoured cruisers, or smaller vessels. The hope was that anything heavier which might attempt to mount a blockade could be enticed by the coast defence ships inside an organised defensive perimeter in which battleships could be engaged by destroyers and torpedo boats.

This was certainly the *modus operandi* of the Swedish coast defence battleships until the middle of the Second World War, with the objective being to destroy an enemy inside coastal waters. Although the strategy was fundamentally defensive, part of its operation did involve a form of 'seduction' with offensive intent. The *Sverige* class' operational tactical deployment was thence turned to more explicit open-sea deterrence and, if necessary, engagement of an enemy. Hence Sweden's, Denmark's and the Netherlands' long term deployment in earlier decades of low freeboard monitors, which were never considered likely to be used outside inshore waters. But for Norway's four coast defence ships of the *Haarfarge* and *Norge* classes, the

COAST DEFENCE FAMILY TREE

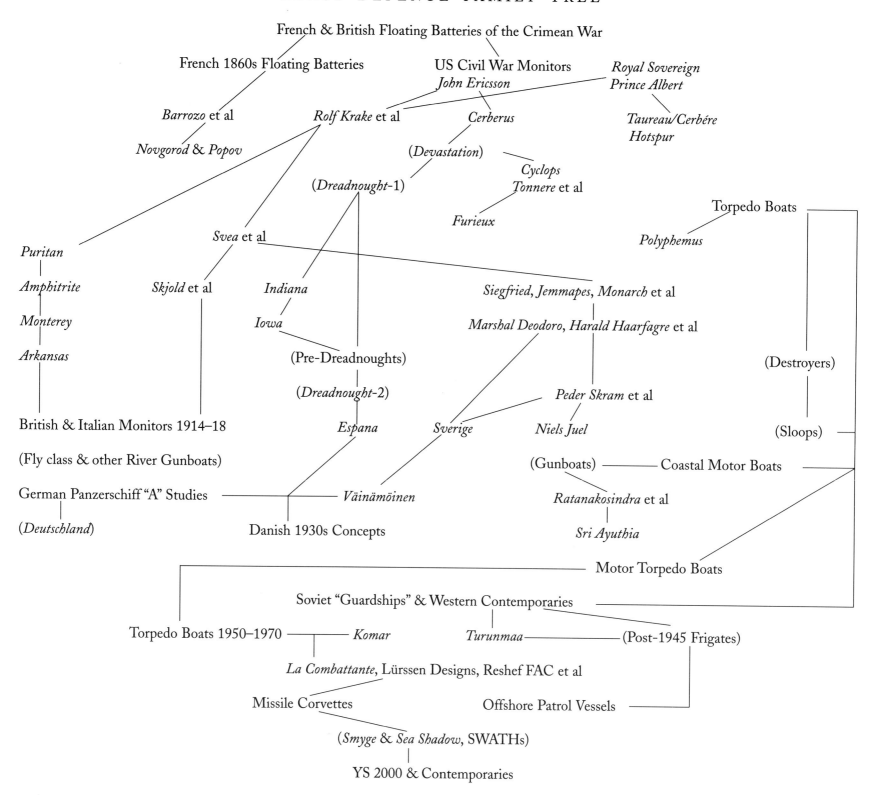

(Note: not included are minelayers, specialised secondary vessels (e.g. destroyers), and vessels reassigned to coast defence)

Polyphemus
The torpedo ram
Polyphemus *was an oddity, more suited to coastal defence than the other roles for which she was touted. The tactics were childish (CMP)*

requirement to provide a localised force multiplier, to use the current vogueish term, meant an ability to shift from one key harbour to another along Norway's 1,000-mile coastline. This explained why both of the aged *Norge* class vessels found themselves at Narvik in April 1940.

An examination of how different types of coast defence ship influenced the development of others, or provoked countermeasures even, explains why the 'family tree' of the coast defence ship until the 1940s had more healthy branches growing from others, than solitary wasted twigs which were doomed to wither and die. That said, there were several embarrassing cul-de-sacs in coast defence ship development. For example, the very low freeboard monitor did have its very obvious limitations outside calm or protected waters, as did rams where the ram was the coast

defence vessel's primary weapon. Meanwhile Russia's circular ironclads *Novgorod* and *Popov* were not exactly pointers to a profitable way forward either.

After *Dreadnought*, comparatively few new coast defence ships were built, although some very interesting designs were produced, notably in Germany, Finland and Denmark. The First World War saw old pre-dreadnoughts join the ranks of the coast defence ships, just as older ironclads of the previous century had done in their twilight years. But the Second World War saw several coast defence ships put to uses for which they had never been intended, for example as mobile anti-aircraft batteries in the case of a number of vessels captured by the Germans.

These developments completed the intriguing story of the classic gun-armed coast defence ship, but its genealogy was not to be brutally cut off at this point, it was simply joined with another, completely different line of development, which started with the torpedo boats of the 1880s and, via the coastal motor torpedo boats of the twentieth century, led to the modern fast attack missile boat and its latest and larger derivative, the modern missile corvette able to operate not only the weapons, but also the complex C³I systems essential for sustained operations in a dense threat environment.

What was the logic behind the chosen armament and levels of armour protection of coast defence ships at different moments during the type's development? How long did they generally take to build and what economies of scale did they offer?

To take the last point, the issue of cost, first: the *Monitor* and the succeeding multiple turret monitors of the American Civil War cost several hundred thousand dollars apiece, $275,000 in the case of *Monitor*. In the same year as Hampton Roads, Napier laid down the first Coles turret ship, the Danish coast defence ship *Rolf Krake*, which was completed at a cost of £74,000. But only a couple of years later, the US monitors *Dictator* and *Puritan* were together estimated to have cost $2.3 million. This high cost should however be set in context against the enormous sum for the period of $62 million spent by the Union on 121 ships 'which were to be rated as useless within a few years'.[1]

Less than ten years later, the Danish coast defence monitor *Gorm* cost £104,000 (very roughly $468–494,000 according to the exchange rate based on the gold standard, which the US joined in the 1870s; earlier sterling/dollar exchange rates are hard to quantify accurately). By early the following century though, the cost differential between capital ships and coast defence ships was narrowing. In 1905 *Dreadnought* had cost around £7 million and less than a decade later the Swedish coast defence battleship *Sverige* cost almost the same amount, £6.725 million or $33.515 million. *Sverige*'s later sisters, *Drottning Victoria* and *Gustav V*, cost a little more at £7.101 million or $35.505 million each.

Given that most coast defence ships' declared purpose was to deter an approach by hostile warships, and given also that economy in armament was invariably also a design objective, the great majority of purpose-designed coast defence ships, monitors included, which were built between 1860 and 1940 carried their main armament in either one or two turrets, each carrying either one or two pieces of ordnance. In the case of central battery or casemate-armour ships, armament was arranged in multiple single guns in batteries on either side of the vessel or, in the case of some ships like the converted Confederate ironclad *Virginia*, in all-round batteries which included both forward and aft-facing armament. In numerous cases, casemated and central battery ships had more gun ports than guns.

There are no instances of turret or barbette coast defence ships armed with more than two guns per turret or barbette,

although in the case of a few vessels there were more than two turrets, as, for instance, in the case of *Royal Sovereign*, on which four turrets carried five 10.5in (279mm), one twin and three singles. In addition, there were some oddities like Denmark's *Skjold* of 1896, which carried just a single main 240mm (9.4in) gun and three single secondary 120mm (4.7in) guns in individual turrets aft arranged in a stern-facing triangle.

The Danes made something of a speciality of curious armament layouts, as shown by *Niels Juel* in its later years, when its primary armament, as completed, of ten 150mm (5.9in) was installed in ten separate shields, the pairs forward and aft being mounted beside one another. In fairness, it should be said that this was a case of *force majeure* because the originally specified armament could not be delivered because of the First World War.

By the twentieth century, after the experiments with casemates and central batteries had been discarded, the general layout of all coast defence ships became more standard. Two single or twin-gun turrets mounted fore and aft, secondary armament either installed at belt level or in turrets in 'B' and 'X' positions or either side amidships or at the quarters, with tertiary light and anti-aircraft armament installed, often without much thought as to arcs of fire, in such spaces as were available.

That said, several exceptions stand out. Surely the classic coast defence ship of the twentieth century, in terms of its simplicity and logic, was the IvS-designed *Väinämöinen* class: four 254mm (10in) in twin turrets fore and aft, eight 105mm (4.1in) AA in twin shields in B and X positions and also either side amidships, with tertiary 40mm and 20mm AA armament dotted around the vessel; this last element of the armament seems to have been added almost as an afterthought. All this was packed into a 3,900 ton hull.

A common denominator of many early coast defence ships was low, and sometimes very low, freeboards, which obviously severely affected seakeeping. This was usually the case with monitors, the freeboard of *Monitor* itself being just 1ft 2in (355.6mm) when fully laden. Without turret or stores, it was just 3in (76mm) in the case of the *Casco* class (1ft 3in [381mm] had been the intention). But the concomitant characteristic of shallow draught enabled monitors to undertake offensive tasks, as demonstrated by the British coastal offence monitors of the First World War. Some ideas outlived their usefulness, such as France's floating batteries of the *Palestro*, *Arrogante* and *Embuscade* classes, while others, like the smaller coast defence ships which are more properly described as armoured gunboats (ranging from the German *Wespe* to the Thai *Ratanakosindra* classes), have survived to this day, albeit in significantly modernised form, providing a link on the family tree of coast defence ships with modern offshore patrol vessels.

In what had been described as a 'penetrating comment' on the monitors, Alexander C Brown, writing in the (US)

Society of Naval Architects and Marine Engineers' journal *Historical Transactions*, pointed out that:

Monitors found their final employment as submarine tenders in World War One (the *Arkansas* class) for which their low freeboard hulls made them well suited. It is significant to note, however, that in this humble capacity they were ministering to the needs of that type of craft which had logically replaced them for as

initially envisaged monitors were designed to combine heavy striking power with concealment and the presentation of a negligible target area.[2]

Certainly in the case of some monitors, like the *Casco* class, a very low silhouette was an original design objective, though it was achieved at a great cost in speed and overall capability. But in general, most early monitor coast defence ships in the fleets of countries which made the discipline

Firing trials against Glatton
The firing trials against Glatton in July 1872 in Portland Roads exposed this early breastwork monitor to some realistic punishment, as recorded at the time in the Illustrated London News (GPH Collection)

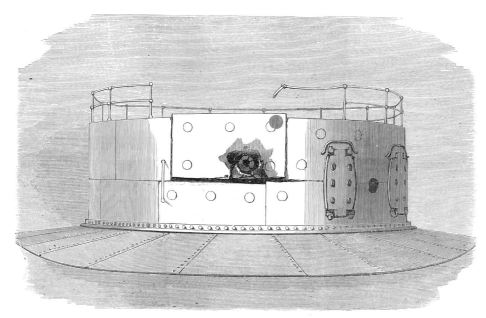

THE TURRET OF H.M.S. GLATTON AFTER THE FIRST SHOT THAT STRUCK.

THE TURRET OF H.M.S. GLATTON: EFFECT OF THE LAST SHOT.

Impact of trials against
Glatton
Depictions of the first and last shots against
Glatton's *turret (which had 12–14in protection), during the firing trials in July 1872, from the* Illustrated London News *(GPH Collection)*

203mm (8in) turrets, which were sufficient to contend with Sweden's contemporary *Svea* class, with its 254mm (10in) 32cal guns. It was simply unfortunate that this Russian trio was sent east to engage Admiral Togo's fleet at Tsushima instead.

The later *Sverige* class, regarded by many as the benchmark for twentieth-century coast defence ships, disposed of 200–150mm (7.9–5.9in) belts, with 200–100mm (7.9–3.9in) for the turrets, which, combined with the main armament of four 280mm (11.1in) was sufficient to contend with contemporary armoured cruisers, though probably not with Russia's *Gangut* class battleships. The *Sverige*s together provided just one of many examples of an incomplete class: originally four vessels had been intended but these could not be completed as neither the funds nor the materials were available.

Choices of main armament were problematical for many coast defence navies. Some, like the Swedes, elected to standardise before *Dreadnought* on a single heavy, though not a battleship-equivalent calibre: in this case 8.3in 44cal. Curiously the Dutch-designed Finnish coast defence ships had four modern Bofors 254mm 45cals, rather than the 280mm twins made by the same company for the *Sverige* class. Whether the Swedes were simply not willing to export a weapon equalling that on its own vessels, or whether the Finns simply decided that the 254mm twin was a more modern, and better mounting, is unclear. In any event, these 254mm were not the equal of the nearest and most likely capital ship adversary, the *Ganguts*, although they were superior to anything else in the Soviet Baltic Fleet.

The smaller coast defence powers also decided on lower calibres as the main armament of their coast defence battleships at times when substantially more powerful armaments were available. The Norwegian Navy's choice of 208mm (8.2in) 44cal for their *Harald Haarfagre* and *Norge* class of 1897 and 1900 respectively are one example, the Dutch choice of 240mm (9.4in) for the *Koningen Regentes* and succeeding coastal battleships is another. In both cases, the weapons chosen were installed because of a combination of cost considerations and a theory that a probable opponent might be an armoured cruiser, though it is hard to penetrate the Norwegian rationale in this regard. Certainly the Dutch had a good case for relying on a capability to ward off armoured cruisers, especially in Far Eastern waters, with the assumption that a serious threat might be dealt with by a more powerful ally such as Britain.

Some countries were more straightforward than others in their definitions of precisely how they regarded their own ships and capabilities. Thus whereas the Swedes were content for their later coast defence ships to be classified as 'battleships', the Danes demonstrated an increasing awareness of the psychological benefits of accuracy. Thus they more often than not used the terms 'armoured ship' ('Panserskibe') or 'armoured coast defence ship' ('Pansrede

their speciality were conceived with low silhouettes the intention.

Armour protection from the early US monitors' typical 3–6in (76–152mm) side armour and 10–11in (254–280mm) for the turrets was as good as anything in service elsewhere in the world at the time, but by 1870, when the *Cerberus* class coast defence monitors had been completed in Britain, up-armouring (to an 8–6in belt) became a characteristic of many successive coast defence classes. Thus by the turn of the century, Russia's unlucky *Admiral Ushakov* class coast defence battleships had 10–4in (254–101mm) belts and

Jacob van Heemskerck
A further view of the Dutch 1908-vintage coast defence ship Jacob van Heemskerck *shows well how some such vessels had much more respectable freeboards, 5.69m in this case at its greatest. She was also capable of long deployments, as her service in the East Indies demonstrated (Deanne Bergin – GPH Collection)*

Norwegian missile Boat
The coast defence ship of the 1970s–80s was often a very small, nimble craft, like Terne, *a* Hauk *class missile/torpedo boat of 1979 vintage, seen firing a Penguin SSM (GPH Collection)*

Kystforsvarsskibe') or simply, as in the case of the low-freeboard vessel *Gorm*, 'armoured battery' ('panserbatteriet'). The Danes never called their vessels battleships and in 1912 the system of nomenclature was simplified further to include the terms coast defence ship ('Kystforsvarsskibe') or even more simply, 'Defensionsskibe'.[3] Similarly, the Finns described their two ships simply as 'Panssarilaivat' or 'armoured ships', taking a leaf out of the Germans' book and their 'Panzerschiffe' of the somewhat more capable *Deutschland* class. But probably there is no equal, in its precision of nomenclature, to the US Navy's description of the *Indiana* class as 'seagoing coastline battleships'.

If most coast defence ships were at least armoured and equipped to fend off or at least contest attacks by armoured cruisers or smaller corsairs, some failed to meet any definition of an acceptable expenditure by a national exchequer. The aforementioned *Niels Juel*, which was too slow and poorly armed to contest anything with anyone is one example, and the Russian circular ironclads *Novgorod* and *Popov* are others.

But what could not be foreseen was that captured coast defence ships should be put to such effective use by the Germans as anti-aircraft ships during the Second World War and, equally, that so many former first-rank predreadnought battleships be reassigned to coastal defence shortly before and during the First World War. Thus did vessels which would otherwise have gone to the breakers earn new leases of life.

Simplicity of superstructure design was another distinguishing feature of most coast defence ships. Most such vessels in the nineteenth century had very basic military masts and monitors had fairly minimal scantling, ships' boats and the like, though some early monitors and other coast defence turret ships had hurricane decks installed.

Comparatively few coast defence ships had extensive pagoda-style conning towers, though the refitted *Sverige*s are an obvious exception.

The characteristics of modern coast defence vessels, missile boats, corvettes and the like are described in Chapter 12, but they all share with their earlier forebears the characteristics of compactness and, until recently, essential simplicity. The present trend towards larger coast defence missile corvettes replacing missile boats has been driven by electronics, rather than weapons, though the requirement for longer range air defence missiles on these vessels is a relatively new development.

It remains surprising that doctrinal attitudes towards coastal defence have not caught up with modern technology, even though coastal offence preoccupations are taking centre-stage with the US Navy. Few medium-sized navies today openly admit that coast defence is their primary mission, yet for all but a handful of fleets, coastal and near-coastal operations, or operations in concert with an ally, are the only aspirations open to them, combined with the testing responsibility of Extended Economic Zone protection. In some cases, coastal defence as a preoccupation is even seen as a doctrinal threat to the procurement of more powerful, ocean-going warships, hence the modern Royal Navy's disinclination to invest in corvettes.

But nonetheless, as the family tree of coast defence ships shows, there is a direct link between the monitors of the 1860s onward and the missile boats and corvettes of the 1990s which inherit an illustrious tradition which continues to show great promise.

1 Gibbons, op.cit., p45.

2 *Monitors of the US Navy*, op.cit., p42.

3 Steensen, op.cit., p199.

CHAPTER 12

Phoenix from the Ashes – Modern Coast Defence Ships

THE APPARENT LESSON OF the success of D-Day, notwithstanding the US Army's sufferings on 'bloody Omaha' beach, was that a determined attacker with sufficient resources could overwhelm any coastal defence system.

Rommel had demanded millions of mines and anti-invasion obstacles and many of these were indeed laid. The one thing he could not know – although he was always privately worried about Normandy – was where the Allies would strike. Hence he was obliged to spread his forces comparatively thinly and, to add insult to injury, he was not allowed control of the German Army's immediately available armoured reserve. For several crucial hours on D-Day this was held back, removing any real chance of defeating the Allies on or close to the beaches.

That the Germans still managed to give the Allies a very hard time on Omaha, and during the battles north of Caen, and later also at the Falaise gap, shows that had Rommel been given complete control of all the available forces, the outcome of D-Day might have been very different, even with the hindrance of the Luftwaffe being unable to seriously contest Allied air superiority. It should be recalled that the Germans did manage to hold out until the very end of the war in several French coastal fastnesses.

The island-hopping campaign of the Pacific war, in which the Japanese were even more determined to hold on to the last, proved that coast defence is also as dependent on the quality and even fanaticism of the defender as it is on the material available to defend the coast in question. The simple tunnel networks of the defenders at places like Iwo Jima, which even the heaviest pre-landing bombardments could not destroy, lengthened many an island campaign by weeks or months. But despite the ferocity of the Japanese defence, the Pacific war demonstrated that an attacker with the magic combination of air and naval superiority, and sufficient soldiery to commit to the assault, could eventually overcome the most dogged resistance.

But the first line of defence, at sea, was wholly inadequate in both Normandy and in the Pacific. In the case of Operation Overlord, the most serious warship loss which the motley collection of large torpedo boats, S-boats and U-boats of the Kriegsmarine could inflict on the Allies was the sinking of a single Norwegian destroyer.

After the Second World War, coast defence went into an apparently irreversible decline for several years. Air power properly deployed, together with command of the sea, could surely ensure that there would no repeats of the fiasco at Gallipoli. That copious air and sea power did not prevent the near disasters at Omaha and Iwo Jima was forgotten.

Some countries though still preserved the integrated coastal defence systems which they felt were their best first line of defence. Although Sweden was the dominant military power in the Baltic for several years after the war, building up a very powerful air force of some 800 aircraft and retaining a strong fleet of fast cruisers of the *Gota Lejon* class and sundry destroyers and two dozen submarines, she did not feel content to abandon her previous preoccupations, although the coast battleships were all disposed of after the war. The Swedish Coastal Artillery remained, with its dense network of guns, controlled minefields, torpedoes and a veritable armada of ramped landing craft to enable units to be moved swiftly around the skerries.

Denmark and Norway too had little to fall back on except some wartime tonnage provided by the British and some captured German vessels. Yet defending their now very exposed coasts against a new threat even more powerful than Germany only reinforced the need for an effective coastal defence, only this time both countries made efforts to get it right.

The sheer quantity of wartime naval tonnage of all types available after the Second World War had the effect of slowing down the pace of naval construction almost everywhere except in the USSR. New classes of large warships commissioned by the West demonstrated some new ideas of how to use warships in the atomic age, but the imperatives driving them were the threats posed by fast snorkel-equipped submarines and jet bombers of the Soviet Navy and Air Force. The abiding reality was that sea power alone could no longer decide the course of most wars (the Falklands conflict being a notable exception), although the naval staffs of all the major powers made assumptions about conflicts which were expected to last a surprisingly long time and planned accordingly.[1]

The lesser powers, especially in Scandinavia, continued to put effort into the development of torpedo boats, which – as long as a war remained conventional – would always pose a credible defensive threat to any adversary which ventured too close. Sweden, Norway and, later, West Germany developed several classes of new torpedo boats which were heavily influenced by the German S-boat designs, as did the Soviet Union and other countries. Also, the development of

Tarantul
This Tarantul *III class missile boat of what was then still the Soviet Black Sea Fleet is seen off Sevastopol on 15 October 1991. The Soviet Union had less than three months to live (Hanny and Leo van Ginderen Collection)*

the wire-guided torpedo provided the torpedo boat with a new lease of life. Vessels like, for example, the Swedish Navy's *Spica* class could lie in wait and despatch an enemy at a considerable range using their wire-guided Tp61 torpedoes. The threat of the torpedo in coastal defence, properly employed, has not diminished with the development of sea-skimming surface-to-surface missiles (SSMs), as they are a low-cost alternative which is far less prone to detection via electronic support measures (ESM) and seduction by electronic countermeasures (ECM).

During the 1950s and 60s, new propulsion systems such as gas turbines and even heavy-calibre guns were proposed or used on some of the major powers' small craft, such as the 4.5in (114mm) Mk1 on the Royal Navy's 'Gay' and 'Dark' class convertible motor torpedo boats (MTBs) or the 3.3in (84mm) CFS 2 gun on the RN's motor gun boat (MGB) *Bold Pioneer*.[2] Meanwhile America's Cuban preoccupations prompted the development of the *Asheville* class patrol craft, armed with a 3in (76mm) 50cal gun, as it was realised that something smaller than a frigate might be needed for engagements with Cuban vessels. But nonetheless these were the exceptions which proved the rule, namely, that the larger powers had little sustained interest in coastal defence.

Sustained is the operative term in Britain's case, because for a time that interest was indeed intense. Britain's *Ford* class seaward defence boats and the MTBs and MGBs of the 1950s were part of a network of fixed and mobile coastal defences primarily aimed at countering Soviet submarines and mines by the use of depth charges, mines and (on just one of the *Ford* class) even the triple-barrelled Squid ahead-throwing anti-submarine (AS) mortar, of which a single-barrelled version was planned for the rest of the class, but never installed. (Squid was, however, installed on the similar Finnish *Ruissalo* class of the late 1950s.)

Although 'existing coast defence guns and mortars were considered ineffective', as Friedman observes, extensive fixed defences were constructed in Britain between 1949 and 1954, including fixed steel obstructions, boom defences and submarine and mine detection equipment.[3]

As for propulsion, the British tested two different propulsion systems on their fast attack craft (FACs) of the 1950s: gas turbines and new lightweight diesels. This work paved the way for a new attitude to the FAC's survivability, as they became progressively more seaworthy and with longer endurance than their wartime forebears. The new British lightweight diesel, the Deltic, powered the Dark class and proved such a success that the US Navy, not having pursued its wartime lead in engines, was obliged to import Deltics for its PTF craft which served in the Vietnam war. Meanwhile the Rolls-Royce RM60A 5,400shp gas turbine was trialled in the steam gunboat *Grey Goose* in 1953, and the operational installation which followed, three Bristol Proteus 3,500shp engines installed in *Brave Borderer* and *Brave Swordsman*, marked a new departure for coastal forces. This in turn led to the export of no less than sixteen derivative craft to Brunei, Denmark, West Germany, Libya and Malaysia, as well as the construction of the RN training 'target' vessels *Cutlass*, *Sabre* and *Scimitar*. These used the same Proteus engines which had been installed in the two 'Brave' class vessels, but uprated to 4,500shp.

As for hulls, the argument in Britain in the early 1950s veered between long, short and medium-length MTBs and designers also fretted about the problems of adequate speed and gun stabilisation, the latter being a problem which has proved surprisingly difficult to tackle on high speed small craft up to this day, although the new US Navy *Cyclone* class patrol boats entering service in the 1990s are fitted with a stabilised weapon system which goes a long way towards solving the problem.

Hull forms were still mostly traditional in the Royal Navy and the US Navy during the immediate post-war period: hard chine or planing MTB hulls which rode the water's surface and thus achieved high speed at the cost of pounding heavily in any kind of sea. The S-boat design which continued to influence many navies had a conventional hull shape which could handle rough seas better, but at a cost in speed. Most current FAC use this more conventional hull design, and the S-boat itself was the basis of the immediate post-war Danish, West German and Norwegian FACs, notably Norway's *Tjeld* class MTBs – all of them diesel-powered. However the Japanese drew on a different inspiration, adopting British hull concepts for their post-war high speed MTBs.

The whole British seaward defence programme of the 1950s depended on mobilisation of very large numbers of vessels. In 1954, this comprised a fleet of eighteen *Ford*s and 104 ex-naval motor launches plus fifty-five trawlers. This would have allowed twenty-seven so-called 'Group 1' ports to be adequately defended after six months' warning and eight key ports given 30 days' notice. (Presumably the USSR would have helpfully neglected to attack during this

October *class*
An Egyptian Navy
variant of the landmark
Komar *class missile boat,*
refitted by Britain's Vosper
Thornycroft, is the
October *class. As refitted*
it carries two twin 30mm
Oerlikon and two Otomat
SSMs (Vosper
Thornycroft)

build-up.) But because this entire seaward defence arrangement 'contributed nothing to Cold War', as Friedman put it, the British government decided in 1956 to concentrate the RN's NATO effort on the Atlantic, effectively sidelining coastal defence of the UK. The decision was confirmed by the 1957 Defence Review.

As an aside, it should be added that worries over seaward defence did not die off before the Royal Navy had displayed its very real concern over the threat to British harbours posed by atomic weapons. The first British nuclear test, in October 1952, was of a 25 kiloton device installed inside the frigate *Plym* which was to demonstrate, among other things, what the effects might be of a nuclear weapon exploding in a harbour. The British even considered the development of their own atomic sea mine, dubbed Cudgel. The idea was to carry Cudgel to Soviet harbours as a side-mounted charge on a midget submarine, which would have itself been towed to Soviet waters by a larger 'mother' submarine. Four such midget X-craft were built in the 1950s and official papers describing Cudgel, released by the Public Record Office, have confirmed that the carriage of this weapon was part of the midget subs' mission.[4] Cudgel, a variant of the 15 kiloton tactical bomb Red Beard, was never built. Ironically, the midget submarines were originally designed to test British defences against similar postulated Soviet craft.

A curious feature of postwar naval development was that despite the clear potential of guided rocketry during the war, so little was done to make more of its use as a tactical offensive weapon. The US and UK expended copious efforts on developing practical surface to air missiles (SAMs), American weapons like Talos and Terrier being somewhat more practical than the British Seaslug. But little was done in these countries or elsewhere (with the exception of Sweden) to develop SSMs for use at sea, although the British did have an idea of using Seaslug as the basis for an offensive weapon – Blue Slug.

It was the Soviet Union which took the logical next step. The USSR saw itself as being very vulnerable to attack by US carrier-based jet bombers armed with nuclear weapons and the development of aircraft like the Douglas Skywarrior justified their concern. Although Stalin had launched a very ambitious naval plan after the war which included cruisers, destroyers and submarines of several classes, the guardship and torpedo boat remained key components of the Soviet naval defensive fabric.

While it would be incorrect to conclude that it was solely the scepticism about conventional warships and technologies displayed by Stalin's eventual successor, Nikita Khruschev, which launched the Soviet Navy into the missile age – serious work began immediately after the war – it was not until the late 1950s that the idea of putting tactical SSMs on small craft was adopted.[5]

The result was a curious hodge-podge of the old and the new. The missile boat with the NATO codename 'Komar' used what was essentially the same hull as the Project 183 ('P-6') torpedo boat – dubbed Project 183R – onto which two bulky SSM launcher-containers were added aft. These turbojet and rocket-powered SSMs were designated P-15 and have been far better known in the West by their NATO codename, SS-N-2A or B Styx, while the P-20 and P-21 were jointly codenamed the SS-N-2C Styx. Various Chinese derivatives exist in the HY-1, HY-2, HY-4 and C-201 series, and are known in the West as CSS-N-2 Silkworm. The 'Komar's only defensive armament was an open twin 25mm AA mounting forward. A target acquisition radar provided location of the enemy and, as long as the little 25.5m long 'Komar' managed to get within 40km of the target, a viable radar-homing threat could be presented to any threatening fleet. Such vessels were still highly vulnerable to air attack and it was partly because of this – and because the NATO powers did not perceive themselves as having any need for such capabilities – that the 'Komar' and succeeding 'Osa' (Project 205) classes (the latter with four SSMs) were not taken very seriously, even though the 39m long 'Osas', with two radar-controlled twin 30mm AA cannon, were far more practical propositions.

These craft were simple and cheap to produce and provided an effective means with which the Soviets could equip their allies and client states during the Cold War. Among the countries so equipped was Egypt, which acquired several 'Komars' and 'Osas' during the 1960s. Following the shattering experience of her defeat by Israel in the Six Day War of June 1967, Egypt was nursing her wounds when an opportunity presented itself to wreak a little revenge. The Israeli Navy, then still equipped with a few Second World War-vintage destroyers, was itself waiting for its own domestically developed SSM – the Israel Aircraft Industries Gabriel – with which to equip a new generation of 'Sa'ar' class patrol boats ordered from France. It is now said that Gabriel used the beam-riding command guidance system of the early Italian Sea Killer SSM.[6] It is necessary to mention this because the Israeli Navy really had no excuse for not understanding the potential of the SSM.

On 21 October 1967, the Israeli destroyer *Elath* (also known as *Eilat*) was unwisely patrolling very close to Port Said when two Styx missiles, fired from two Egyptian 'Komars' which never left harbour, wrecked her machinery spaces. The ship was finished off an hour later by a third missile. The panic in Western naval circles which followed this event was akin to the torpedo boat scare of the 1880s.

The scale of the panic was a little misplaced – if only because there were soon some effective counters to the SSM – but the missile boat had certainly arrived. Apart from the bruised Israelis, who quickly learned the lesson and concentrated on building up their Gabriel-equipped flotilla, another country which now launched a crash development of an effective SSM was France, whose state-owned Aéro-spatiale quickly produced the MM38 Exocet sea-skimmer – a far greater threat than the Styx with its parabolic arc trajectory. Even so, Styx remained a potent weapon, as Indian 'Osas' were to show when they sank Pakistan's destroyer *Khaibar* during the 1971 war. However the Gabriel-armed Sa'ars which savaged the Egyptian and Syrian fleets without loss to themselves in 1973 were able to shoot down Styx with 0.50in (12.7mm) heavy machine gun fire. Some fifty Styx were fired and failed to hit a single Israeli vessel. The Israelis by contrast sank three Syrian 'Komars' and two 'Osa Is', among other craft, while Egypt lost three to five FAC, including two 'Komars' and some of the four 'Osa Is' which Egypt is known to have lost around this time. This extraordinarily one sided performance was ascribed to better seakeeping in battle and, crucially, better ECM.

The October War's first night included the first missile boat against missile boat engagement, the Battle of Latakia in which five Israeli boats avoided two Styx salvoes and sank three Syrian craft with Gabriel, although the third was finally despatched by gunfire. In another key battle two days later, off Damietta, six Israeli FAC sank three Egyptian vessels, two with Gabriel and the third with gunfire.[7]

These engagements proved that the missile-armed FAC represented a quantum leap over the torpedo boat and, with their long range punch, could be rightly regarded as the worthy successor to the powerfully armed coast defence ship of old, not simply as a better-armed torpedo boat. Just as powerful 8in to 11in guns on coast defence ships of a previous generation could deter and just as the ships which carried them could represent a convincing fleet in being, so also the missile-armed FAC represented a completely new form of naval warfare: the small craft with a weapon which could truly contest large expanses of sea space.

But it is instructive to bear in mind a few key points. Israel's early triumphs were at least as attributable to the quality of Israeli electronic warfare as to the reliability of the Gabriel itself. The importance of the electronic innards of the modern SSM cannot be overstated.

There is a story from the Falklands War, relating to Exocet, which illustrates this point. It is said that the British asked the French government precisely what standard of electronic counter-counter measures (ECCM) fit was installed in the seeker heads of Argentina's Exocets. Subsequent events cannot be described for legal reasons, but the alleged upshot was that the British learned that the French defence ministry had no way of forcing the manufacturer of the seeker to reveal details of the microchip and its circuits intended to defeat countermeasures. The British had been promised that the most advanced seeker would be restricted to themselves and the French Navy. They were angry that the French could not prove that they had kept their promise, although subsequently it turned out that the Argentine Exocets did not have the advanced seeker. Ex-

Yugoslav Osa
Seen returning to its coastal hide on the Yugoslav coast (before the horrors of the 1990s), is a Yugoslav Navy Osa *class missile boat, armed with four SS-N-2 SSMs and two twin 30mm automatics. Such hides are used by several countries in Scandinavia, the Middle East and Asia (GPH Collection)*

ocet, being vulnerable to 'chaff' because of its so-called 'pseudo-proximity' fuse which works through the seeker to calculate where a target should be, partly on the basis of information fed into the missile before launch, needs an ECM system which can discriminate between true and false targets.

Another point is that SSMs are not necessarily designed to sink a target. The key issue is to impair or shatter a target's ability to continue its mission. With a 165kg warhead, Exocet was clearly going to badly damage any target it hit, the Mach 0.9 impact of such a warhead being compared by some to the impact of a 13.5in battleship shell. But single shells did not sink their targets, unless the hit was very lucky. At least as damaging to a target besides the warhead is the remaining fuel contained by a sea-skimming SSM. Naval sources say the warhead of the Exocet which hit the British destroyer *Sheffield* on 2 May 1982 during the Falklands War did not explode, but the missile's fuel nonetheless started a fierce fire. The ship itself was rendered inoperable, despite the efforts of damage control teams, but the ship itself did not sink until 9–10 May, as she was being towed to Ascension Island. The sinking was unexpected. During the 1980–88 Iran-Iraq War, the frequent Exocet and other missile attacks on tankers and other vessels in the Gulf caused damage, but few sinkings.

Besides Israel and France, other countries were also catching up fast with their own SSM developments including, most importantly, the USA, with the McDonnell Douglas RGM-84 Harpoon, and Italy, first with the Sistel Sea Killer and then with Otomat, a turbojet and rocket-powered hybrid developed by OTO Melara in collaboration with France's Matra. Norway meanwhile adapted the powerplant of the American Bullpup air-to-surface missile to its own SSM, the little Penguin originally developed by Kongsberg Vapenfabrikk, now known as Norsk Forsvarstekuologi. This weapon was small enough to be fitted to diminutive vessels like the *Storm* class and was also bought by the Swedish Navy for its *Hugin* class FAC. Sweden was obliged to do this because, although she had put SSMs of her own design (the Rb 08A) on *Halland* class destroyers during the 1960s, she had not developed an SSM small enough for installation on a FAC, preferring to rely instead on the fairly heavy torpedo armament of the six wire-guided Tp61s of the *Spica* class.

Sweden did eventually develop her own compact SSM in the Saab Missiles RBS15 which re-equipped the *Spica*s and has also been installed on Sweden's coastal corvettes, as well as on FACs in the Finnish, Croatian and Yugoslav (Serb-Montenegrin) navies.

But, although both South Africa and Taiwan copied the Gabriel (as the Skorpioen and Hsiung Feng 1 respectively) and the Otomat was also sold to several navies, the pre-eminent SSMs of the 1970s to the 1990s were Exocet and Harpoon in their various guises, the most recent being Exocet MM40 Block II and Harpoon Block 1D, and, surprisingly, the hardy Styx and Silkworm, of which the most recent versions can present a genuine sea-skimming threat.

The MM40 Block II started life as a French clandestine project. The missile is said to be able to fly corkscrew manoeuvres to bypass a ship's defences and is also capable of doglegging, switching direction by up to 90 degrees. With the ability to operate in sea states of up to 7 and with improved ECCM, the weapon is probably as advanced as a subsonic SSM can be today. The Block ID Harpoon by contrast is believed to be capable of flying 'clover-leaf' pattern missions in which a target missed on a first attempt can be attacked on a second pass. The weapon's improved range is useful for this purpose, as it apparently cannot benefit from mid-course correction. If correct, this is a curious omission, as Gabriel, for example, does benefit from this feature, as do most Russian weapons. It certainly provides one explanation why the latest Israeli Sa'ar 5 corvettes carry a mixed battery of Harpoons and Gabriels.

The most recent SSM developments present a far from uniform view of the priorities for future weapons. Thus Matra Defense successfully argued against the proposed joint development, together with OTO Melara, of a super-

sonic version of Otomat which had been dubbed Otomach, on the grounds that high speed was not vital in order to pierce a warship's defences. Fellow French company Aérospatiale, maker of the Exocet, disagrees and has thus been involved in a long, troubled effort to develop just such a weapon, called ANS, in collaboration with Germany. Extraordinary claims were made for ANS. Besides a 100km range in a so-called 'lo-lo-lo' profile (i.e. beneath the radar horizon until it came within range of the warship's surface surveillance radar and ESM), it was claimed to have a 15 G manoeuvrability limit (as opposed to just 5 G for Exocet). Exocet itself, in its latest MM40 Block II version, is a much improved missile, still with a 70km range, but able to perform violent manoeuvres to avoid defences, and maintain a sea-slimming profile in sea states of up to 7. It has now also emerged that Block II can spot the radar pulses directing close-in weapons systems (CIWS) like Phalanx and Goalkeeper, severely complicating the task of warship defence.

The MM40 Block II has now been ordered for several countries' FACs including those of Malaysia and Oman. As mentioned later, another user is Qatar in its shore-based coast defence role. That weapons like this are now widely available for coastal defence uses, either on corvettes and FACs, or in shore-based batteries, has further upped the technical ante against those who might attack an enemy coastline.

Russia's willingness to market very sophisticated supersonic weapons like the Chelomey design bureau's ramjet-powered Yakhont, which can probably reach speeds of Mach 3.5 in the terminal attack mode, and cruise at Mach 2.0–2.5 over ranges of up to 300km, shows that this ante will be further upped in favour of the coastal defender with a deep pocket. Such a weapon – if married to the advances of the Block II Exocet – will be very difficult to counter for the foreseeable future.

Following the development of the Exocet and Harpoon in particular, new life was given to the builders of small warships, as they now turned out a large number of missile-armed FACs for navies in Europe and the developing world. Many such navies were now able to replace obsolete and larger wartime tonnage with craft which could pack a truly formidable punch.

Typical of the genre were the *Combattante II* FAC, built by Constructions Mécaniques de Normandie (CMN) for numerous navies. Invariably armed with a quartet or, latterly, octet of SSMs with an OTO Melara 76mm 62cal COMPACT dual-purpose mounting forward and a smaller calibre AA weapon (usually a twin Oerlikon 35mm or Breda 40mm) aft, this class provided a new power to several navies which, like their torpedo-equipped forebears of the 1880s, could now contest far larger areas of sea than the coast defence fleets of old, thanks to the range of their new weapons.

They were also for the most part conventionally-hulled as

opposed to the planing hulls once favoured by the British and there is thus a direct lineage between today's Lürssen-built FAC and the S-boats of the Second World War.

During the 1970s and 1980s it became almost *de rigeur* for smaller navies without true blue water pretensions to acquire small flotillas of these FACs, which became increasingly complex as builders offered more impressive electronic warfare (EW) and ESM fits, better command systems and, in the case of a few classes, ASW armament and even helicopter flight-decks too (witness the Lürssen-built 57m vessels of the United Arab Emirates' fleet).

But during this time a mistake was being made by the manufacturers offering the designs and the navies buying them. The attempt to cram everything into a small hull meant that inevitably these craft could not include a sufficiently capable command system, let alone longer range air defences. There was no reason why these vessels could not be built with larger displacements, apart from a new orthodoxy – or conservatism – which said that size was not everything, therefore was not necessary.

Even though the Israelis have shown, with their *Reshef* class FAC which displace some 415 tons, that extra displacement does confer some seakeeping advantages and other benefits which enable FAC like these to travel long distances like the Haifa to Eilat route via the Cape, most FAC-equipped navies stuck with smaller displacements and less potent equipment fits.

Although much can be said about the sluggishness of the Iraqi war effort during the 1991 Gulf conflict, the fact remains that however good the Iraqi effort may have been, there was probably little which any Iraqi FAC could have done to counter helicopters firing air-to-surface missiles (ASMs) from just outside the range of the FAC's defensive battery. The mauling of the Iraqi Navy by, mostly, the Sea Skua-armed Lynx helicopters of the Royal Navy and the Intruder attack aircraft of the US Navy, showed that the day of the rudimentary FAC was over and that an era which began with the sinking of the *Eilat* was over. (It should however be noted that reliable sources have told the author that the Iraqi attempt to use the Lürssen-built 'TNC 45' FACs captured from Kuwait was hampered by the removal of key operating codes and manuals before seizure.)

Since 1991 a discernible change has occurred in which the new benchmark is a corvette-sized vessel able to take on at least the ASM-armed helicopter and which is also able to ship a decent command, control and communications (C3) suite, to say nothing of meaningful EW and ESM. The result can be seen, for instance, in Vosper Thornycroft's 83m corvette design, of which two have been sold to Oman. Besides eight Exocet MM40s and the ubiquitous 76mm 62cal, these vessels carry, *inter alia*, an octuple Thomson-CSF Crotale SAM launcher able to tackle the helicopter at standoff ranges of up to 13km, while sea-skimming missiles can be tackled out to 6.5km.

However, Sea Skua's maximum range is 15km, and reportedly the Aérospatiale AS 15TT of similar dimensions can do a little better than that, while the ASM version of Penguin, the Mk 3, which has been bought for US Navy LAMPS helicopters, can reach 40km+. Obviously there would be little a modern FAC or corvette could do to counter the aircraft or helicopter launching AM 39 Exocet or Harpoon ASMs, with their even longer ranges.

This development of larger corvettes to tackle the ASM threat has perhaps finally explained the earlier thinking in the former Soviet Union which gave rise to the Project 1234 ('Nanuchka' class) 'small missile ships' (variously described in the West as corvettes or large FAC). Western commentators were originally somewhat bemused by this 1970s-vintage class and its successors, armed with six SS-N-9 SSMs, a twin SA-N-4 SAM launcher (with twenty missiles with a 13km range) and a twin AK-257 57mm AA aft. At 675 tons full load, they were large by comparison with other FACs and carried an impressive self-defence capability, further improved in subsequent versions (Project 1234.1 and others) which substituted a single 76.2mm AK-176 DP gun and a 30mm AK-630 Gatling CIWS for the twin 57mm. They are reported to be poor sea boats though, and Western observers were surprised that no attempt was made to put any ASW equipment on this relatively large FAC hull, especially given the copious ASW equipment fit of the Project 1124 ('Grisha' class).

An even more impressive vessel than either Project 1234 or Vosper's 83m corvette, albeit one which is probably not affordable to most of the world's navies, is the Israeli *Sa'ar 5* corvette built by America's Litton Ingalls under the Foreign Military Sales programme. Claimed to be the world's most

Turunmaa
After 1947 Finland was bound by the restrictive terms of the Treaty of Paris which forbade the Finns a meaningful naval force, or so those who drafted it thought. Turunmaa, at barely over 600 tons, was the answer in the 1960s: a compact equivalent of sorts of the intelligence which went into the Väinämöinen *of an earlier generation, equipped with a very powerful Bofors 4.7in 46cal automatic gun (CMP)*

Göteborg
The Swedish coastal corvette Göteborg *shows the direction which coastal defence is taking in the 1990s: larger, stealthier, more seaworthy hulls with space for a more resilient defensive electronic and weapons suite. Driven by the requirement for an ASW platform, the Swedes have followed a trend pursued by other navies for other reasons. Either way, the newer coast defence missile corvettes today are more often than not equipped with some form of surface-to-air missile or close-in weapons system (CelsiusTech)*

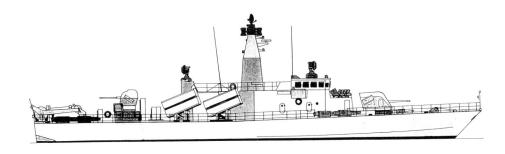

heavily-armed surface warship for its displacement, it carries eight Harpoon, eight Gabriel 3, a 20mm Mk-15 Phalanx CIWS and no less than thirty-two IAI Barak vertical-launch SAMs in a very compact silo – among other weapons.

Germany is also following suit in that it has decided that its large fleet of, at the time of writing, thirty-eight FACs is of little apparent use now that the Cold War is over and there is no apparent immediate threat in the Baltic. In 1994 the Bundesmarine adopted the decision in principle to replace these vessels with fifteen larger corvettes displacing 1,000 tons or more which can serve in both the coastal defence and ocean-going roles – budgets permitting. Across the Baltic, Sweden's *Göteborg* class coastal corvettes, developed in part as a response to the spate of serious violations of her waters by suspected Soviet submarines during the 1980s, have already shown the Germans the way forward with their extraordinarily compact arrangement of 57mm and 40mm guns, eight RBS-15 SSMs and four Tp42 ASW torpedoes plus Elma ASW grenade launchers on a 425 ton (full load) hull which yet also manages to pack in an effective command and fire control, radar and sonar suite.

Still in the Baltic, it is worth also making the observation that perhaps the earliest indicator of the direction contemporary naval developments are taking had been provided two decades earlier, when Finland built her two 605 ton (770 ton full load) corvettes *Turunmaa* and *Karjala*. Because of the provisions of the 1947 Treaty of Paris, Finland was at that time forbidden not only guided missiles, but also torpedoes, submarines and a navy with more than 10,000 tons of vessels in total. This forced the Finns to build small, yet the corvettes were armed with a Bofors 120mm (4.7in) 46cal gun which was easily the most powerful gun to be operationally installed since the Second World War on such a small warship.

It is hard to avoid the observation that in these tiny corvettes, which were otherwise originally armed with two Bofors 40mm 70cal, a twin 30mm, two Soviet-supplied RBU-1200 unguided ASW rocket launchers and depth charges, the Finns built the nearest anyone has come to a modern gun-armed pure coast defence ship. There is even something in their appearance which provides a reminder of earlier, larger coast defence stablemates such as the *Väinämöinen*.

Another coast defence navy, Thailand's, also displayed similar tendencies around this time, perhaps with the memory of the *Sri Ayuthia* in mind. The Thais ordered a British-built frigate in 1969 – *Makut Rajakumarn* – which, in a period when stern helicopter flightdecks or stern-mounted SAMs and ASW armament were *de rigeur*, instead shipped two 4.5in Mk.8s fore and aft. Another navy which did something similar though, albeit with 3in (76mm) guns, was South Korea with its *Ulsan* class frigates. There were – and are – many old destroyers and frigates of wartime vintage with traditional gun arrangements, but other than Thailand's no other non-communist navy of the 1960s and 1970s had ordered a major

warship in which large-calibre gunnery arranged fore and aft was the primary anti-surface vessel armament.

The benefits of a powerful mixed general purpose armament on a hull smaller than those deployed with their current fleet has not been lost on the US Navy. At the time of writing, three American shipyards – Ingalls, Newport News and Trinity Marine – were chasing a Kuwaiti contract for several so-called 'Offshore Missile Vessels', corvettes in reality. The solutions offered by these yards have apparently impressed an unintended potential customer, the US Navy, which is said to be considering the acquisition of a 90m corvette.

Such a policy change towards smaller warships which can yet contest substantial littoral areas should not come as a surprise. The writing has been on the wall since October 1992 and the publication of the US Navy's and US Marine Corps' doctrinal White Paper *From the Sea*. This document, an effort to take the US Navy beyond its Cold War preoccupations, talks extensively about operations in littoral waters, not necessarily always offensive. The strategy concludes that 'the shift in strategic landscape means that naval forces will concentrate on littoral warfare and manoeuvre from the sea'.[8] It is against this background also that vessels such as the *Cyclone* class patrol boats (based incidentally on the British Vosper Thornycroft *Ramadan* class design), and the new *Osprey* class mine countermeasures (MCM) vessels are being acquired. These developments therefore represent a complete shift in US Navy thinking, away from pure blue water obsessions.

One aspect of modern coastal defence has not yet been touched on, but is becoming increasingly relevant to cash-starved navies. Many modern navy and coastguard vessels whose secondary military function is, effectively, coastal defence or the defence of sovereign home territory, have primary purposes which are civilian and more or less peaceful in nature. Modern offshore patrol vessels (OPVs) perform the role of protection of the extended economic zone (EEZ) which may not be strictly 'coastal' in the accepted sense, but which is dictated by the distance between a given area of sea and the nearest national territorial landfall.

Disputes ranging from the argument over who is the rightful owner of uninhabitable outcrops of rock like Rockall, disputed by Britain and Ireland, or the far more dangerous wrangle between several countries over the Spratly Islands in the South China Sea, have at their core worries over who controls the economic resources of a given area. Wars have started for more slender reasons and the OPVs which must police EEZs or economically significant waters of disputed status must ideally be able to act as policeman or warrior in not wholly unequal measure.

Some vessels, such as the Norwegian Coastguard's *Nordkapp* class OPVs, Denmark's *Thetis* class fishery patrol frigates or the French Navy's *Floréal* class surveillance frigates, have unambiguous military potential, equipped as they are

Floréal
Typical of the modern offshore patrol vessel is France's 'surveillance frigate' Floréal, *an ocean-going vessel built cheaply to mercantile standards, armed with basic anti-surface threat weapons like the modernised 100mm gun forward and reconditioned MM38 Exocets. She also carries a helicopter, but no sonar or ASW equipment and is thus at the top end of the pure OPV range, even if she is described as a frigate (Chantiers de l'Atlantique)*

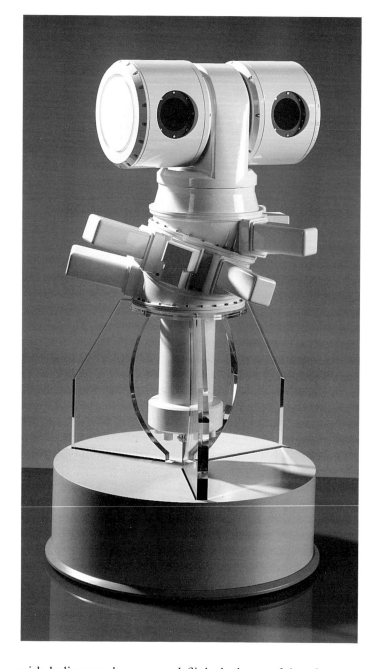

such vessels, although some weaknesses like the *Floréals'* lack of any sonar could not easily be corrected in a crisis. Nonetheless, these vessels, and their similar helicopter-equipped counterparts serving in navies such as those of Ireland, Mexico and Spain, represent an effective means of, if not coastal defence *per se*, of performing essential sovereignty protection tasks in peacetime in the EEZ, while at the same time providing a limited capability for war.

In one sense, their coastal 'defence' applications are unambiguous and very useful. Unlike many warships which either spend their time in port, in refit, or in the open ocean on purely military duties, the sheer familiarity which these vessels' crews have with their EEZ patrol area or coastal area of interest enables them to perform a more informed surveillance mission than warships assigned to the classic OPV/EEZ protection task.

No matter how weak a country may be, or how unimpressive an OPV's armament may be, the presence of such a vessel near a coast or in an area of economic interest effectively sends a message to the potential miscreant – or enemy. For all practical purposes, that implicit message goes something like this: 'I represent the state and its interests. To overcome these you must commit aggression or show hostility towards me and, if you do, I will resist you to the best of my abilities'. And, he might add, 'I will make sure that there is hell to pay if you do fire on me, ram me or make a run for it'.

Some patrol vessels assigned to the OPV task are far smaller than their 2,000–3,000 ton helicopter-equipped stablemates, and are solely useful for the fishery patrol or surveillance task, but not much more, but here again a synergy can be seen between their peacetime roles and the coast defence task. Denmark, for example, possesses a fairly substantial fleet of very small patrol vessels equipped with not much more than a navigational radar and a machine gun or cannon.

Manned by the Home Guard, their role is essentially one of surveillance. The new 80 ton MHV 800 class, with a crew of just eight, perform the role of surveillance of coastal waters, harbour control, the protection of naval ports and search and rescue. Some twenty-five vessels were planned but the programme has been delayed by funding restrictions.

Obviously, practically any seaworthy craft can perform such a function and many navies or coastguards operate similar craft to the MHV 800s, but what is interesting is their *modus operandi*, which is essentially limited to the maximum that is within the vessel's potential. A more ambitious marriage of traditional coast defence surveillance preoccupations with EEZ protection and with at least one vital military task has been provided by Canada, which at the time of writing had just commissioned the first of a new class of a dozen Maritime Coastal Defence Vessels

with helicopter hangars and flightdecks, useful main guns (Bofors 57mm Mk 2 in the case of the *Nordkapps*, OTO Melara 76mm 62cal on the *Thetis* class and Creusot-Loire 100mm on the *Floréals*), plus actual, or facilities for, SSMs. Light guns (usually 20mm) nearly always grace such vessels, while the relatively new phenomenon of effective 'bolt-on' light SAM armament, such as Matra's Simbad twin launcher for the Mistral SAM, make it possible to turn ships which are 'fitted for, but not with' into effective coastal combatants. In the case of the *Nordkapps*, their wartime purpose has been stated as including coastal convoy escort.

The addition of helicopters to OPVs provides a relatively simple means of adding an ASW or anti-ship capability to

Smyge
This craft is Smyge, *a revolutionary concept-warship built in Sweden to trial the technologies which will now be incorporated in the future YS-2000 programme, among others. Low radar reflectivity is a key element of modern Swedish naval design. In this concept vehicle, the proposed gun installation is aft and retractable. Stealth will give coastal defence forces a new edge (GPH Collection)*

(MCDVs), the *Kingston* class, which combine MCM with EEZ protection, sovereignty protection, and surveillance in one hull.

Canada has been bedevilled by a long history of ambitious defence plans since the Second World War which has not been matched by funding, and the MCDVs are essentially an effort by the Canadian Navy to get 'back to basics'. At 713 tons (light) and 920 tons (full load), the 15kt MCDVs will be armed with only one 40mm gun and a pair of 12.7mm heavy machine guns, two modular minesweeping systems and a module for a remote controlled MCM submersible. With an 18-day endurance, their peacetime role will be offshore patrol and coastal surveillance.

New hull concepts, such as SWATH (Small Waterplane Area, Twin Hull) or trimarans (now under serious investigation in the UK for a future frigate application), may also lend themselves to coastal defence applications of one form or another. But unless the exotic nature of some related future technologies can be kept within tolerable cost limits, these are unlikely to be applied for humbler roles, unless or until they become so familiar and trusted as to make their application to coastal defence *de rigeur*.

A lead in one area of new technology is already being shown in MCM vessels, which increasingly use hulls made of glass reinforced plastic or some such material. This new technology cannot be avoided for coastal defence or any other future naval application – stealth.

The basic rules which apply to any vessel wishing to reduce the various signatures which identify it to the world are essentially the same for all vessels, although MCM craft have obvious particular needs. Briefly, the identifiable signatures are: acoustic, electronic, infra-red (IR), magnetic and radar cross-section (RCS). Magnetic signature reduction is critical to MCM vessels' operations and survival, while the provision of a low RCS is ideally achieved at the ship design stage.

There are some very stealthy vessels about today, such as the French *La Fayette* and British Type 23 frigates, while other warships can avail themselves of panels of radar absorbent materials (RAM) which, appropriately positioned, can reduce a warship's detectability or disguise it.

Any technology which reduces a coast defence vessel's RCS or detectability, such as simple noise-reduction and IR-reduction measures, will turn the potential advantage in favour of the less well armed defender, especially if, as on designs of the new generation Swedish YS 2000 missile boats, weapons and other above-decks paraphernalia are RCS-shielded or concealed. Work on this design is still in the definition phase at its future builder, Karlskronavarvet, but the intention is to produce a vessel with similar or better stealth properties than the revolutionary trials vessel *Smyge* (the word means 'stealth' in Swedish).

This surface effect ship (SES) has validated the theory and the Swedish Navy is set to blaze a new path in coastal defence with the YS 2000 class when they appear around the turn of the twentieth century. They will be armed with the Bofors 57mm 70cal Mk 3 gun, RBS 15 SSMs, ASW torpedoes and unspecified other armament, which will include at least provision for point-defence SAMs.

Norway's Kvaerner Mandal may build a slightly less ambitious missile SES to replace current FACs and it would not be premature to conclude that other navies will follow suit. The US Navy is certainly very interested in stealth on coastal or small craft and funded, together with the former Defense Advanced Research Projects Agency (formerly DARPA, now simply known as ARPA), the construction of the Lockheed-designed and built *Sea Shadow* stealth test SWATH vessel.

This entered service in total secrecy in 1983. It displaces 560 tons full load, and can make 15kts, care of a pair of GM Detroit Diesel 12V149 TI diesels driving two shafts in the outer 'wings' of the SWATH hull. Radar and communications masts are retractable and the ship can trim down by the stern. Precise RCS characteristics have obviously not been revealed, but *Sea Shadow* is said to have greatly advanced the US Navy's understanding of the stealth discipline – not surprising since the builder also designed the F-117A stealth strike aircraft.[9]

These kinds of stealth and new hull technologies, together with user-friendly weapons such as ever smaller vertical launch missiles, fired from silos rather than bulky trainable launchers, will allow the small warship of the future to hide and survive, while carrying a very worthwhile offensive and defensive battery. As ever, affordability will determine a nation's arsenal, but it will no longer be so clear-cut that a great sea power will always overwhelm a small one only interested in defending its own coastline and waters of sovereign or economic interest. After all, for anyone who is interested, there is no shortage of information on what mistakes have been made in the past – and what solutions have shown promise.

1 See Norman Friedman, *The Postwar Naval Revolution* (London, 1986) for an account of the thinking of the US, British, Soviet and other naval staffs after the war. See also Eric Grove, *Vanguard to Trident – British Naval Policy since World War II* (London, 1987) for an account of British naval strategy and the long war which the Admiralty assumed was possible.

2 Friedman, ibid, pp206–7.

3 Ibid, pp201–11 for the history of post-war British inshore craft.

4 George Paloczi-Horvath, 'Royal Navy's Nuclear Sea Mine Plans Revealed', *NAVINT*, Vol.7 No.5, 10 March 1995, p8.

5 For descriptions of Soviet naval thinking at the time, see Friedman, ibid, and John Jordan, *Modern Soviet Warships* (London, 1984). For another good account of strategic thinking and weapons in the Soviet Navy between 1945 and 1964, see Steven J Zaloga, *Target America* (Novato, California, 1993).

6 Norman Friedman, *The Naval Institute Guide to World Naval Weapons Systems 1991/92 & 1994 Update* (Annapolis, Maryland, 1991 & 1994). New details on Gabriel are found in the 1994 Update, p21.

7 *Conway's All the World's Fighting Ships 1947–1982, Part II: The Warsaw Pact and Non-Aligned Nations* (London, 1983), see Egyptian (pp301–04), Israeli (pp437–41) and Syrian (pp447–8) sections for descriptions of the fighting in the 1973 October War.

8 Scott R Gourley, 'From the Sea – The New Direction', *Defence*, February 1993, p46.

9 Bérnard Prezelin (Ed.), *The Naval Institute Guide to Combat Fleets of the World 1995* (Annapolis, Maryland, 1995), for latest details of the various OPVs, surveillance vessels, MCDVs, stealth vessels and the like which are described in this chapter.

CHAPTER 13

Modern Fixed and Mobile Coastal Defence

MODERN FIXED AND MOBILE shore-based coastal defences represent an attempt to square the circle of providing effective cover over, if not over a whole coastline, then certainly its most vulnerable or important points – and at the lowest cost. Essentially the choices involved in stationary or mobile coast defence from the shore involve educated guesswork about where an enemy or potential adversary might choose to strike.

The irony of successful deterrence is that one can never know precisely what elements of a deterrent package might have swayed an adversary's decision not to attack, but clearly there are some obvious probabilities. The geography of Scandinavia favours the defender and the strategically significant fjord or skerry can be protected with moderate ease against all but the most determined attacker by the usual combination of mines, shore-fired torpedoes and SSMs – provided that control of the air can at least be contested. Major ports and naval forces are obvious defence priorities, as are exposed coastlines within a manageable distance of a key objective – such as a capital city – but otherwise the defender has in the past always had more 'key points' to defend than reasonably sized forces with which to shield them.

What has radically altered this assessment of the classic coast defence dilemma is the appearance of the SSM. Whereas torpedoes and coastal artillery – mobile or not – can only provide protection out to at most a few tens of kilometres, some SSMs can reach out to 150km, completely altering the balance in favour of the well-equipped and astute defender – provided he can protect both this asset and the means of target detection and fire control from attack.

Lessons learned from post-1945 experiences of coastal defence have generally confirmed the validity of the above analysis. When coastal defence or, as in Normandy in 1944, the ability to respond quickly failed, the results were catastrophic. MacArthur's landing at Inchon in 1950, which so completely turned the tables against the outflanked North Koreans, is an obvious case in point. It is perhaps less fair to criticise the Egyptian performance against the Anglo-French forces in 1956, although some of the usual measures such as the sinking of blockships were used. It was no accident though that, after Suez, Nasser made sure that Egypt was well-equipped with Soviet-supplied coast defence missiles and long range guns.

There was little opportunity for classic coast defence operations in most of the brush-fire wars of the 1960s to 1990s, although the mere threat of attack from the sea apparently played an major role in misleading Saddam Hussein about the Allied coalition's intentions in 1991. The mere presence of substantial US Marine landing forces was enough to provoke the laying of thousands of mines off Kuwait, many of which still lurk in the shallows outside those channels which were cleared by coalition minehunters.

An opportunity for the classic application of coast defence disciplines presented itself to the hapless Argentineans defending the Falkland Islands during their brief occupation in 1982. The problem, as ever in coast defence, was that there were simply not enough troops and equipment. The Falklands conflict is the most interesting recent example of the opportunities presented, and challenges faced, in attempting to mount any kind of viable coast defence.

Thus the settlement at San Carlos was indeed identified by the Argentines as a possible landing point, but the forces available to harass the British landing on 21 May were meagre, comprising just sixty-two men, two 106mm recoilless guns and two 81mm mortars at Fanning Head, a towering headland overlooking the approach to the landing beaches. This well-positioned, if small, sub-company strength force was dislodged by a cleverly devised combination of attack and negotiation involving the Royal Marines' Special Boat Service.

What is worth remembering about this skirmish in which the British prevailed is that had those two Argentine guns and two mortars been brought to bear on the ships quietly sailing into San Carlos Water, there is no doubt that they could have done incalculable damage – out of all proportions to the size of the Argentine force engaged. After all, the Argentines would have learned precisely this lesson a month and a half before when, on 3 April 1982, their corvette *Guerrico* was badly damaged at South Georgia by a combination of withering small arms fire and 84mm and 66mm anti-tank rockets, all in the hands of a tiny 22-strong Royal Marines garrison.

A third engagement during the Falklands conflict is also of crucial relevance to this narrative as it was the first known occasion when an SSM was fired against a warship from a land site. On 13 June, following an earlier failed attempt to attack British ships bombarding Port Stanley on 27–28 May, a jury-rigged twin MM38 Exocet SSM installation mounted

(left) Exocet MM40
Currently the most popular coast defence missile outside of the former Communist bloc is the Exocet in various versions. Here an MM40 'Batterie Cotiére' is seen being fired from a 6x6 mobile launcher (Aerospatiale)

Exocet MM38
A further variant of coastal Exocet was Vosper Thornycroft's Excalibur system, deployed at Gibraltar in the 1980s, which used MM38 missiles as fired from the usual shipborne launchers of the time, but fitted on a flat-bed trailer-launcher. The British had memories of the fate of Glamorgan *in mind . . . (Vosper Thornycroft)*

on a trailer engaged the *County* class destroyer *Glamorgan*. An Exocet caused severe damage to the ship, whose crew knew of the Exocet threat but miscalculated its range. The author has heard that the mistake was described by an observer afterwards as a case of 'cutting across the penalty area'. The war ended on the next day, but it is tempting to conclude that the 'gun line' of warships bombarding Port Stanley might have been withdrawn to a slightly safer distance had the war continued.[1]

Interestingly, the British learned the lesson and after the war contracted Vosper Thornycroft to devise a trailer-mounted twin MM38 Exocet launcher called Excalibur, which was installed for a few years at Gibraltar. The trailer had an integral Type 1006 radar and power generation, but the mounting is understood to have now been withdrawn from Gibraltar.

Weapons like the shore-based versions of Exocet and Harpoon, with essentially the same characteristics as their shipborne variants, clearly represent the most potent shore-based coast defence solution currently available, although heavy artillery is another, while a third approach – so far not yet widely adopted – is unguided rocketry.

In no country, except perhaps the Scandinavian nations, is coast defence taken so seriously that it is regarded as a primary mission of the armed forces. It is thus not surprising that it has been in Scandinavia that the most coherent, rational approach to the problem has been taken, with impressive results given these countries' severely squeezed defence budgets.

Sweden has one of the most developed coast defence systems of any country in the world today, and perhaps the best equipped. The Coastal Artillery is a separate arm of service within the navy and as such is equipped, not only with both coastal artillery and missiles, but also with its own dedicated fleet of patrol craft, minelayers and, of crucial importance to the provision of mobile coastal defence, amphibious vessels.

Coast defence 120mm emplacement
Another Swedish concept, now in service, is the Bofors 120mm 62cal ERSTA installation. The magazine, servicing and gun-cooling arrangement can be seen in this cutaway (Bofors)

The gunnery has been extensively modernised and comprises the Bofors 120mm 62cal ERSTA turret in fixed mountings, supplemented by fixed 75mm mountings. The ERSTA turret has a maximum 27km range, which like the 75mm fixed guns fire from well-concealed turrets disguised to appear like rocky outcrops. A deep magazine and servicing and cooling system lie beneath the ERSTA turret, which draws target information from a NobelTech 9 KM 400 surveillance radar.

Significant though these fixed guns are for Sweden's defence, the provision of mobile weaponry is an increasing trend and these assets comprise 120mm guns including Bofors CD-80 Karin guns, 55cal weapons which have been specially designed for the coastal defence role, as well as 75mm and 40mm AA guns. Supporting them are 81mm mortars for close-range defence. The Karin fires the same shell as the ERSTA turret but an enhanced range shell which can reach out to 30km is also available.

A very important future coast defence project is the STARKA system being developed by NobelTech for both the Swedish and Norwegian coastal artillery for service from 1997–98. This will use mobile 155mm howitzers firing from pre-prepared positions, from which they can swiftly withdraw, either to other positions or to safer cliffside hides. A request for studies went out to industry in February–March 1992. They began in the following April and the project moved on surprisingly quickly given its sheer complexity. Trials of appropriate systems were intended to be complete by June 1995, to be followed by production orders for the self-propelled artillery. Sweden's Bofors, France's GIAT and Britain's VSEL have all showed interest in providing the armament. Assuming the project is funded, the howitzers are likely to be 39cal weapons, although longer 48 cal or the future NATO long range standard of 52cal, had not been ruled out.[2]

Sweden's coastal defence missile arsenal is truly formidable. For long-range protection, there is the Saab RBS-15KA SSM fired from a four-round truck launcher, plus the RBS-08A and RB-52 SSMs, the latter being French-supplied SS-11 wire-guided missiles which are being replaced for close-range defence by the Rockwell AGM-114A Hellfire – known to the Swedes as the RBS-17. This provides a form of coastal defence which can be carried and deployed by one man. Some 700 were originally ordered in 1987, with ninety launchers, to equip twenty-five battalions to replace the thirty-two RB52 battalions.

The RBS-15KA is identical to the ship-launched version, being powered by two booster rockets and a Microturbo TR160 turbojet, and has a maximum range of 100km. The missile's resistance to countermeasures has been improved under a mid-life update contract awarded in 1991. The RBS-17 Hellfire, marketed by Rockwell as Shore Defence Hellfire, is a lightweight man-portable weapon system derived from the anti-tank missile. Besides the modified

missile itself, the system consists of an El Op Portable Advanced Laser (PAL) designator with an 8km range for targeting, a compact, foldable tripod launcher, and launch control equipment. The missile itself has a blast fragmentation warhead instead of the anti-armour warhead of the air-launched Hellfire and its autopilot is also modified to allow it to be fired at a 10 or 20 degree elevation, instead of the horizontal of an anti-tank helicopter's weapon pylon. The RBS-17 can lock on to its target before or after launch.

Finally, naval craft in Swedish Coastal Artillery service currently consist of a fleet of nine coastal and sixteen inshore minelayers, plus eighteen patrol craft and no less than 150 landing craft of various types to move troops and artillery around the densely island-strewn Swedish archipelago. All of these coast defence assets are organised into six coastal artillery brigades within which there are fifty-three static defence and a dozen mobile units, including amphibious defence and minelaying formations.

In the late 1980s Norway decided to overhaul its elderly coast defence network and in June 1990 a contract was awarded by the Royal Norwegian Navy's Material Command to Norsk Forsvarsteknologi (NFT) to modernise all the minefields and torpedo batteries at the Norwegian Coastal Artillery's fortresses along Norway's very long coastline. Nine controlled minefields and shore-mounted torpedo batteries are being modernised and three more are being added, these minefields and torpedoes all being controlled from the fortresses, the last of which will be complete in June 1997. The programme involves the modernisation of five minefields and four torpedo batteries, with the addition of two new minefields at Namsen Fjord and in Tromso and one more torpedo battery at Namsen Fjord at a total cost of NKr 700 million ($93 million). The first of the modernised complexes was being readied at the time of writing near Bergen.

The minefields are receiving a new weapons control system based on NFT's KMC 9000 tactical fire control console with new Saab electro-optical and Terma radar sensors. The existing mines are being modernised with new sensors and command and communication systems. Safety for innocent shipping is a priority and the mines can be automatically deactivated when required.

The torpedoes will similarly be modernised, as will their loading and mid-course correction arrangements and the above-water tubes will be replaced by submerged ones. All these minefields and torpedo batteries are also being provided with new communications equipment and a complete training package. Incredibly, the Norwegians still use not only the venerable British Mk8 torpedo for coastal defence, but also the T1, a Norwegian-built, German-designed G-7a of 1940s vintage. It is not clear if these weapons will remain in service beyond the completion of the new programme; Norway is a Tp61 user, its variant being the Tp617, and it would seem logical to standardise on this 533mm weapon.

Unofficial sources quoted in 1992 said that Norway then had twenty-six coastal fortresses and fifty artillery batteries and there were still twenty-six coastal fortresses in early 1995, equipped with 75mm, 90mm, 105mm, 120mm, 127mm and 150mm guns. The 105mm and 150mm are German relics of the Second World War which have been modernised. The further modernisation of the rest of Norwegian coastal artillery has involved the installation of Bofors 120mm ERSTA guns and new 90mm guns, plus AA defences which include 20mm armoured turrets from NFT which use Rheinmetall Rh 202 20mm guns. This remarkable little turret, with 360 degree traverse and 50 degree elevation, has a 150 degree field of view and a sight with 8x magnification.

Norway may also benefit in 1997–98 from the aforementioned joint Swedish-Norwegian STARKA project for new mobile 155mm artillery, for which the Norwegian designation is IM-battery. However at the time of writing there was some uncertainty over Norwegian commitment to further coastal defence expenditure. Coastal protection is not cheap: in 1992 the cost of a Norwegian coastal fort was officially stated to be NKr 819 million or $160 million, providing an indicator of the investment involved. Strangely, one weapon which has not yet entered service with Norway's coastal defences is NFT's Penguin SSM, although the Norwegian Defence Ministry has looked at launcher options including a truck launcher with six missiles. The weapon is in very widespread use on sundry Norwegian FACs and on F-16A/B fighters. In the coast defence role, Penguin Mk.2 could achieve a range of between 25 and 27km.

One other Scandinavian country which does use shore-fired SSMs though is Denmark, which as already mentioned has two batteries of 100km+ range McDonnell Douglas Harpoon 1Cs taken from the decommissioned 1960s-built frigates *Niels Juel* and *Herluf Trolle*. Danish company NEA Lindberg designed and manufactured the specialist equipment used in this conversion. Each battery comprises two Scania launch vehicles with quad launchers plus a Scania command vehicle, all these vehicles towing their own generators on support trailers.

Otherwise Denmark still retains coastal artillery at Stevns and Langeland forts, where of ten 150mm guns taken from German battleships, four at Stevns fort are in two twin SKC/28 mountings taken from the *Gneisenau*. These forts were reduced to reserve status in 1983 but are put through their paces by reservists once a year, firing live ammunition and supported by coastal radar networks. One 1994 report said only one fort was still operational while another said Denmark still uses ex-US 3in (76mm) 50cal naval mountings for coastal defence. There were also six other forts until recently equipped with a wide range of artillery including 210mm, 170mm, 150mm, 120mm and 105mm with, until 1983, 40mm guns for protection against air threats.

Hellfire
The lightest current coastal defence missile system is the Hellfire, from McDonnell Douglas. A variant of the helicopter-fired anti-tank missile, the Shore Defence Hellfire is now in service with the Swedish Coastal Artillery (McDonnell Douglas)

RBS15
Yet another Swedish concept, and the most popular internationally, is the coast defence anti-ship missile, in this case a Bofors RBS15 seen at launch from its mobile transporter-launcher (Bofors)

STARKA
The Swedish Coastal Artillery's STARKA concept, under study from 1992, which has also been offered to Norway, is based on the premise that future coastal artillery will survive longer if it is mobile. STARKA uses pre-prepared, hidden positions along a coastline, from which self-propelled artillery can suddenly emerge and then withdraw after firing, using a variation on 'shoot and scoot' tactics (GPH Collection)

Finland, like its Scandinavian neighbours, has always respected the usefulness of coastal defence and today fields five RBS-15KA quad launchers, plus copious static artillery, comprising 170 M-54 130mm guns, M-60 122mm and D-10T 100mm tank turrets (from decommissioned T-55 tanks), organised in two army coast artillery regiments and three independent battalions, one of them mobile.[3]

The emphasis on coastal defence shown by Scandinavian countries is still shared by a surprisingly large number of countries, although this is still mainly a preoccupation of the major powers, several European nations and a handful of Latin American and Asian states. In Africa for example, only one sub-Saharan country, Angola, is known to possess a coastal defence system – with a Soviet-supplied SS-C-1 Sepal battery at Luanda. Cost is clearly an obvious factor in discouraging the acquisition of specialised coast defence capabilities in Africa.

Similarly, in the rest of Western Europe beyond Scandinavia, only Spain and Portugal have dedicated coast defence units. Portugal's are equipped with six 234mm,

9.2in Vickers pattern weapons installed in the 1950s (Ireland's 9.2in guns and their 1938 vintage shells were kept in working order as late as the early 1980s).

Meanwhile Spain still has a galaxy of coastal artillery in two groups in the Balearics and at her North African enclaves of Ceuta and Melilla, with other guns stationed near the strait of Gibraltar – what the Spanish call 'el Estrecho'. These units have seventeen Vickers Model 1926 381mm 45cal (15in), sixteen Vickers Model 1912 305mm 50cal (12in) and ninety-seven 152mm. The 305mm guns were removed from the previously described small battleships *Espana* and *Jaime I* upon decommissioning. Eight are stationed near the straits at Punta Paloma Baja, Punta Caraminal and at Cadiz/San Fernando. Also guarding the straits are two 381mm (15in) at Punta Paloma Alta – the largest such artillery still in use anywhere.[4]

Elsewhere in Europe – besides Turkey's 1950s-supplied 9.2in (234mm) guns – coast defence is only of interest to the former Warsaw Pact. Bulgaria has two regiments and twenty batteries with 150 100mm and four SM-4–1 130mm, plus

SS-C-1b Sepal and SS-C-3 Styx SSMs. Poland's army has 3,100 men in six battalions with 152mm M-1937, plus three SS-C-2B battalions. Romania's navy has 1,000 men with thirty-two 130mm, while in Ukraine, 5,000 troops under navy command in a reserve coast defence division have seventy-two towed D-30 and twenty-three self-propelled (SP) 2S1 artillery and twenty-four 2S9 SP combined gun/mortars.

Lastly, Russia has 29,500 coast defence soldiers, but only 4,500 are in identified coast defence artillery and rocket troop units, with forty SS-C-1b SSMs, plus SS-C-3 and SS-C-4 defending base approaches. Also still in use is elderly 130mm SM-4-1 artillery. It should be noted that the first coast defence missile was the Soviet Union's SS-C-2, locally designated Komet, which entered service in 1958 and re-sembled a scaled-down MiG-15 fighter. Outside the War-saw Pact, Komet saw service with Cuba, Egypt and Syria.

Just as Russia led then, she is at least in a position to lead now, although lack of funding is the major hurdle. The Chelomey design bureau has thus designed a coast defence variant of its state-of-the-art Yakhont ramjet-powered supersonic anti-ship missile – appropriately named Bastion.

Russia and Spain are not alone in using old coastal artill-ery. Astonishingly, sixteen American-supplied First World War 155mm GPFM-3 guns are still being used for coastal defence in Chile, controlled by a Chilean-developed system using commercial microcomputers – an example of how the marriage of the very old and the new can provide a cost-effective defence. The guns include French-made M1917A1s with American breech and firing mechanisms. The Americans also supplied such weapons to Peru and Venezuela. The latter are no longer in service, although there are still eighteen of the former. Elsewhere in Latin America, the Brazilian Army is still a major user of coast

Norwegian minefield Norway has been updating its complex web of coastal controlled minefields and shore-fired torpedo batteries in the 1990s. This illustrates the system package being delivered (Kongsberg Defence)

artillery, with 240 guns, comprising 305mm, 152mm and 150mm, 120mm and even 75mm and 57mm, in two coast and air defence artillery brigades. The Cuban Navy still mans two SS-C-3 SSM units, plus 152mm M-1937, 130mm M46 and 122mm M1931/7 artillery.

In the Middle East, the only export opportunity for the Franco-Italian coastal Otomat SSM has been in Egypt, whose army also mans 130mm SM-4–1 guns under navy command – weapons originally acquired very much with the memory of Suez in mind. The Qatar Navy meanwhile deploys four quad launchers for MM40 Exocet SSMs. Less sophisticated perhaps are the Silkworms fielded by the Pasdaran Inqilab, Iran's Revolutionary Guard Corps, which also deploys artillery under joint command with the Iranian Navy. Unclear though is the status of the 130mm SM-1–1 guns in Yemen, following the civil war between north and south.

In Asia only the major powers can afford coastal defences. China's naval Coastal Regional Defence Forces have around thirty-five artillery and SSM regiments in twenty-five coast defence regions protecting key points, fielding HY-2, HY-4 and C-201 (Silkworm) SSMs, plus 130mm, 100mm and 85mm guns. The Japanese Ground Self Defence Force has plans for fifty-six truck-mounted sextuple launchers for the Mitsubishi SSM-1 SSM (also referred to as the Type 88), for which a requirement for 384 missiles was stated in 1988 (hence Type 88), when the first six truck-mounted launchers were funded. The SSM-1 is a turbojet-powered weapon with two rocket boosters and a range of 150km. At 225kg, the warhead is substantially heavier than Exocet's 165kg, but only marginally heavier than Harpoon's 221.5kg.

While South Korea's Marines are another user of coastal Harpoon, North Korea's navy has two regiments with Silkworm in six sites, plus 152mm M-1937, 130mm SM-4–1, and 122mm M-1931 and M-1937 guns. In Taiwan, one navy SSM battalion is equipped with locally-built Gabriel copies, the Hsiung Feng. Taiwan is also said still to be using for coastal defence US 5in 38cal guns taken from surplus destroyer tonnage.

There is one other country in Asia which has started to take coastal defence so seriously that in 1992 it set up a special command for the purpose. Under naval command, Thailand's Air and Coastal Defence Command has been set up specifically to protect the Thai eastern seaboard, site of a major current infrastructure development. With 8,000 men, the command may expand to 15,000 if the southern seaboard development project takes off. A coastal defence regiment based at Sattahip has 155mm and 130mm guns, while an air defence regiment has Chinese AA guns and man-portable SAMs.[5]

Shore-based coast defence systems may be dominated by gunnery, SSMs and, in Scandinavia, controlled minefields and shore-based torpedo batteries, but a 'cheap and cheer-ful' alternative with the benefit of mobility is unguided rocketry of the 'Katyusha' or BM-21 variety, as operated by former Eastern bloc nations and its Western equivalents. Russia's Rosvoorouzhenie defence sales agency is presently marketing the BM-21/22 'Grad' bombardment rocket launcher as, *inter alia*, a coast defence weapon.

Clearly any country equipped with a bombardment rocket system such as the potent US Multiple Launch Rocket System (MLRS), which was to put to such deadly use by the US and British armies during the 1991 Gulf war, could in theory also use it for coastal defence, although this is unlikely. The same could be said of the Russian Smerch rocket launcher system. Cost is one reason, the need for specialised training appropriate to the coast defence mission is another, and the desire of armies to preserve such a valuable asset for its primary field mission is a third.

However there are cheaper alternatives other than the usual BM21 and its former Eastern bloc derivatives, which are now being either widely exported or made available on the export market. For example Brazil's Avibras has recently been marketing its Astros II system, comprising a truck-mounted launcher for unguided rockets which can reach out to targets between 10 and 70km away, using different types of multiple warheads and dual-purpose munitions. The rockets themselves are offered in three variants, the SS-30, SS-40 and SS-60. Astros II effectively represents a low-cost alternative to MLRS.

At the other end of the scale a similar, although much smaller, weapon is the 68mm Rocket System offered by Belgium's Forges de Zeebrugge, first shown at the 1992 Bourget Naval exhibition. A pair of rocket pods, analogous to similar pods carried by attack aircraft and combat helicopters, would be managed by a GRCS fire-control computer, firing multi-dart or unitary rounds out to a maximum range of 6km.

Beyond SSMs, guns and bombardment rockets, there is of course the humble mine. It remains the coast defence weapon par excellence. Practically everyone can afford it. One does not need a dedicated minelayer to deliver it (the Libyans are suspected of once having used civilian ferries for the job in the Red Sea) and, with luck, it can even be laid without an enemy suspecting. The technology of mine warfare and mine countermeasures (MCM) is beyond the scope of this narrative, but a few salient points can be made. Mines come in various guises, responding to acoustic, magnetic or pressure signatures and of course the contact mine is still with us – the Iranians used M-08 mines in 1987, of Soviet design and North Korean manufacture, which were derived from a Russian 1898-vintage mine used in the Russo-Japanese War in 1904–05. Some countries, like Russia for example, are manufacturing mines which have been specifically designed for the littoral environment and Russia has even developed specialised river mines, such as the magnetic MIRAB which, despite their venerable history (dating back to 1939) remain a potent threat in estuaries. The most recent Russian innovations have included coastal defence mines which, upon detection of a target, launch torpedoes at them – breathing new life into the traditional Scandinavian shore-based torpedo battery.

At the time of writing, there were at least eighteen countries known to be manufacturers of sea mines, including not only 'the usual suspects', but also newcomers such as Chile, Iraq, South Africa and Taiwan. As the technology spreads, and as sophisticated MCM becomes ever more expensive and MCM hulls ever fewer, it is hard to avoid the conclusion that here, too, is another area of coastal defence where the advantage has shifted even further in favour of an appropriately equipped and canny defender. In the 1982 Falklands War the British did not risk their excellent 'Hunt' class minehunter-sweepers, leaving minesweeping to expendable deep-sea trawlers which had been taken up from trade. After the war, with the threat of other hostile action removed, the 'Hunts' did clear some mines though.

A final point on mines: their use by Iraq in 1990–91 did not alter the Gulf War's outcome, but imagine a situation in which there is no alternative line of approach except direct attack via a small coastline, a modern Gallipoli if you will. In such a situation coastal minefields could play a strategic role, potentially turning the tables completely against the attacker – especially if the defender can also control the electronic environment.

Here is one other aspect of modern shore defence – the combination of weapons, their fire control systems, modern information technology and communications – which in sure hands can provide the defender with another advantage. The adoption of a 'systems approach' to the coast defence problem is now changing strategists' attitudes, especially given that coastal surveillance assets, such as mobile radars, can easily be put to useful civilian as well as military use. Some surveillance systems can also be containerised, lending mobility and ease of maintenance, witness the containerised multi-sensor surveillance systems developed by Thorn EMI for use at the Royal Navy's Faslane submarine base.[6]

The awareness of such possibilities, combined with the example being provided by Scandinavian nations in how a modern coast defence network should be established is still curiously lost on some analysts. But the message is spreading.

An informative paper on electronic support measures in the littoral environment, presented to the 1995 International Maritime Defence Exhibition, explains the complexity of electronic warfare operations in a dense threat – and electronic emitter – environment. The paper observes that: 'land-based threats will maximise the use of terrain screening to the offshore forces in the littoral which will restrict the sensor detection range [that is, of the vessel offshore], thereby limiting the battlespace in which the

[ship's] defensive systems must react'. For the naval task force operating off a defended coastline, the effects of such terrain screening will increase the need to detect multiple electronic emitters (radars and so forth) and the need for very rapid data fusion techniques if the vessel offshore is to stand a realistic chance of surviving in the face of an organised coastal defence.[7]

It should be recalled that sea-skimming coastal-launched Exocets or Harpoons, let alone their supersonic replacements in the future, would have to be detected, decoyed or destroyed in seconds, rendering the realism of sustained littoral operations by blue water naval forces

MLRS
If you line up a Multiple Launch Rocket System (MLRS) launcher within range of a threatening fleet, that fleet could be seriously disabled if required. The potential of long range bombardment rocket systems in coastal defence applications is only now being properly understood. Competitors to the US MLRS are being marketed by Russia and Brazil (Loral Vought Systems)

Manta
The ever-present coastal threat, the mine, in this case an Italian Manta shallow water 'anti-invasion' mine, with acoustic and magnetic fuses. Weight is 220–240kg, the shelf life is 30 years, the effective life after being laid is over a year. The mine remains the most cost-effective coast defence weapon, if you know where to put them (Misar)

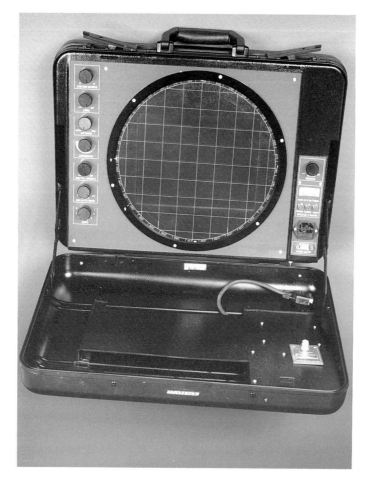

Pilotwatch
A transportable radar monitoring system suitable for coastguard use is the UK's Pilotwatch. The case is shown opened with the radio antenna connection in the lid, with liquid crystal display status indicators and control switches in the case's body (Thornson Thorn Missile Systems)

the cost and material, but also the lives, necessary for an amphibious assault on a well-defended coastline despite the US Navy's and Marine Corps' October 1992 doctrinal White Paper, *From the Sea*, and its emphasis on littoral warfare.

In the last analysis, it is always the calibre of the people involved which matters the most, but the question has to be asked: in an age of potentially dense high technology threat environments, in seriously contested coastal waters, will democratic nations with accountable legislatures ever again accept the risk of casualties comparable to Iwo Jima or 'bloody Omaha'?

It is no accident that the US Marine Corps has developed helicopter lift to, hopefully, just beyond an enemy's coast into such an art form. The Leathernecks may sing about the 'shores of Tripoli', but they would ideally prefer not to have to actually wade ashore on them, especially if that enemy's arsenal is graced with SSMs, guns, minefields and the like. Of course the alternative, as at San Carlos, is to try to pick a lightly defended landing zone – and hope for the best – even it means a long journey to your final destination.

1 Martin Middlebrook, *Task Force – The Falklands War, 1982* (Harmondsworth, Middlesex, England – Revised Edition, 1987). The South Georgia engagement is described on pp58–61; the Fanning Head engagement on pp206–7; the Exocet attack on *Glamorgan* on pp353–5.

2 George Paloczi-Horvath, 'New Directions for Coastal Defence', *Defence*, June 1993, p14.

3 Information on modern coastal artillery, SSM characteristics and deployment, mines and other coast defence weapons is drawn chiefly from Friedman, ibid; *The Military Balance 1994–1995*, International Institute of Strategic Studies, Brassey's, (London, 1994); George Paloczi-Horvath & Kay Atwal, 'Protecting the Shore', *Defence* (October 1992), pp14–19; Jonathan Portman, 'Upgrading Coastal Defences', *Defence Systems Modernisation* (August 1992), pp26–7.

4 *Defensa*, No.183/184, (Madrid, July/August edition, 1993), pp74 & 79.

5 *Jane's Defence Weekly*, 3 December 1994, p18.

6 Portman, *Defence Systems Modernisation*, ibid.

7 Dr A G Self, Lockheed Canada Inc., *The Littoral – Some Implications for ESM Systems*, paper presented to the International Maritime Defence Exhibition, Greenwich, London, 1995.

potentially very dangerous indeed. Whether the mission is invasion, sanctions enforcement (as in the Adriatic during the conflicts in the former Yugoslavia) or mere sabre-rattling, tarrying off a hostile coast can be more dangerous than ever.

It is hard to avoid the conclusion that as the major powers' tolerance of high casualties in war has generally decreased over the past half century – because of the experience of Vietnam, Afghanistan or wherever – it is increasingly unlikely that nations will be willing to invest not only

Afterword

WHAT ARE THE ENDURING lessons of the history of coastal defence, for the attacker as well as the defender? Part of the intellectual problem which both specialists and historians have in taking a balanced view of this discipline is that, since Mahan, it has been very hard to find evidence of coastal defence being among the classic preoccupations of maritime thinkers concerned with grand strategy. The traditional view, to the extent that any serious intellectual consideration was given to the subject at all, was that coastal defence was merely a mechanistic adjunct to the main game: you either had enough destroyers, torpedo boats, minefields, guns and troops to defend your shoreline – with air support to match – or you didn't. According to this outlook, more complex and subtle coast defence calculations were meaningless and anyway, since 1940, they summoned up unkind parallels with 'Maginot line' thinking and could hence be safely overlooked.

The result, more often than not, was that with the exception of those countries which demonstrated an understanding of the strategic value for themselves of an integrated coastal defence, very few countries took coastal defence seriously at all until they had to – or until it was too late.

But, as this study has tried to show, from the floating batteries of the Crimean War to the unwieldy monitors and ironclads of the American Civil War, from *Prince Albert* to *Devastation*, purpose-designed coastal warships have had an influence on the development of naval design far greater than their humble original purposes might at first have indicated.

Though there were some Americans who were so bedazzled by the new technology that they believed their monitors could take on far more powerful European adversaries, most realistic observers of the time knew well the limitations of these craft. And yet, *Monitor* proved to be both an inspiration, a source of desperation – and a deterrent. One important major study of the Battle of Hampton Roads which unfortunately only came to the author's attention after the main body of this book was written describes the impression which both *Monitor* and her redoubtable opponent *Virginia* created in the minds of those who saw them, served on them, or fought against them.

Monitor caused desperation to her crew simply because of her very low freeboard. Her paymaster wrote that: 'Our decks are constantly covered with a sea of foam pouring from one side to the other as the deck is inclined, while at short intervals a dense green sea rolls across with terrible force, breaking into foam at every obstruction offered to its passage'[1].

That the Union had felt obliged to so rapidly construct what was essentially an armoured, steam-powered raft to defend her ports and coast against Confederate marauders was a reflection of her weakness at the outset of the Civil War. Despite her implicit industrial strength, the Union lacked the iron-cased seagoing warships which were beginning to grace the fleets of France and Britain. America's foremost shipbuilder, Donald McKay, had called for a US response to European progress, saying: 'It would be easy for us to build in one year, a fleet of 500 to 600 men-of-war ships, from a gunboat to the largest of iron-cased frigates'[2]. This was of course somewhat optimistic, especially when more sober minds were concentrated on simply trying to keep one particular frigate, the *Merrimack*, out of Confederate hands. This effort failed. *Merrimack* was transformed into the ironclad *Virginia*, and the inconclusive Battle of Hampton Roads in 1862 was the result.

William Davis' book makes a number of interesting observations. One is that John Ericsson's design for *Monitor* was only one of six designs for turrets vessels to be submitted to Commodore Joseph Smith's examining board[3]. Another illuminating sideline is that the original contract called for the vessel to be capable of making six knots under sail![4] A further point is the sheer strangeness of *Monitor*'s appearance to anyone who saw her at the time. One such observer, upon setting eyes on the curious Union vessel, was moved to say that: 'No words can express the surprise with which we beheld this strange craft, whose appearance was tersely and graphically described by one of my oarsmen, "A tin can on a shingle."'[5]

Whatever the fallbacks of *Monitor* and its contemporaries – and both *Monitor* and *Virginia* came to ignominious ends – their layout and concept nevertheless inspired a line of development which ultimately culminated in the *Sverige*, the *Dhonburi* and the *Väinämöinen* and, via different lines of development, both the *Dreadnought*s and all the battleships of the first half of the twentieth century.

The idea of mustering some tantalising, equaliser of a force on a small or modest hull with which to overcome a more powerful warship is as old as maritime warfare. But the classic coast defence ship, either when included in a balanced fleet or when it led a fleet, and when it was built in sufficient numbers, could contribute to a very meaningful 'fleet in being'. Powerful navies, like France's for instance, considered them as essential adjuncts to the main fleet. Lesser navies had few other options and, realistically, the construction of effective coastal defence battleship fleets was the only credible strategy.

But the fact is that only a very few countries managed to develop such strategies and construct meaningful flotillas of these vessels. Sweden had a dozen coastal battleships in service in 1906 (after the launching of *Oscar II* in the previous year), while France had no fewer than fifteen (of very mixed capabilities) in the same year. But the latter were part of a much larger fleet, originally constructed very much with a British threat in mind. By 1906, following the commissioning of *Dreadnought* and the establishment of the 'Entente Cordiale' with Britain two years before, many of these vessels' original purpose had been eradicated. Nevertheless, some proved useful in the First World War, as shown in Chapter 7.

Yet only Sweden and, arguably, Denmark and the Netherlands with their nine coast defence ships apiece in 1906, ever had a truly meaningful coast defence battleship force at any one time. In the Danish case, some of the vessels still around in the early twentieth century were very old. The rest of the coast defence navies never had more than a handful, or fewer, of the type at any one time. Norway had four ships from 1900 to 1940, while the Thais had four in the late 1930s (if you include the two 886 ton *Ratanakosindra* class vessels, that is).

So, if their numbers were so small in most countries, what was the point of having them at all? Why not simply spend money on, say, an armoured cruiser (very popular around the turn of the century), or a mixed fleet of destroyers, submarines and, at the most, cruisers in later years?

The latter approach was precisely the course chosen by the Netherlands, although this was more by default as that country's ambitious plans to build capital ships, first battleships and later battlecruisers, never came to anything. The former approach of reliance on armoured cruisers was partly chosen by the likes of Argentina and Spain, although the Spanish learned at Santiago in 1898, in a very painful manner, just why armoured cruisers could not be a credible answer to battleships with superior gunnery and armour.

But what could have been an answer, in the right location, might have been a coast defence ship with armour comparable to the battleships of the period. In the context of this debate, the decision to design or build modern coast defence ships after the *Sverige* class is more significant. Finland with the *Väinämöinens*, and Denmark with its stillborn concepts of the 1930s, showed that very considerable batteries and respectable armour could yet be provided on small shallow draught hulls.

It may be of interest to readers that a useful source of information on Ingenieur-Kantoor voor Scheepsbouw (IvS), the Dutch firm which designed *Väinämöinen*, is William Manchester's massive study of the German armaments and steel family Krupp. This describes in detail how the restrictions of the Versailles Treaty were evaded by the establishment of IvS – 'the heart of Krupp's Dutch complex' – in The Hague 'with the approval and co-operation of Admiral Behncke's Marineleitung in Berlin'. A careful reading of these pages establishes a strong indirect link between *Väinämöinen* and the 'Panzerschiff' *Deutschland*[6].

In the light of such impressive designs and concepts, it is tempting to wonder what might have happened at Narvik in 1940 if the Norwegians had been equipped with modern vessels comparable to the *Väinämöinen*s. There seems little doubt that, in capable hands, two such vessels might have wiped out the German destroyer force which fell upon Narvik that April. Whether a better-equipped Norwegian fleet could have altered the course of history, or at least the Narvik campaign, is of course a moot point, although there is no shortage of opinions which hold that the latter's outcome was not inevitable[7].

If classic gun-armed coast defence ships never managed to alter the course of actual maritime conflicts, they certainly inspired further developments of the genre which played a major role in the creation of the big gun battleship, as well as contributing to the design process which spawned intermediate ideas like Germany's 'Panzerschiffe'. As outlined in Chapter 8, these vessels were difficult to classify when they were designed, 'armoured ship' being a meaningless or euphemistic term to most foreign observers, leading to such hyperbole as their description by the British as 'pocket battleships', a term which the Germans never used. Today, they are perhaps best described as armoured cruisers. In this connection, it is interesting to note that Britain continued this habit of not sharing the German view of their capital ships, *Gneisenau* and *Scharnhorst* being described as battleships by the Germans and battlecruisers by the British, who felt that their inferior armour and – compared to most battleships – their inferior gunnery merited the description.

In at least one case, that of Sweden, coast defence battleships and the rest of the network of coastal defence so painstakingly constructed in that country, posed an effective deterrent to much more powerful potential adversaries like Germany and the Soviet Union and as such influenced the course of greater events in northern Europe.

The demise of the battleship after the Second World War and the creation of wholly new military technologies, ranging from the atom bomb to the guided missile, seemed to make a nonsense of the idea of coastal defence. (The same assumption was made by observers reflecting on many other military technologies, from armoured vehicles to artillery and conventional manned military aircraft.) Still, many countries chose to retain their coastal gunnery after 1945 and, in time, a totally new coastal defence vessel in the fast missile boat was created whose primary weapon had a far greater range than the torpedo boat with limited seakeeping which it replaced.

Almost a century and a half after the *Monitor*, the modern missile corvette is the true inheritor of the mantle once worn by the gun-armed coast defence ship. In designs such as the trimaran frigate and corvette concepts now being investigated by shipyards and, for example, the Ministry of Defence in Britain, the coast defence missile corvette is even leading the way towards wholly new hull forms. It is a fair bet that within the next generation, the trimaran hull form might take its place in several of the world's navies.

As such, one generic type of vessel – the coast defence ship – will have again shown that just as it can be renewed to cope with new threats, it can also be modernised in order to seize a technical lead, just as the turret ship *Prince Albert*

had done in the 1860s, inspiring a whole new range of vessels which, as the 'Family Tree' of coast defence ships shows, led directly to the largest battleships. Thus has the coast defence ship earned its place in history.

1 William C. Davis, *Duel between the First Ironclads*, (Pennsylvania, 1994), p2. Edition, with new material, of a work first published in New York in 1975.

2 Ibid. p6.

3 Ibid. p19.

4 Ibid. p42.

5 Ibid. p118.

6 William Manchester, *The Arms of Krupp 1587–1968* (London, 1969), pp395–6. See also pp422, 424, 426 & 464.

7 For instance, Waage, *The Narvik Campaign*, op. cit.

Trimaran corvette
In 1995 Vosper Thornycroft outlined an extraordinary design aimed at the export market: a guided missile corvette with a trimaran hull. Among its benefits are the positioning of the helicopter hangar and flight deck further forward than usual, with the result that helicopters could be operated in higher sea states. The concept will be put to the test when Britain completes a trials trimaran in the late 1990s. (Vosper Thornycroft)

Update

THIS BOOK WAS WRITTEN between 1993 and 1995, but since its completion the world of coastal defence has obviously not been standing still. It is a mark of the pace of change in naval technology that there have been sufficient new developments either not recorded or not mentioned in detail in Chapters 12 and 13 to justify this update on where the discipline of coast defence stood in the spring of 1996.

The trend towards the construction of larger missile corvettes instead of the building of fast attack missile boats in the 200–500 tonne range has continued. In the Middle East, Oman has led the way with its contract for two 83m vessels built by Britain's Vosper Thornycroft, the first of which was delivered in early 1996. These vessels are interesting in that they were designed with the experience of the 1991 Gulf War in mind and include an improved command and control suite. As outlined in Chapter 12, a common criticism of fast attack missile boats has been their weak command, control, communications and intelligence (C3I) suites. In the case of Oman's vessels, this requirement is addressed by the Tavitac system from France's Thomson-CSF.

Brunei has also followed Oman's example and ordered three so-called 'Offshore Patrol Vessels' (OPVs) from Britain's Yarrow Shipbuilders in late 1995. These will be 1,500 tonne missile corvettes broadly similar to Oman's, but the Sultan of Brunei doubtless feels that discretion is the better part of valour and a suitably unthreatening euphemism is better than a more appropriate designation. Another Far

Eastern country taking the same approach is Malaysia, which, at the time of writing, was about to choose a design for its so-called 'New Generation Patrol Vessel'. By all accounts, these missile- and helicopter-equipped ships will in truth be well-armed light frigates, albeit with the primary role of patrolling Malaysia's extensive Exclusive Economic Zone (EEZ), which as this book has shown is but a further extension of the classic coastal defence role. This tendency to underplay the capabilities of the modern missile corvette has also been demonstrated by Kuwait, which uses the bland term 'Offshore Missile Vessel' to describe its future missile corvette.

What is responsible for this outbreak of naval euphemisms? A possible reason is the fact that virtually all the navies which have decided to order missile corvettes in the 1990s are, in effect, trading up from smaller, less capable fast attack craft and, in so doing, are fuelling regional arms races. This is quite evident in both the Middle East and Far East, two growth areas for this type of vessel. Malaysia has also taken advantage of the availability of several *Assad* class missile corvettes originally bought by Iraq but never delivered because of the Gulf War, ordering two from their Italian builders, Fincantieri. They have now been extensively modified for Far Eastern service.

One area, though, where missile corvettes have prompted neither an arms race nor linguistic escapism is the Baltic, where Sweden placed an order for the first two 600 tonne *YS 2000* missile corvettes in October 1995. These will use the stealth technologies investigated by the experimental craft *Smyge* (described in Chapter 12) and will replace

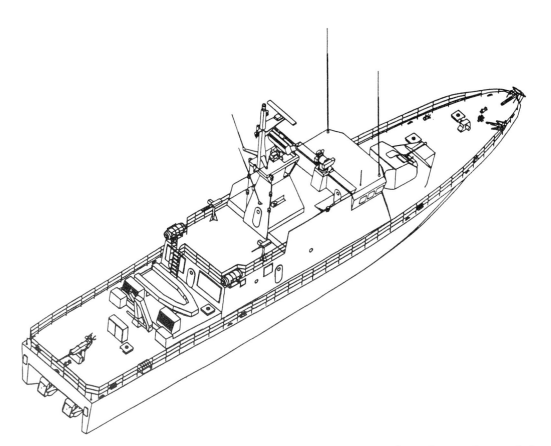

PB-37BRL
Just as there is a trend away from smaller fast attack missile boats to larger corvettes, some navies are choosing to put short-range anti-ship missiles on small patrol boats. The PB-37BRL patrol boat, eight of which have been ordered from France by the Kuwaiti Navy, is one example. As this book went to press, its anti-ship missiles had not yet been chosen. (CMN)

smaller fast attack craft in the Swedish Navy. Across the Baltic, Germany will do the same whenever it finances the fifteen corvettes which will replace its missile boats. Because this project has been delayed, the Bundesmarine is considering a service life extension programme for its Type 148 missile boats. This could include the installation of a quad 27mm Drakon close-in weapon system and a new command system.

The Middle East and Far East are also the growth areas for another, entirely different type of coastal defence craft, the development of which is more a response to improved missile technology than some ill-considered addition of another spiral to regional arms races.

Two navies, Kuwait's and the Philippines', have decided to arm small patrol boats with short-range anti-ship missiles rather more modest than the Exocets and Harpoons which equip most fleets. These weapons, British Aerospace's Sea Skua SL and Aerospatiale's MM-15, are both derivatives of helicopter-launched weapons described in Chapter 12. In the case of Kuwait's PB37BRL boats, a capability is being provided to install short-range surface-to-air missiles (SAMs), namely a sextuple Sadral launcher for Matra's Mistral SAM. The C3I fit of the Kuwaiti craft is also impressive for the vessel's size. This is a derivative of Tavitac, the system on Oman's corvettes. The Philippines requires the same kind of patrol boats, equipped with the same generic type of missile. However these developments will not tip

the balance away from the trend towards larger, rather than smaller, missile boats and corvettes.

Just as a number of navies in the Middle East and Far East have chosen to describe their missile corvettes as what they are not, most operators of genuine OPVs – including a few new ones – have remained content to describe them for what they are. Two new designs which have recently been chosen by Mauritius and Morocco are intriguing examples of how good compromises can be reached between economy and innovation. Their primary purpose is to patrol national EEZs, and their armament is either negligible or non-existent, although in the case of Morocco's *Rais Bargach*, the first vessel of the class was unarmed at its delivery, while the second carries a 40mm gun forward. The four ships of this class (the first was launched in October 1995) have one very useful feature for the EEZ patrol role: an enclosed well at the stern which allows the easy launch and recovery of a rigid inflatable boat to transport boarding parties to vessels under investigation. There is also room for 30 soldiers in addition to the 24 crew.

Vigilant, the 75m, 1,350 tonne Mauritian vessel was launched in December 1995 and is equally interesting for other reasons. Designed by Canada's W.C.M.G., it is being built by Chile's Asmar shipyard – a new force in world naval construction. The sleek craft resembles the most elegant of fast luxury yachts and will be capable of carrying a helicopter and of reaching a 'hot pursuit' speed of 22 knots and a

Rais Bargach
The service provided by offshore patrol vessels is another form of coastal defence. This very economical 64m, 600 tonne French-built vessel, the Moroccan Navy's Rais Bargach, *was handed over in December 1995. Seakeeping is said to be excellent. Remarkably, the vessel was unarmed at delivery and the Moroccans seemed sanguine about leaving things that way, though she can mount a 76mm gun if required. (Leroux & Lotz)*

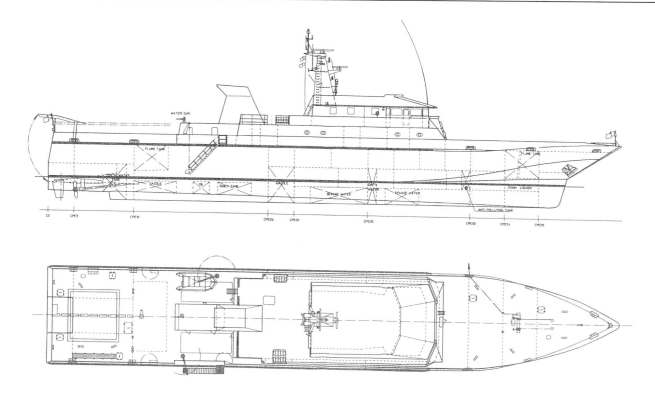

cruise speed of 19 knots, with a range of 6,500 nm. The craft will carry either a 40mm or 30mm gun, though it could mount a 76mm. The vessel will be a good example of 'for, but not with' capabilities and straddles the line between the corvette with an unambiguous military purpose and the OPV intended to protect the EEZ. In this respect, Asmar's vessel is significantly cheaper than, for example, the French *Floréal* class intended for the same missions.

Several countries continue to update their fixed coastal defences. As usual, Scandinavia leads the way. As outlined in Chapter 13, Norway launched a project to modernise its coastal defences in 1992 and has now added a £71 million order for twelve mobile coastal defence military units to replace fixed coastal artillery. It is significant that despite the ending of the Cold War, Norway has managed to find the money for this despite the belief in some quarters that new coast defence systems are unaffordable. Norway has bought the shore-fired RBS-17 Hellfire missile as already acquired for the Swedish Coastal Artillery. Another £45 million order has been placed for laser designators, C3 equipment and assault craft to transport Norwegian Coastal Artillery units. These assault craft will consist of sixteen aluminium-hulled *Stridsbåt 90N* craft which have been ordered from Sweden's Dockstavarvet. Sweden uses the same type of 18 tonne vessel and, like Norway, deploys these

15.9m craft for transporting coastal artillery units around its coastline. Norway has an option to buy another four to sixteen boats, while the Swedish Coast Artillery is also now testing British-built ABS *M-10* hovercraft for the same role.

A more passive, but equally effective form of coastal defence are the surveillance capabilities which now equip Egypt's forces. They have lately been updating their Coastal Border Surveillance System (CBSS) by adding electro-optical equipment. This consists of coastal pedestal-mounted infra-red and TV cameras which can identify ship targets located by CBSS by day or night.

Change has not been confined to technology in the months since the main text of this book was completed. In December 1995 Britain's Royal Navy published a new document, *The Fundamentals of British Maritime Doctrine*, which outlines the UK's post-Cold War naval strategy[1]. This pays particular attention to 'littoral' concerns, also reflecting the principal focus of the new US naval policy paper, *From the Sea*. The British doctrine talks about coast offence and amphibious operations, but only refers to modern coast defence in an oblique way when it very briefly discusses 'Combat Operations in Defence of Forces Ashore'. But the doctrine also contains many useful examples of both recent and more distant naval conflicts in order to provoke debates among the naval officers of the future.

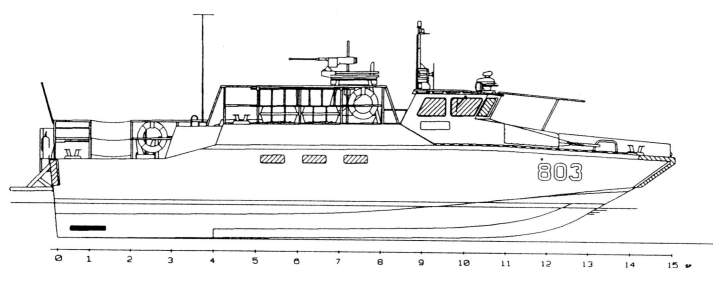

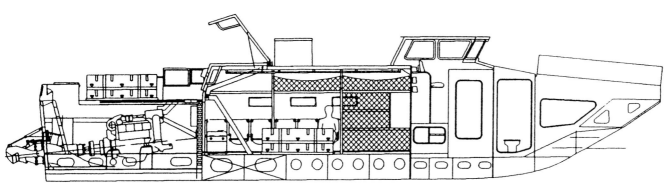

Stridsbåt 90N
Coastal defence takes many forms in Scandinavia. One such is the transporting of coastal artillery units between the coast and islands, and across fjords. Norway has ordered 16 of these Swedish-built, 18 tonne Stridsbåt 90N *aluminium-hulled assault craft for her coastal artillery. Sweden also uses the type (Dockstavarvet)*

One of these examples is a comment entitled 'Gallipoli – How Not to Fight', which bears quoting in full for reasons which will become apparent.

The Allied maritime operations in 1915–16 to exploit the possibilities of strategic leverage and pass through the Dardanelles with a fleet that would force Turkey out of the war, were a case study in how not to mount a joint operation. The initial plan, to carry out the operation with ships alone, reflected the lack of a joint approach at the military strategic level. The original campaign plan underestimated the power of the mutually supporting gun and mine defences, and was finally abandoned because of a failure at the tactical level to neutralize them sufficiently. When amphibious landings on the Gallipoli peninsula eventually took place, inadequacies in command and control resulted in failure to achieve their objectives. There was no doctrine for such operations and tactical commanders did not realize what was expected of them. A second wave of landings failed for the same reasons. The result was stalemate on the ground and the landing forces were eventually withdrawn in a meticulously planned evacuation that was the most successful part of the whole affair. A campaign imaginatively conceived at the grand strategic level failed because of strategic, operational and tactical errors.

This accurate, if damning summary could equally apply to most of those examples of failed coast defence operations described in this book. It also spells out how effective coast defences can take advantage of the particular weaknesses of an adversary. As the new British maritime document later explains, the British managed to improve their grasp of strategy and tactics when they retook the Falkland Islands from Argentina in 1982. In 1996 they established a headquarters at Northwood for their new Joint Rapid Deployment Force which will hopefully prevent mistakes such as those made at Gallipoli from ever being repeated.

Given that major Western powers like Britain are likely to be involved in coastal operations in future, either offensive or for the purpose of surveillance or sanctions monitoring, the improving coastal defence capabilities of many countries around the world will be of more than passing interest to them. As this book has tried to show, these can only be ignored at an attacker's peril.

1 *The Fundamentals of British Maritime Doctrine* (*BR 1806*), Directorate of Naval Staff Duties, The Defence Council (Ministry of Defence, London, 1995)

Appendix A: Purposed-designed Coast Defence Vessels

For the purposes of clarity and because of their influence on subsequent coast defence ship design, Appendix A includes US Civil War monitors described in Chapter 2, but not river monitors or vessels which were uncompleted, uncommissioned or which reappeared under the guise of the 'great repairs', in which case they are listed when they were first actually brought into service. Appendix A also includes purpose-designed monitors (British and Italian) used in coastal *offence* roles in the First and Second World Wars, and Soviet guard ships.

In the case of a class, the first of class, or name ship, is followed by other names; the date given is for the launch or completion of the first of class; details provided are for the first of class or name ship unless otherwise indicated. Armament and armour are generally recorded in inches and fractions thereof, except where primary sources refer only to metric measurements or where metric measurements materially clarify a point of detail which is impractical to record in a different way.

For the purposes of clarity, all vessels are listed according to the chapter in which they are first described in detail, by country, and in order of launch, completion or commissioning of first of class. This does not mean that vessels are not mentioned later on (see index). For instance, where coast defence ships of the early twentieth century were put to other uses by the German Kriegsmarine, this is discussed in Chapter 9. Sources for these appendices are as referred to in the footnotes to each chapter or basic source works referred to in the first chapters to which they apply.

Reference: Chapter 2

United States

Class	Launch/Comp	Displacement	Propulsion/speed	Armour	Main armament
Monitor	30.1.1862	987t	320ihp = 6kts	4.5–2in side & 9–8in turret	2 x 11in
Passaic, Catskill, Lehigh, Montauk, Nahant, Nantucket, Patapsco, Sangamon, Weehawken	30.8.1862	1875t	320ihp = 7kts	5–3in side & 11in turret	1 x 15in SB, 3 x 11in
Roanoke	conversion completed 4.1863	4395t	440ihp nominal = 6kts	4.5–3.5in side & 11in turret	2 x 15in, 2 x 11in
Onondaga	29.7.1863	2551t	610ihp = 7kts	5.5in side & 11in turret	2 x 15in, 2 x 8in
Canonicus, Catawba, Mahopac, Manayunk, Manhattan, Oneota, Saugus, Tecumseh, Tippecanoe	1.8.1863	2100t	320ihp = 8kts	5–3in side & 10in turret	2 x 15in
Miantonomoh, Agamenticus, Monadnock, Tonawanda	15.8.1863	3400t	1400ihp = 9–10kts	5in side & 10in turret	4 x 15in
Dictator	26.12.1863	4438t	3500ihp = 11kts	6–1in side & 15in turret	2 x 15in
Milwaukee, Kickapoo, Chickasaw, Winnebago	4.2.1864	1300t	9kts	3in side & 8in turret	4 x 11in
Casco, Chimo, Naubuc, Nausett, Shawnee, Shiloh, Squando, Suncook, Tunxis	7.5.1864	1175t	600ihp = 5kts	3in side & 8in turret	2 x 11in

Reference: Chapter 2

United States

Class	Launch/Comp	Displacement	Propulsion/speed	Armour	Main armament
Confederate States					
Virginia	conversion completed 17.2.1862	4500t	7–9kts	4in casemate	6 x 9in, 2 x 7in, 2 x 6.4in
Virginia (II)	2.1863	–	5kts	6–5in casemate	2 x 7in, 4 x 6.4in
Stonewall	21.6.1863	1400t	1200ihp = 10kts.	4.5–3.5in side & 4.5in turret	1 x 10in, 2 x 6.4in

Reference: Chapter 3

Great Britain

Class	Launch/Comp	Displacement	Propulsion/speed	Armour	Main armament
Royal Sovereign	20.8.1864	5080t	2460ihp = 11kts	5.5–4.5in belt & 10.5–5.5in turret	5 x 10.5in
Prince Albert	23.5.1864	3687t	2128ihp = 11kts	4.5in belt & 10.5–5.5in turret	4 x 9in
Cerberus, Magdala	2.12.1868	3344t	1369ihp = 9.75kts	8–6in belt & 10–9in turret	4 x 10in
Abyssinia	19.2.1870	2901t	1200ihp = 9.5kts	7–6in belt & 10–8in turret	4 x 10in
Glatton	8.3.1871	4912t	2870ihp = 12kts	12–10in belt & 14–12in turret	4 x 10in
Hotspur	19.3.1870	4331t	3500ihp = 12.6kts	11–8in belt & 10.5–8in gunhouse	1 x 12in, 2 x 64pdr
Rupert	12.3.1872	5440t	4630ihp = 13.5kts	11–9in belt & 14–12in turret	2 x 10in, 2 x 64pdr
Cyclops, Gorgon, Hecate, Hydra	18.7.1871	3480t	1660ihp = 11kts	8–6in belt & 10–9in turret	4 x 10in
Scorpion, Wyvern	7.1863	2751t	1450ihp = 10.5kts	4.5–2in belt & 10–5in turret	4 x 9in
Bellisle, Orion	completed 1878	4870t	4040ihp = 12.99kts	12–6in belt & 10.5-8in battery	4 x 12in, 4 x 20pdr

Reference: Chapter 4

France

Class	Launch/Comp	Displacement	Propulsion/speed	Armour	Main armament
Palestro, Paixhans, Peiho, Saigon	Completed 9.1862	1508–1539t	150nhp = 7kts	4.7–4.3in side	12 x 6.4in
Arrogante, Implacable, Opioniatre	Completed 1.1865	1490t (1412t others)	470ihp = 6.77kts	4.7in belt & 4.3in battery	9 x 6.4in
Embuscade, Imprenable, Protectrice, Refuge	Completed 1.1866	1555t	440ihp = 7.5kts	5.5in belt & 4.3in battery	4 x 7.6in
Taureau	Completed 1866	2433t	1790ihp = 12.5kts	6in belt & 4.7in barbette	1 x 9.4in
Cerbère, Bouledogue, Belier, Tigre	Completed 10.1868	3532t	1800ihp = 12–12.5kts	8.7–7in belt & 7in turret	2 x 9.4in
Tonnere, Fulminant	Completed 1879	5765t (*Fulminant* 5871t)	4200–4500ihp = 13.7kts	13–10in belt & 13–12in turret	2 x 10.8in

Reference: Chapter 4

France					
Class	**Launch/Comp**	**Displacement**	**Propulsion/speed**	**Armour**	**Main armament**
Tempête, Vengeur	Completed 1879	4793t (*Vengeur* 4635t)	2000ihp = 11.7kts (*Vengeur* 10.7kts)	13–10in belt & 14–12in turret	2 x 10.8in (*Vengeur* 2 x 13.4in)
Rochambeau (ex-USS *Dunderberg*)	Commissioned in France 1870	7800t	4500ihp = 15kts	3.5–2.5in belt & 4.5in casemate	Rearmed with 4 x 10.8in & 10 x 9.4in
Onondaga (ex-USS *Onondaga*)	Commissioned in France 1867	2551t	610ihp = 7kts	5.5in max side & 11in turret	Rearmed with 4 x 9.4in
Russia					
Bronenosetz, Edinorog, Koldun, Latnik, Lava, Perun, Stryeletz, Tifon, Uragan, Vyeshtchun	Completed 1865–66	1565t	340–530ihp = 6.5–8kts	9–3in side & 10in turret	2 x 9in
Smerch	Completed 1865	1460t	700ihp = 8kts	4.5in side & 6–4.5in turret	4 x 60pdr
Charodeika, Russalka	Completed 1868	2100t	875ihp = 8.5kts	4.5in side & 6in turret	4 x 9in
Admiral Lazarev, Admiral Greig	Completed 1869	3820t (*Greig* 3768t, 3462t designed)	2020ihp = 10.5–11kts	4.5in side & turret	6 x 9in
Admiral Chichagov, Admiral Spiridov	Completed 1870	3925t (*Spiridov* 3851t, 3,492t designed)	2030ihp = 10.5kts	6in side & 6in turret	4 x 9in
Novgorod	Completed 1874	2491t	3000ihp = 6–7kts	9–7in side & 9in barbette	2 x 11in
Popov	Completed 1877	3550t	4500ihp = 8kts	16–14in side & 9in barbette	2 x 12in
Italy					
Palestro, Varese	5.9.1865	2165t	930ihp = 8kts	4.75in side & citadel	4 x 200mm, 1 x 165mm
Guerriera, Voragine	12.5.1866	1821t	454–588ihp = 6.3kts	5.5in side	12 guns
Alfredo Cappellini, Risoluta, Faa di Bruno, Audace	24.12.1868	631t	210ihp = 12kts	4.75in max	1 gun
Prussia/Germany					
Arminius	20.8.1864	1800t	1440ihp = 11kts	4.5in belt & turret	4 x 210mm
Wespe, Viper, Biene, Mucke, Scorpion, Basilisk, Camaleon, Crocodil, Salamander, Natter, Hummel	1876	1139t	8–9kts	8in breastwork	1 x 305mm
Denmark					
Rolf Krake	1863	1320t	750ihp = 9.5kts	4.5in side & turret	4 x 68pdr
Lindormen	1868	2048t	1500ihp = 12kts	5in side & 5.5in turret	2 x 9in
Gorm	1870	2313t	1600ihp = 12.5kts	7in side & 8in turret	2 x 10in
Odin	1872	3170t	2300ihp = 12kts	8in side & battery	4 x 10in
Helgoland	1878	5332t	4000ihp = 13.75kts	12–8in belt & 10in barbette/battery	1 x 12in, 4 x 10.2in
Sweden					
John Ericsson, Thordon, Tirfing	1865	1476t	380ihp = 7kts	4.75in hull & 10.25in turret	2 x 9.4in
Loke	1871	1574t	430ihp = 8.5kts	5in hull & 17.5–15in turret	2 x 9.4in

Reference: Chapter 4

Norway Class	Launch/Comp	Displacement	Propulsion/speed	Armour	Main armament
Skorpionen, Mjolner, Thrudvang	1866	1425t (others 1490t)	330ihp (others 450ihp) = 6 kts (others 8kts)	5in hull & 12in turret	2 x 10.5in
Thor	1872	1975t	600ihp = 8kts	7in hull & 14in turret	2 x 10.5in
Netherlands					
Heiligerlee, Krokodil, Tijger	1868	1520t	630–680ihp = 8.25–9kts	5.5in side & 11–8in turret	2 x 9in
Bloedhond, Cerberus	1869	1656t (*Cerberus* 1559t)	680ihp (*Cerberus* 534ihp) = 7.7kts (*Cerberus* 7kts)	5.5in side & 11–8in turret	2 x 9in
Adder, Haai, Hyena, Luipaard, Panter, Wesp	1871	1555t	560–740ihp = 7–8kts	5.5in side & 11–8in turret	2 x 9in
Draak	1877	2198t	807ihp = 8.4kts	8–5.5in side & 12–9in turret	2 x 11in
Matador	1878	1968t	690ihp = 7.5kts	5.5–4.5in side & 12–9in turret	2 x 11in
Greece					
Basileos Georgios	1867	1774t	2100ihp = 12.2kts	7–6in belt & 6in battery	2 x 9in
Turkey					
Lutfi Djelil, Hifzi Rahman	1868	2540t	2000ihp = 12kts	5.5in belt, 3in side & 5.5in turret	2 x 8in, 2 x 7in
Portugal					
Vasco da Gama	1876	2384t	3000ihp = 10.3kts	9–4in belt & 10–6in battery	2 x 10.2in
Brazil					
Barrozo	1864	1354t	420ihp = 9kts	3.8in–2.5in belt & battery	2 x 7in, 2 x 68pdr
Brasil	1864	1518t	975ihp = 11.3kts	4.5–3in belt & battery	4 x 7in, 4 x 68pdr
Tamandare	1865	980t	273ihp = 8.5kts	3.8–2.5in belt & battery	2 x 5.8in, 2 x 68pdr
Lima Barros	21.12.1865	1330t	2100ihp = 12kts	4.5–3in belt & turret	4 x 7in
Rio de Janeiro	–	–	–	4in belt	–
Bahia	6.10.1865	1008t	1200ihp = 10kts	4.5in belt & turret	2 x 7in
Silvado	1866	1150t	947ihp = 10.7kts	4.5–3in belt & turret	4 x 5.8in
Mariz e Barros, Herval	1866	1196t (*Herval* 1353t)	600ihp = 9kts	4.5–3in belt & battery	2 x 7in, 2 x 68pdr (*Herval* 4 x 7in)
Cabral, Colombo	1866	1033t	750ihp = 10.5kts	4.5–3in belt & battery	2 x 5.8in, 2 x 68pdr (*Colombo* 4 x 7in)
Sete de Setembro	1874	2172t	2000ihp = 10.5kts	4.5in belt & battery	4 x 9in
Javary, Solimoes	1874	3543t	2200ihp = 10kts (*Solimoes* 11.2kts)	12in belt, 12–11in turret	4 x 10in
Argentina					
La Plata	29.8.1874	1500t full load	750ihp = 9.5kts	6in belt & 9–8in turret	2 x 7.8in

Reference: Chapter 5

France

Class	Launch/Comp	Displacement	Propulsion/speed	Armour	Main armament
Tonnant	Completed 1884	5010t	2000ihp = 11.6kts	18–13.5in belt & 14.5in max barbettes	2 x 13.4in
Furieux	Completed 2.1887	5925t	4600ihp = 13kts	18–13in belt & 8in turret	2 x 13.4in
Fusée, Flamme, Grenade, Mitraille	Completed 5.1885	1073t	1500ihp = 12.5kts	9.5–4in belt & 8–4.7in barbette	1 x 9.4in
Achéron, Cocyte, Phlegeton, Styx	Completed 2.1888	1690t (*Phlegeton, Styx* 1767t)	1600ihp = 11.6–13kts	8in turret & belt	1 x 10.8in
Jemmapes, Valmy	Completed 1894	6476t	9000ihp = 16.7kts	18–10in belt & 18in turret	2 x 13.4in
Bouvines, Amiral Tréhouart	Completed 12.1894	6681t	8500ihp = 16.5–17kts	18–10in belt & 18in turret	2 x 12in

Germany

Class	Launch/Comp	Displacement	Propulsion/speed	Armour	Main armament
Siegfried, Beowulf, Frithjof, Heimdall, Hildebrand, Hagen, Odin, Ägir	Completed 19.4.1890	3691t	5000ihp = 14.5kts	7–9.5in belt & 8in turret & barbette	3 x 240mm

(**NB** see also Chapter 7 for discussion on different data for these ships)

Austria-Hungary

Class	Launch/Comp	Displacement	Propulsion/speed	Armour	Main armament
Monarch, Wien, Budapest	Completed 11.5.1898	5547t	8500ihp = 17.5kts	220–270mm belt & 250mm turret	4 x 240mm

Russia

Class	Launch/Comp	Displacement	Propulsion/speed	Armour	Main armament
Admiral Ushakov, Admiral Seniavin, General Admiral Graf Apraksin	Completed 1895	4971t	5750ihp = 16kts	10–4in belt & 8in turret	4–10in
*Grozyaschi, Gremyashchi, Otvajni**	Completed 1891	1627t	2050–2500ihp = 13–14kts	5.5–2.5in belt	1 x 9in, 1 x 6in
*Khrabri**	Completed 1897	1735t	2100ihp = 14kts	5–3.5in	2 x 8in, 1 x 6in

*classified as armoured gun vessels, rather than coast defence ships, but merit inclusion for completeness

United States

Class	Launch/Comp	Displacement	Propulsion/speed	Armour	Main armament
Puritan	Commissioned 10.12.1896	6060t	3700ihp = 12.4kts	4–6in belt, 8in turret & 14in barbette	4 x 12in
Amphitrite, Monadnock, Terror, Miantonomoh	For details see Chapter 5, Table 1, p. 60				
Monterey	Commissioned 13.2.1891	4084t	5250ihp = 13.6kts	13–5in belt, 8–7.5in turret & 13-11.5in barbette	2 x 12in, 2 x 10in
Arkansas, Nevada, Florida, Wyoming	Commissioned 28.10.1902	3225t	2400ihp = 12.5kts	11–5in belt, 10–9in turret & 11–9in barbette	2 x 12in
Indiana, Massachusetts, Oregon	Commissioned 20.11.1895	10,288t	9000ihp = 15kts	18–4in belt & 15in turret	4 x 13in

Sweden

Class	Launch/Comp	Displacement	Propulsion/speed	Armour	Main armament
*Svea, Göta, Thule**	1886	3051t	3640ihp = 14.7kts	11.5–8in belt & 11.5–9.5in turret	2 x 10in
Oden, Thord, Niord	1897	3445t	5350ihp = 16.5kts	9.5in belt & 8in turret	2 x 10in
Dristigheten	1900	3445t	5400ihp = 16.5kts	8in belt & 8–6in turret	2 x 8.3in

Reference: Chapter 5

Sweden Class	Launch/Comp	Displacement	Propulsion/speed	Armour	Main armament
Äran, Wasa, Tapperheten, Manligheten	1902	3592t	6500ihp = 17kts	7in belt & 7.5–5in turret	2 x 8.3in
Oscar II	1905	4584t	9000ihp = 18kts	6–4in belt & 7.5–5in turret	2 x 8.3in
Denmark					
Tordenskjold	1880	2462t	2600ihp = 12.75kts	no belt armour, 8in barbette	1 x 14in, 3 x 14in TT
Iver Hvitfeldt	1886	3392t	5100ihp = 15.25kts	11.5–7in belt & 8.5in barbette	2 x 10.2in
Skjold	1896	2160t	2400ihp = 14kts	9–7in belt & 10in turret	1 x 9.4in
Herluf Trolle, Olfert Fischer	1899	3494t	4200ihp = 15.5kts	8–7in belt & 7–6in turret	2 x 9.4in
Norway					
Harald Haarfagre, Tordenskjold	1.1897	3858t	4,500ihp = 16.9kts	7–4in belt & 8–5in turret	2 x 8.2in
Norge, Eidsvold	3.1900	4165t	4500ihp = 16.5kts	6in belt & 9–5in turret	2 x 8.2in
Netherlands					
Reinier Claszen	1891	2440t	2315ihp = 12.5kts	4.75in belt & 11in turret	1 x 8.2in, 1 x 6.7in
Evertsen, Piet Hein, Kortenaer	1894	3464t	4700ihp = 16kts	6–4in belt & 9.5in barbette	3 x 8.2in
Koningen Regentes, De Ruyter, Hertog Hendrik	1900	5002t	6500ihp = 16.5kts	6–4in belt & 10–5in turret & barbette	2 x 9.4in
Marten Harpertzoon Tromp	1904	5210t	6400ihp = 16.5kts	6–4in belt & 8–5in turret & barbette	2 x 9.4in
Jacob van Heemskerck	1906	4920t	6400ihp = 16.5kts	6–4in belt & 8–5in turret & barbette	2 x 9.4in
Brazil					
Marshal Deodoro, Marshal Floriano	18.6.1898	3162t	3400ihp = 15kts	13.7–5.9in belt & 8.6in turret	2 x 9.4in
Argentina					
Independencia, Libertad	11.12.1890	2330t	2780ihp = 14.2kts	8in belt & 8—6in barbette/5in gunhoods	2 x 9.4in

Reference: Chapter 6

Sweden					
Class	**Launch/Comp**	**Displacement**	**Propulsion/speed**	**Armour**	**Main armament**
Sverige, Drottning Victoria, Gustav V	Completed 10.5.1917	7125t	25,400bhp (23,910bhp others) = 22.5kts	200–150mm belt & 200–100mm turret	4 x 11.1in, 8 x 6in
Denmark					
Peder Skram	2.5.1908	3735t	5400ihp = 16kts	195–155mm belt & 190–160mm turret	2 x 9.4in
Niels Juel	3.7.1918	3800t	5800ihp = 16kts	195–155mm belt & 150mm gunshield	10 x 5.9in
Netherlands					
De Zeven Provincien	Completed 6.10.1910	6530t	8000ihp = 16kts	150–100mm belt & 248mm turret	2 x 11in
Spain					
Espana, Alfonso XIII, Jaime I	Completed 23.10.1913	15,452t	15,500shp = 19.5kts	8–4in belt & 8in turrets	8 x 12in

Reference: Chapter 7

Great Britain					
Class	**Launch/Comp**	**Displacement**	**Propulsion/speed**	**Armour**	**Main armament**
Humber, Severn, Mersey (ex-Brazilian *Javary, Solimoes, Madeira*)	Completed 11.1913	1260t	1450ihp = 9.5kts	3–1.5in belt, 4in turret face & 3.5in barbette	2 x 6in
Abercrombie, Havelock, Raglan, Roberts	Completed 5.1915	6150t	2000ihp = 10kts designed (6/6.5kts actual for *Raglan* & *Roberts*)	4in internal belt & 10in turret face & 8in barbette	2 x 14in
Lord Clive, General Craufurd, Earl of Peterborough, Sir Thomas Picton, Prince Eugene, Prince Rupert, Sir John Moore, General Wolfe	7.1915	5900–6150t legend	2310ihp = 7kts	6in belt, 10.5in turret face & 8in barbette	2 x 12in
Marshal Soult, Marshal Ney	Completed 11.1915	6670t legend	1500bhp = 6kts	4in internal belt & 13in turret face & 8in barbette	2 x 15in
M 15, M 16–28	Completed 6.1915	540t legend	800ihp (560/600/640bhp for several others) = 11 kts	No armour besides 4in front gunshield/1.25in sides	1 x 9.2in
M 29, M 30–33	Completed 6.1915	355t legend	400ihp = 9kts	No armour besides 3in front gunshield	2 x 6in
Erebus, Terror	9.1916	8000t	6,000ihp = 12kt	4in internal belt, 13in turret face & 8in barbette	2 x 15in
Gorgon, Glatton (ex-Norwegian *Nidaros, Bjorgvin*)	Completed 6.1918	5700t nominal	4000ihp = 12kts	7–3in belt, 8in turret faces & 8–6in barbette	2 x 9.2in
Italy					
Alfredo Cappellini	1915	1452t	265ihp = 3.5kts	400mm turret	2 x 15in
Faa di Bruno	30.1.1916	2854t	465ihp = 3kts approx.	2.9m concrete cofferdam & 60mm barbette & 20–70mm turret	2 x 15in

Reference: Chapter 7

Finland

Class	Launch/Comp	Displacement	Propulsion/speed	Armour	Main armament
Väinämöinen, Ilmarinen	28.12.1930	3900t	6000bhp = 16kts	50–55mm belt & 100mm turret	4 x 10in

Siam/Thailand

Ratanakosindra, Sukhothai	21.4.1925	886t	850ihp = 12kts	2.5–1.25in belt	2 x 6in
Sri Ayuthia, Dhonburi	21.7.1937	2265t	5200bhp = 15.5kts	2.5in belt & 4in turret	4 x 8in

Reference: Chapter 9

Britain

Class	Launch/Comp	Displacement	Propulsion/speed	Armour	Main armament
Roberts, Abercrombie	Completed 27.10.1941	7973t (*Abercrombie* 8536t)	4800shp = 12.5kts	5–4in belt, 13–5in turret & 8in barbette	2 x 15in

Soviet Union (guardships)

Uragan, Smerch, Taifun, Tsyklon, Groza, Vikhr, Burya, Purga, Snieg, Tucha, Shkval, Shtorm, Burun, Grom, Mietel, Vyuga, Molniya, Zarnica	1929	450t	6290shp = 23kts	–	2 x 4in/3.9in
Dzerzhinskiy, Kirov	1934	810t	4500bhp = 18.5kts	–	3 x 4in
Rubin, Brilliant, Saphir, Zhemtchug	1936	550t	2300bhp = 17kts	–	1 x 4in
Yastreb, Berkut, Gryf, Kondor, Korshun, Oryol, Sokol, Voron	1940–41	906t	23,000shp = 31kts	–	3 x 3.9in
Albatros, Chaika, Fregat, Krechyet, Orlan, 'VI', Kaguar, Leopard, Pantera, Bys, Tigr, Yaguar	1943	920t	12,300shp = 25kts	–	3 x 3.9in

Appendix B
Other Warships Reassigned to Coastal Defence

Reference: Chapter 5

Japan *Hei Yen* (ex-Chinese *Ping Yuen*) coast defence ironclad

Reference: Chapter 7

Britain *Majestic* class battleships: *Hannibal, Illustrious, Jupiter, Magnificent, Mars, Victorious*
Canopus class battleships: *Canopus, Glory, Goliath*
Triumph class battleships: *Swiftsure*
King Edward VII class battleships: *Britannia, Dominion, Hindustan*
Dreadnought class battleship: *Dreadnought*

Germany *Brandenburg/Wörth* class battleships: *Wörth, Brandenburg*

France *Terrible* class barbette ship: *Requin*
Henri IV class battleship: *Henri IV*

Italy *Duilio* class turret ship: *Dandolo*
Italia class battleship: *Italia*
Re Umberto class battleship: *Re Umberto*
Ruggiero di Lauria class battleship: *Andrea Doria*

Austria-Hungary *Erzherzogin Stephanie* class barbette ship: *Erzherzogin Stephanie*
Erzherzog Rudolf class barbette ship: *Erzherzog Rudolf*

Russia *Ekaterina II* class barbette ship: *Georgi Pobiedonosets*

United States *Chicago* class cruiser: *Chicago* (one of thirty-two large to small vessels serving with the US Naval Militia which provided a coast defence or at least surveillance capability)

Japan *Petropavlovsk* class battleship: *Tango* (ex-Russian *Poltava*)
Fuji class battleship: *Fuji*
Imperator Alexander II class barbette ironclad: *Iki* (ex-Russian *Nikolai I*)
Admiral Ushakov class coast defence battleships: *Mishima, Okinoshima* (ex-Russian *Admiral Seniavin, General Admiral Graf Apraksin*)

Turkey *Avni Illah* class casemate ironclad (as built): *Muin-i-Zaffer*
Brandenburg/Wörth class battleships: *Torgud Reis, Heireddin Barbarossa* (ex-German *Weissenburg, Kurfürst Friedrich Wilhelm*)

Greece *Mississippi* class battleships: *Kilkis, Lemnos* (ex-US *Mississippi, Idaho*)

Reference: Chapter 9

Germany *Braunschweig* class battleship: *Hessen* (classified as coast defence ship in Reichsmarine service)

Italy *San Giorgio* class armoured cruiser: *San Giorgio*

Glossary

A (B, X & Y) position/turret. location of turrets from fore to aft

AA. anti-aircraft

approx. approximately

ASW. anti-submarine warfare

barbette. originally open-topped armoured enclosure containing gun mounting, fitted with armoured hoods from 1890s, then identified as turret (q.v.)

belt. hull side armour

bhp. brake horsepower

cal. calibre (i.e. the length of a gun, expressed as a multiplication of its barrel internal diameter)

casemate. armoured box on ironclads from within which guns were operated, singly or severally

cemented. 'Krupp cemented', face-hardened nickel-chromium steel armour

centre-pivot. open mounting with gunshield revolving on small diameter ring of rollers, operating on deck-mounted pivot plate

corsair. raiding vessel operating against trade

cm. centimetre

CODOG. combined diesel and gas turbine arrangement

COGOG. combined gas and gas turbine arrangement

ECM. electronic countermeasures

ESM. electronic support measures

FAC. fast attack craft

fighting top. conning tower or mast-mounted command and rangefinding position

ft. feet; foot

Harvey. Harvey face-hardened steel armour (further hardened if alloyed with nickel)

HA. high angle

hp. horsepower

ihp. indicated horsepower

in. inch

kiloton. Nuclear weapon yield measurement – 1,000 tons of TNT equivalent

lb. pound(s)

MCM. mine countermeasures

MTB. motor torpedo boat

m. metre(s)

mm. millimetre(s)

nhp. nominal horsepower

psi. pounds per square inch

QF. quick-firer/firing

redoubt. in this book's context, section of ironclad enclosed behind armour

SAM. surface-to-air missile

SES. surface effect ship (hovercraft)

shp. shaft horsepower

SSM. surface-to-surface missile

superfiring. turret on higher deck and *en echelon* with another turret, e.g. A & B turrents, X & Y turrets (q.v.)

TT. torpedo tube

tumblehome. inward curve of ship's side above water line, (also turtle backed)

turret. revolving armoured gunhouse

USN. United States Navy

USS. United States Ship

x. multiplication or disposition of armament, expressed as number of mountings times number of barrels, e.g. 4 × 2 = four twin mountings

Index

Page numbers in italics refer to illustrations and tables.